Commercial's

AF813996

THE RESERVE BANK OF INDIA ACT, 1934

(Act 2 of 1934)

[As amended vide

DoR LIC No. S1371/23.03.025/2024-25, dt. 4-6-2024]

Alongwith

- **Reserve Bank of India (Note Refund) Rules, 2009**
  [As amended vide Noti. RBI/DCM (NE) No. 631/08.01.01/2018-19, dt. 5-9-2018]
- **Reserve Bank of India (Board for Financial Supervision) Regulations, 1994**
- **Application for a Certificate of Registration to commence/ carry on the Business of a non-making Financial Institution**
- **Reserve Bank Commercial Paper Directions, 2012**
- **Reserve Bank of India Monetary Policy Committee and Monetary Policy Process Regulations, 2016**
- **Reserve Bank - Integrated Ombudsman Scheme, 2021**
- **Electoral Bond Scheme, 2018**
  (As amended vide SO 5163(E), dt. 7-11-2022, w.e.f. 7-11-2022)
- **Registration of Assignment of Receivables (Reserve Bank) Regulation, 2022**
- **Registration of Factors (Reserve Bank) Regulations, 2022**

COMMERCIAL LAW PUBLISHERS (INDIA) PVT. LTD.

WITH THE BLESSINGS OF MATA VAISHNO DEVI

Published

by

Sandeep Garg

COMMERCIAL LAW PUBLISHERS (INDIA) PVT. LTD.

HEAD OFFICE:

4239/1, Shakahar Bhawan,

Ansari Road, Daryaganj, New Delhi-110002

Phones : 43502008, 43011562, 43452009

e-mail : commercialhouse@yahoo.co.in,

naveen commercialhouse@gmail.com

Website : commerciallawpublishers.com

Printed at

TAJ PRESS, NOIDA

INTRODUCTORY

The Reserve Bank of India Act, 1934 is an Act to constitute a Reserve Bank of India to regulate the issue of bank notes and the keeping of reserves with a view to securing monetary stability in India and generally to operate the currency and credit system of the country to its advantage. A bank is an institution, of great value in the commercial world, empowered to receive deposits of money, to make loans, and to issue its promissory notes, (designed to circulate as money, and commonly called "bank-notes" or "bank-bills") to perform any one or more of these functions. It is an institution, usually incorporated with power to issue its promissory notes intended to circulate as money (known as bank notes); or to receive the money of others on general deposit, to form a joint fund that shall be used by the institution, for its own benefit, for one or more of the purposes of making temporary loans and discounts; of dealing in notes, foreign and domestic bills of exchange, coins, bullion, credits, and the remission of money; or with both these powers, and with privileges, and in addition to these basic powers, of receiving special deposits and making collections for the holders of negotiable papers, if the institution sees fit to engage in such business.

The term bank is usually restricted in its application to an incorporated body; while a private individual making it his business to conduct banking operations is generally denominated a banker.

The preamble to the Reserve Bank of India Act states that in the present disorganisation of the monetary systems of the world it is not possible to determine what will be suitable as a permanent basis for the Indian monetary system, but whereas it is expedient to make temporary provision on the basis of the existing monetary system, and to leave the question of the monetary standard best suited to India to be considered when the international monetary position has become sufficiently clear and stable to make it possible to frame permanent measures. The Act provides for a bank to be called the Reserve Bank of India which shall be constituted for the purposes of taking over the management of the currency from the Central Government and of carrying on the business of banking in accordance with the provisions of this Act. The bank shall be a body corporate by the name of the Reserve Bank of India, having perpetual succession and a common seal, and shall by the said name sue and be sued. With regard to the management of the bank, the Central Government may from time to time give such directions to the bank as it may, after consultation with the Governor of the bank, consider necessary in the public interest. Subject to any such directions, the general superintendence and direction of the affairs and business of the bank shall be entrusted to a Central Board of Directors which may exercise all powers and do all acts and things which may be exercised or done by the bank. Save as otherwise provided in the regulations made by the Central Board, the Governor and in his absence a Deputy Governor nominated by him in his behalf, shall also have powers of general superintendence and direction of the affairs and the business of the bank, and may exercise all powers and do all acts and things which may be exercised or done by the bank.

This book comprising the Reserve Bank of India Act, 1934 ***as amended vide DoR LIC No. S1371/23.03.025/2024-25, dt. 4-6-2024***, the Reserve Bank of India (Note Fund) Rules, 2009 ***as amended vide Noti. RBI/DCM (NE) No. 631/08.01.01/2018-19, dt. 5-9-2018***; the Reserve Bank of India (Board for Financial Supervision) Regulations, 1994; Application for a Certificate of Registration to Commence/Carry on the business of a

Non-banking Financial Institution; the Reserve Bank Commercial Paper Directions, 2012; the Reserve Bank of India Monetary Policy Committee and Monetary Policy Process Regulations, 2016; the Reserve Bank - Integrated Ombudsman Scheme, 2021; Electroral Bond Scheme, 2018 (as amended vide SO 5163(E), dt. 7-11-2022, w.e.f. 7-11-2022; Registration of Assignment of Receivables (Reserve Bank) Regulations, 2022; Registration of Factors (Reserve Bank) Regulations, 2022 would serve the purpose of having an overall view of the subject in issue.

A creative feedback from the learned readers, bringing to our notice any mistake, error or omission or discrepancy that might have crept in this book in spite of our sincere efforts to avoid those, is most welcome, for it will help us to improve the overall quality, style and presentation of the book in the forthcoming editions.

PUBLISHERS

CONTENTS

THE RESERVE BANK OF INDIA ACT, 1934

CHAPTER I
PRELIMINARY

CHAPTER II
INCORPORATION, CAPITAL, MANAGEMENT AND BUSINESS

CHAPTER III
CENTRAL BANKING FUNCTIONS

CHAPTER V
PENALTIES

THE RESERVE BANK OF INDIA (NOTE REFUND) RULES, 2009

THE RESERVE BANK OF INDIA (BOARD FOR FINANCIAL SUPERVISION) REGULATIONS, 1994

CHAPTER I
INTRODUCTORY

THE ELECTORAL BOND SCHEME, 2018

THE RESERVE BANK - INTEGRATED OMBUDSMAN SCHEME, 2021

CHAPTER I
PRELIMINARY

CHAPTER II
OFFICES UNDER THE RESERVE BANK - INTEGRATED OMBUDSMAN SCHEME, 2021

CHAPTER III
POWERS AND FUNCTIONS OF THE OMBUDSMAN

CHAPTER IV
PROCEDURE FOR REDRESSAL OF GRIEVANCE UNDER THE SCHEME

THE RESERVE BANK OF INDIA ACT, 1934

(Act 2 of 1934, dt. 6-3-1934)

[*As amended vide DoR.LIC No. S1371/23.03.025/2024-25, dt. 4-6-2024*]

An Act to constitute a Reserve Bank of India.

WHEREAS it is expedient to constitute a Reserve Bank for India to regulate the issue of Bank notes and the keeping of reserves with a view to securing monetary stability in [1][India] and generally to operate the currency and credit system of the country to its advantage;

[2][AND WHEREAS it is essential to have a modern monetary policy framework to meet the challenge of an increasingly complex economy;

AND WHEREAS the primary objective of the monetary policy is to maintain price stability while keeping in mind the objective of growth;

AND WHEREAS the monetary policy framework in India shall be operated by the Reserve Bank of India;]

It is hereby enacted as follows:—

CHAPTER I
PRELIMINARY

1. Short title, extent and commencement

(1) This Act may be called the Reserve Bank of India Act, 1934.

[3][(2) It extends to the whole of India [4][xxx]]

(3) This section shall come into force at once, and the remaining provisions of this Act shall come into force on such date or dates[5] as the [6][Central Government] may, by notification in the Gazette of India, appoint.

TO PRE-EMPT

The Reserve Bank of India Act is an Act to constitute a Reserve Bank of India whereas it was felt expedient to constitute a Reserve Bank of India to regulate the issue of bank-notes and the keeping of reserves with a view to securing monetary stability in India and generally to operate the currency and credit system of the country to its advantage. It was also felt in the present disorganisation of the monetary systems of the world it is not possible to determine what will be suitable as a permanent basis for the Indian monetary system. And also it was felt expedient to make temporary provision on the basis of the existing monetary system, and to leave the question of the monetary standard best suited to India to be considered when the international monetary position has become sufficiently clear and stable to make it possible to frame permanent measures.

2. Definitions

In this Act, unless there is anything repugnant in the subject or context,—

[7][xxx]

---

1 Substituted for "British India" by the AO 1948.
2 Substituted by Act 28 of 2016, w.e.f. 27-6-2016.
3 Substituted by the AO 1950.
4 Words "except the State of Jammu and Kashmir" omitted by Act 62 of 1956, w.e.f. 1-11-1956.
5 Sections 2 to 19, 47, 50 to 52, 55 to 58 and 61 enforced on 1-1-1935 and the other sections on 1-4-1935.
6 Substituted for "G.G. in C" by the MO 1937.
7 Clauses (a) and (ai) omitted by Act 61 of 1981, w.e.f. 12-7-1982.

[1][(aii)] "the Bank" means the Reserve Bank of India constituted by this Act;

[2][(aiii) "Bank for International Settlements" means by body corporate established with the said name under the law of Switzerland in pursuance of an agreement dated the 20th January, 1930, signed at The Hague;]

[3][(aiv) "bank note" means a bank note issued by the Bank, whether in physical or digital form, under section 22;]

(b) "the Central Board" means the Central Board of Directors of the Bank;

[4][xxx]

[5][(bva) "Consumer Price Index" means the Consumer Price Index Combined published by the Government of India from time to time;]

[6][[7][(bvi) "Deposit Insurance Corporation" means the Deposit Insurance Corporation established under section 3 of the Deposit Insurance Corporation Act, 1961 (47 of 1961);]

[8][xxx]

[9][xxx]

[10][(bviiia) "Exim Bank" means the Export-Import Bank of India established under the Export-Import Bank of India Act, 1981 (28 of 1981);]

[11][(bix) "foreign currency" and "foreign exchange" have the meanings respectively assigned to them in the Foreign Exchange Regulation Act, 1973 (46 of 1973);

(c) "Industrial Finance Corporation" means the Industrial Finance Corporation of India established under the Industrial Finance Corporation Act, 1948 (15 of 1948);]

[5][(ci) "inflation" means the year wise change in monthly Consumer Price Index expressed in terms of percentage;

(cii) "inflation target" means the inflation target determined in accordance with sub-section (1) of section 45ZA;]

[12][(ca) "International Development Association" means the "Association" referred to in the International Development Association (Status, Immunities and Privileges) Act, 1960 (32 of 1960);

(cb) "International Finance Corporation" means the "Corporation" referred to in the International Finance Corporation (Status, Immunities and Privileges) Act, 1958 (42 of 1958);

(cc) "International Monetary Fund" and "International Bank for Reconstruction and Development" means respectively the "International Fund" and the "International Bank", referred to in the International Monetary Fund and Bank Act, 1945;]

---

1 Clause (aa) re-lettered as clause (aii) by Act 23 of 1965, w.e.f. 1-3-1966.
2 Inserted by Act 51 of 1974, w.e.f. 13-12-1974.
3 Inserted by Finance Act, 2022 (No. 6 of 2022), dt. 30-3-2022.
4 Clauses (bi), (bii), (biii), (biv) and (bv) omitted by Act 61 of 1981, w.e.f. 12-7-1982.
5 Inserted by Act 28 of 2016, w.e.f. 27-6-2016.
6 Inserted by Act 47 of 1961, w.e.f. 1-1-1962.
7 Clause (bbb) re-lettered as clause (bvi) thereof by Act 23 of 1965, w.e.f. 1-3-1966.
8 Clause (bvii) omitted by Act 53 of 2003, w.e.f. 2-7-2004.
9 Clause (bviii) omitted by Act 61 of 1981, w.e.f. 12-7-1982.
10 Inserted by Act 28 of 1981, w.e.f. 1-1-1982.
11 Substituted by Act 24 of 1978, w.e.f. 21-7-1978.
12 Inserted by Act 51 of 1974, w.e.f. 13-12-1974.

[4][(cci) "Monetary Policy Committee" means the Committee constituted under sub-section (1) of section 45ZB;]

[1][(ccc) "National Bank" means the National Bank for Agriculture and Rural Development established under section 3 of the National Bank for Agriculture and Rural Development Act, 1981 (61 of 1981);]

[2][(ccci) "National Bank for Financing Infrastructure and Development" means the Institution established under section 3 of the National Bank for Financing Infrastructure and Development Act, 2021;

(cccii) "other development financial institution" means a development financial institution licensed under section 29 of the National Bank for Financing Infrastructure and Development Act, 2021;]

[3][(cccc) "National Housing Bank" means the National Housing Bank established under section 3 of the National Housing Bank Act, 1987 (53 of 1987);]

[4][(cccci) "Policy Rate" means the rate for repo-transactions under sub-section (12AB) of section 17;]

[5][xxx]

[6][(cv) "Reconstruction Bank" means the Industrial Reconstruction Bank of India established under section 3 of the Industrial Reconstruction Bank of India Act, 1984 (62 of 1984);]

(d) "rupee coin" means [7][xxx] rupees which are legal tender [8][[in [9][India]] under the provisions of the Indian Coinage Act, 1906 (3 of 1906); [10][xxx]

(e) "scheduled bank" means a bank included in the Second Schedule;

[11][(el) "Small Industries Bank" means the Small Industries Development Bank of India established under section 3 of the Small Industries Development Bank of India Act, 1989 (39 of 1989);]

[12][(ea) "Sponsor Bank" means a Sponsor Bank as defined in the Regional Rural Banks Act, 1976 (21 of 1976);]

[13][[14][(eb)] "State Bank" means the State Bank of India constituted under the State Bank of India Act, 1955 (23 of 1955);]

[15][xxx]

[16][(fi) "State Financial Corporation" means any State Financial Corporation established under the State Financial Corporations Act, 1951 (63 of 1951);]

[17][xxx]

1 Ins. by Act 61 of 1981, w.e.f. 12-7-1982.
2 Inserted by Act 17 of 2021, w.e.f. 19-4-2021.
3 Inserted by Act 53 of 1987, w.e.f. 9-7-1988.
4 Inserted by Act 28 of 2016, w.e.f. 27-6-2016.
5 Clauses (ci), (cia), (cii), (ciii), (civ), (cv) omitted by Act 61 of 1981, w.e.f. 12-7-1982.
6 Inserted by Act 62 of 1984, w.e.f. 20-3-1985.
7 Word "silver" omitted by Act 62 of 1948, w.e.f. 1-1-1949.
8 Inserted by the MO 1937.
9 Substituted for "the States" by Act 32 of 1951, w.e.f. 1-11-1951.
10 Word "and" omitted by the M.O. 1937.
11 Inserted by Act 39 of 1989, w.e.f. 7-3-1990.
12 Inserted by Act 21 of 1976, w.e.f. 26-9-1975.
13 Inserted by Act 23 of 1955, w.e.f. 1-7-1955.
14 Clause (ee) re-lettered as clause (eb) thereof by Act 21 of 1976, w.e.f. 26-9-1975.
15 Clause (f) omitted by Act 61 of 1981, w.e.f. 12-7-1982.
16 Inserted by Act 24 of 1978, w.e.f. 21-7-1978.
17 Clauses (f) to (k) omitted by Act 11 of 1947, w.e.f. 1-4-1947.

[1][(g) "Unit Trust" means the Unit Trust of India established under section 3 of the Unit Trust of India Act, 1963 (52 of 1963);]

[2][(h) "agricultural operations", "central co-operative bank", "co-operative society", "crops", "marketing of corps", "pisciculture", "regional rural bank" and "State co-operative bank" shall have the meanings respectively assigned to them in the National Bank for Agriculture and Rural Development Act, 1981 (61 of 1981);

(i) "co-operative bank", "co-operative credit society", "director", "primary agricultural credit society", "primary co-operative bank" and "primary credit society" shall have the meanings respectively assigned to them in Part V of the Banking Regulation Act, 1949 (10 of 1949).]

COMMENTS

Sec. 2(aii)

Bank is an institution, of great value in the commercial world, empowered to receive deposits of money, to make loans, and to issue its promissory notes, (designed to circulate as money and commonly called "bank-notes" or "bank bills" or to perform any one or more of these functions. It is an institution, usually incorporated with power to issue its promissory notes intended to circulate as money (known as bank notes); or to receive the money of others on general deposit, to form a joint fund that shall be used by the institution, for its own benefit, for one or more of the purposes of making temporary loan and discounts; of dealing in notes, foreign and domestic bills of exchange, coin, bullion, credits, and the remission of money; or with both these powers, and with the privileges, in addition to these basic powers, of receiving special deposits and making collections for the holders of negotiable paper, if the institution sees fit to engage in such business. The term "bank" is usually restricted in its application to an incorporated body; while a private individual making it his business to conduct banking operations is generally denominated a "banker".

Sec. 2(bvi)

Sec. 3 of the Deposits Insurance and Credit Guarantee Corporation Act, 1961 lays down the provision for the establishment and incorporation of Deposit Insurance Corporation. It says the Central Government shall, by notification in the Official Gazette, establish a corporation by the name of the Deposit Insurance Corporation which shall be a body corporate having perpetual succession and a common seal with power, subject to the provisions of this Act, to acquire, hold or dispose of property and to contract, and may by the said name, sue or be sued. Any reference in this Act to the Deposit Insurance Corporation shall, on and from the date on which Chapter II of the Deposit Insurance Corporation (Amendment and Miscellaneous Provisions) Act, 1978, comes into force, be construed as a reference to the Deposit Insurance and Credit Guarantee Corporation. The head office of the corporation shall be at Bombay, but it may, with the previous sanction of the Reserve Bank, establish branches or agencies in any other place in India.

Sec. 2(bviiia)

Export-Import Bank of India Act, 1981 is an Act to establish a corporation to be known as the Export-Import Bank of India for providing financial assistance to exporters and importers, and for functioning as the principal financial institution for coordinating the working of institutions engaged in financing export and import of goods and services with a view to promoting the country's international trade and for matters connected therewith or incidental thereto.

Sec. 2(bix)

Under s. 2(m) of the Foreign Exchange Management Act, 1999, "foreign currency" means any currency other than Indian currency. Under s. 2(h) of Foreign Exchange Management Act, 1999, "foreign exchange" means foreign currency and includes, (i) deposits, credits and balances payable in any foreign currency, (ii) drafts, travellers' cheques, letters of credit or bills of exchange,

---

1 Inerted. by Act 52 of 1963, w.e.f. 1-2-1964.
2 Inserted by Act 61 of 1981, w.e.f. 12-7-1982.

expressed or drawn in Indian currency but payable in any foreign currency, (iii) drafts, travellers cheques, letters of credit or bills of exchange drawn by banks, institutions or persons outside India, but payable in Indian currency.

Currency in the context connotes coined money and such bank-notes or other paper money as are authorised by law and do in fact circulate from hand to hand as the medium of exchange. The term 'money' is synonymous with currency and imports any currency, token, bank notes or other circulating medium in general use as the representative of value.

Sec. 2(ccc)

National Bank under s. 3 of the National Bank for Agricultural and Rural Development Act, 1981 providing for the establishment of national bank for agricultural and rural development and capital thereof lays down that with effect from such date as the Central Government may, by notification in the Official Gazette, appoint, there shall be established for the purposes of this Act, a bank to be known as the national bank for agriculture and rural development. The bank shall be a body corporate with the name aforesaid having perpetual succession and a common seal with power, subject to the provisions of this Act, to acquire, hold and dispose of property and to contract, and may by that name sue and be sued. The head office of the National Bank shall be at Bombay or at such other place as the Central Government may, by notification, specify. The National Bank may establish offices, branches, or agencies at any place in India, and with the previous approval of the Central Government and in consultation with the Reserve Bank, at any place outside India.

Sec. 2(cccc)

Sec. 3 of the National Housing Bank Act, 1987 providing for establishment and incorporation of national housing bank says that with effect from such date as the Central Government may, by notification, appoint, there shall be established for the purposes of this Act, a bank to be known as the national housing bank. The bank shall be a body corporate with the name aforesaid having perpetual succession and a common seal with power, subject to the provisions of this Act, to acquire, hold and dispose of property and to contract, and may by that name sue and be sued. The head office of the National Housing Bank shall be at Bombay or at such other place as the Central Government may, by notification, specify. The National Housing Bank may establish offices, branches, or agencies at any place in India, and with the previous approval of the Reserve Bank at any place outside India.

Sec. 2(cv)

Sec. 3 of Industrial Reconstruction Bank of India Act, 1984 providing for establishment and incorporation of Reconstruction Bank lays down that with effect from such date as the Central Government may, by notification, in the Official Gazette, appoint, there shall be established, for the purposes of this Act, a corporation to be known as the industrial reconstruction bank of India. The reconstruction bank shall be a body corporate with the name aforesaid having perpetual succession and a common seal with power, subject to the provisions of this Act, to acquire, hold and dispose of property and to contract, and may by that name sue and be sued. The head office of the Reconstruction Bank shall be at Calcutta and the Reconstruction Bank may establish offices, branches, or agencies at any other place, whether in, or outside, India.

Sec. 2(ea)

Sec. 2(g) of Regional Rural Banks Act, 1976 defines "sponsor bank" a bank by which a regional rural bank has been sponsored.

Sec. 2(h)

Under s. 2(a) of National Bank for Agricultural and Development Act, 1981, agriculture includes horticulture, animal husbandry, forestry, dairy and poultry farming, pisci-culture and other allied activities, whether or not undertaken jointly with agriculture and the expression "agricultural operations" shall be construed accordingly. Under s. 2(d) of the abovesaid Act, "Central Co-operative Bank" means the principal co-operative society in a district in a State, the primary object of which is the financing of other co-operative societies in that district, provided that in addition to such principal society in a district, the State Government may declare any one or more co-operative societies carrying on the business of financing other co-operative societies in that district to be also or to be a Central Co-operative Bank or Central Co-operative Banks within the meaning of the definition.

Crops include products of agricultural operations. Such products of the soil as are annually planted, severed, and saved by manual labour, as cereals, vegetables, grass maturing for harvest or harvested, etc. but not grass on lands used for pasturage. In its more general signification, means all products of the soil that are grown and raised annually and gathered during a single season.

CHAPTER II

INCORPORATION, [1][CAPITAL], MANAGEMENT AND BUSINESS

3. Establishment and incorporation of Reserve Bank

(1) A bank to be called the Reserve Bank of India shall be constituted for the purposes of taking over the management of the currency from the [2][Central Government] and of carrying on the business of banking in accordance with the provisions of this Act.

(2) The Bank shall be a body corporate by the name of the Reserve Bank of India, having perpetual succession and a common seal, and shall by the said name sue and be sued.

COMMENTS

The Reserve Bank of India should be a bank which is a body corporate having a perpetual succession and a common seal and it can sue and be sued.

[3][4. Capital of the Bank

The capital of the Bank shall be five crores of rupees.]

5. [4][xxx].

6. Offices, branches and agencies

The Bank shall, as soon as may be, establish offices in Bombay, Calcutta, [5][Delhi and Madras] [6][xxx] and may establish branches or agencies in any other place in India [7][xxx] or, with the previous sanction of the [8][Central Government] elsewhere.

[9][7. Management

(1) The Central Government may from time to time give such directions to the Bank as it may, after consultation with the Governor of the Bank, consider necessary in the public interest.

(2) Subject to any such directions, the general superintendence and direction of the affairs and business of the Bank shall be entrusted to a Central Board of Directors which may exercise all powers and do all acts and things which may be exercised or done by the Bank.

[10][(3) Save as otherwise provided in regulations made by the Central Board, the Governor and in his absence the Deputy Governor nominated by him in his behalf, shall also have powers of general superintendence and direction of the affairs and the business of the Bank, and may exercise all powers and do all acts and things which may be exercised or done by the Bank.]]

1 Substituted for "SHARE CAPITAL" by Act 62 of 1948, w.e.f. 1-1-1949.
2 Substituted for "G.G. in C." by the MO 1937.
3 Substituted by Act 62 of 1948, w.e.f. 1-1-1949.
4 Omitted by the Reserve Bank (Transfer to Public Ownership) Act,1948 (62 of1948), w.e.f. 1-1-1949
5 Substituted for "Delhi, Madras and Rangoon" by Act 11 of 1947, w.e.f. 1-4-1947.
6 Words "and a branch in London" omitted by Act 24 of 1955, w.e.f. 8-5-1955.
7 Words "or Burma" omitted by Act 11 of 1947, w.e.f. 1-4-1947.
8 Substituted for "G.G. in C." by the MO 1937.
9 Substituted by Act 62 of 1948, w.e.f. 1-1-1949.
10 Substituted by Act 32 of 1951, w.r.e.f. 1-1-1949.

8. Composition of the Central Board, and term of office of Directors

[1][(1) The Central Board shall consist of the following Directors, namely:—

(a) a Governor and [2][not more than four] Deputy Governors to be appointed by the Central Government;

(b) four Directors to be nominated by the Central Government, one from each of the four Local Boards as constituted by section 9;

(c) [3][ten] Directors to be nominated by the Central Government; and

(d) [4][two Government official] to be nominated by the Central Government.]

(2) The Governor and Deputy Governors shall devote their whole time to the affairs of the Bank, and shall receive such salaries and allowances as may be determined by the Central Board, with the approval of the [5][Central Government]:

[6][PROVIDED that the Central Board may, if in its opinion it is necessary in the public interest so to do, permit the Governor or a Deputy Governor to undertake, at the request of the Central Government or any State Government, such part-time honorary work, whether related to the purposes of this Act or not, as is not likely to interfere with his duties as Governor or Deputy Governor, as the case may be:]

[7][PROVIDED FURTHER that the Central Government may, in consultation with the Bank, appoint a Deputy Governor as the Chairman of the National Bank, on such terms and conditions as that Government may specify.]

(3) A Deputy Governor and the Director nominated under clause (d) of sub-section (1) may attend any meeting of the Central Board and take part in its deliberations but shall not be entitled to vote:

[8][PROVIDED that when the Governor is, for any reason, unable to attend any such meeting, a Deputy Governor authorised by him in this behalf in writing may vote for him at that meeting.]

(4) The Governor and a Deputy Governor shall hold office for such term not exceeding five years as the [9][Central Government] may fix when appointing them, and shall be eligible for re-appointment.

[10][A Director nominated under clause (c) of sub-section (1) shall [11][xxx] hold office for a period of four years [12][and [13][shall be eligible for reappointment:

PROVIDED that any such Director shall not be appointed for more than two terms, that is, for a maximum period of eight years either continuously or intermittently.]]]

A Director nominated under clause (d) of sub-section (1) shall hold office during the pleasure of the [9][Central Government.]

---

1 Subsstituted by Act 62 of 1948, w.e.f. 1-1-1949.
2 Substituted for "three" by Act 18 of 1964, w.e.f. 1-7-1964.
3 Substituted for "six", ibid, w.e.f. 1-7-1964.
4 Substituted for "one Government official" by Act 12 of 2012, w.e.f. 1-2-2012.
5 Substituted for "G.G. in C." by the MO 1937.
6 Inserted by Act 35 of 1962, w.e.f. 15-9-1962.
7 Inserted by Act 61 of 1981, w.e.f. 12-7-1982.
8 Substituted by Act 54 of 1953, w.e.f. 30-12-1953
9 Substituted for "G.G. in C." by the M.O. 1937.
10 Substituted by Act 62 of 1948, w.e.f. 1-1-1949.
11 Words, brackets and figure "subject to the provisions of sub-section (6)" omitted by Act 18 of 1964, w.e.f. 1-7-1964.
12 Inserted by Act 51 of 1974, w.e.f. 13-12-1974.
13 Substituted for "thereafter until his successor shall have been nominated" by Act 4 of 2013, w.e.f. 18-1-2013.

(5) No act or proceeding of the Board shall be questioned on the ground merely of the existence of any vacancy in, or any defect in the constitution of, the Board.

[1][xxx]

(7) A retiring Director shall be eligible for re-nomination.]

[2][9. Local Boards, their constitution and functions

(1) A Local Board shall be constituted for each of the four areas specified in the First Schedule and shall consist of five members to be appointed by the Central Government to represent, as far as possible, territorial and economic interests and the interests of co-operative and indigenous banks.

(2) The members of the Local Board shall elect from amongst themselves one person to be the chairman of the Board.

[3][(3) Every member of a Local Board shall hold office for a term of four years and [4][shall be eligible for reappointment:

PROVIDED that any such member shall not be appointed for more than two terms, that is, for a maximum period of eight years either continuously or intermittently].]

(4) A Local Board shall advise the Central Board on such matters as may be generally or specifically referred to it and shall perform such duties as the Central Board may delegate to it.]

10. Disqualifications of Directors and members of Local Boards

(1) No person may be a Director or a member of a Local Board who—

(a) is a salaried Government official[5][xxx] [6][xxx], or

(b) is, or at any time has been, adjudicated an insolvent, or has suspended payment or has compounded with his creditors, or

(c) is fund lunatic or becomes of unsound mind, or

(d) is an officer or employee of any bank, or

[7][(e) is a Director of banking company within the meaning of clause (c) of section 5 of the [8][Banking Regulation Act, 1949 (10 of 1949)], or of a co-operative bank.]

(2) No two persons who are partners of the same mercantile firm, or are Directors of the same private company, or one of whom is the general agent of or holds a power of procuration from the other, or from a mercantile firm of which the other is a partner, may be Directors or members of the same Local Board at the same time.

(3) Nothing in clause (a), clause (d) or clause (e) of sub-section (1) shall apply to the Governor, or to a Deputy Governor or to the Director nominated under clause (d) of sub-section (1) of section 8.

---

1 Sub-section (6) omitted by Act 18 of 1964, w.e.f. 1-7-1964.
2 Substituted by Act 62 of 1948, w.e.f. 1-1-1949.
3 Substituted by Act 51 of 1974, w.e.f. 13-12-1974.
4 Substituted for "thereafter until his successor shall have been appointed and shall be eligible for reappointment" by Act 4 of 2013, w.e.f. 18-1-2013.
5 Words "or a salaried official of a State in India" omitted by AO 1950.
6 Words "or Burma" omitted by Act 11 of 1947, w.e.f. 1-4-1947.
7 Substituted by Act 23 of 1965, w.e.f. 1-3-1966.
8 Substituted for "Banking Companies Act, 1949" by Act 51 of 1974, w.e.f. 13-12-1974.

11. Removal from and vacation of office

(1) The [1][Central Government] may remove from office the Governor, or a Deputy Governor or [2][any other Director or any member of a Local Board]:

[3][xxx]

[4][(2) A Director nominated under clause (b) or clause (c) of sub-section (1) of section 8 shall cease to hold office if without leave from the Central Board he absents himself from three consecutive meetings of the Board convened under sub-section (1) of section 13.]

(3) The [1][Central Government] shall remove from office any Director, and the Central Board shall remove from office any member of a Local Board, if such Director or member becomes subject to any of the disqualifications specified in sub-section (1) or sub-section (2) of section 10.

(4) A Director or member of a Local Board removed or ceasing to hold office under the foregoing sub-sections shall not be eligible for re-appointment either as Director or as member of a Local Board until the expiry of the term for which his appointment was made.

(5) The [5][xxx] nomination [6][xxx] as Director or member of a Local Board of any person who is a member of [7][Parliament or the Legislature [8][of any State]] shall be void, unless within two months of the date of his [5][xxx] nomination [6][xxx] he ceases to be such member, and if any Director or member of a Local Board is elected or nominated as a member of [9][Parliament or any such Legislature], he shall cease to be a Director or member of the Local Board as from the date of such election or nomination, as the case may be.

(6) A Director may resign his office to the [1][Central Government], and a member of a Local Board may resign his office to the Central Board, and on the acceptance of the resignation the office shall become vacant.

12. Casual vacancies and absences

(1) If the Governor or a Deputy Governor by infirmity or otherwise is rendered incapable of executing his duties or is absent on leave or otherwise in circumstances not involving the vacation of his appointment, the [1][Central Government] may, after consideration of the recommendations made by the Central Board in this behalf, appoint another person to officiate for him, and such person may, notwithstanding anything contained in clause (d) of sub-section (1) of section10, be an officer of the Bank.

[10][xxx]

1 Substituted for "G.G. in C." by the M.O. 1937.
2 Substituted for "any other Director" by Act 32 of 1951, w.e.f. 1-11-1951.
3 Proviso omitted by Act 62 of 1948, w.e.f. 1-1-1949.
4 Substituted, ibid.
5 Word "appointment" omitted, ibid.
6 Words "or election" omitted, ibid.
7 Certain words substituted by the AO 1950.
8 Substituted for "of a Part A State or a Part C State" by Act 32 of 1951, w.e.f. 1-11-1951.
9 Substituted for "any such Legislature or Council" by the AO 1950.
10 Sub-section (2) omitted by Act 62 of 1948, w.e.f. 1-1-1949.

(3) Where any casual vacancy in the office of any member of a Local Board occurs [1][xxx] the Central Board may nominate thereto any [2][xxx] person recommended by the [3][other] members of the Local Board.

(4) Where any casual vacancy occurs in the office of a Director other than the vacancies provided for in sub-section (1), the vacancy shall be filled [4][by the Central Government].

(5) A person nominated [5][xxx] under this section to fill a casual vacancy shall [6][xxx] hold office for the unexpired portion of the term of his predecessor.

13. Meetings of the Central Board

(1) Meetings of the Central Board shall be conveyed by the Governor at least six times in each year and at least once in each quarter.

(2) Any [7][four Directors] may require the Governor to convene a meeting of the Central Board at any time and the Governor shall forthwith convene a meeting accordingly.

(3) The Governor, or [8][if for any reason, he is unable to attend,] the Deputy Governor authorised by the Governor under the proviso to sub-section (3) of section 8 to vote for him shall preside at meetings of the Central Board, and, in the event of an equality of votes, shall have a second or casting vote.

[9]**[xxx]**

17. Business which the Bank may transact

The Bank shall be authorised to carry on and transact the several kinds of business hereinafter specified, namely:—

(1) the accepting of money on deposit without interest from, and the collection of money for, [10][xxx] the [11][Central Government], [12][[13][xxx] the [14][State] Government [15][xxx] [16][xxx] local authorities, banks and any other persons:

[17][(1A) The accepting of money as deposits, repayable with interest, from banks or any other person under the Standing Deposit Facility Scheme, as approved by the Central Board, from time to time, for the purposes of liquidity management;]

(2) (a) the purchase, sale and rediscount of bills of exchange and promissory notes, [18][drawn on [19][and payable in India]] and arising out of *bona fide* commercial or trade transaction bearing two or more good signatures, one of which shall

---

1 Words "otherwise than by the occurrence of a vacancy in the office of a Director elected by the Local Board" omitted by Act 62 of 1948, w.e.f. 1-1-1949.
2 Word "qualified" omitted, ibid.
3 Substituted for "elected", ibid.
4 Substituted for certain words ibid.
5 Words "or elected" omitted, ibid.
6 Words, brackets and figure "subject to the proviso contained in sub-section (4)" omitted, ibid.
7 Substituted "three Directors" by Act 18 of 1964, w.e.f. 1-7-1964.
8 Substituted for "in his absence" by Act 24 of 1955, w.e.f. 8-5-1955.
9 Sections 14, 15 and 16 omitted by the Reserve Bank (Transfer to Public Ownership) Act, 1948 (62 of 1948), w.e.f. 1-1-1949.
10 Words "the Secretary of State" omitted by the AO 1948.
11 Substituted for "G.G. in C." by the MO 1937.
12 Substituted for "L.G.s" by the MO 1937.
13 Words "the Federal Railway Authority" omitted by the AO 1948.
14 Substituted for "Provincial" by the AO 1950.
15 Words "the Government of Burma, the Burma Railway Board," omitted by Act 11 of 1947, w.e.f. 1-4-1947.
16 Words and letter "Part B States" omitted by Act 32 of 1951, w.e.f. 1-11-1951.
17 Inserted by Act 13 of 2018, w.e.f. 28-3-2018.
18 Substituted for "drawn on and payable in India" by the MO 1937.
19 Substituted for "India or Burma and payable in India or Burma" by Act 11 of 1947, w.e.f. 1-4-1947.

be that of a scheduled bank [1][or a State co-operative bank] [2][or any financial institution, which is predominantly engaged in the acceptance or discounting of bills of exchange and promissory notes and which is approved by the Bank in this behalf] [3][xxx] and [4][maturing,—

(i) in the case of bills of exchange and promissory notes arising out of any such transaction relating to the export of goods from India, within one hundred and eighty days, and

(ii) in any other case, within ninety days,

from the date of such purchase or rediscount exclusive of days of grace;]

(b) the purchase, sale and rediscount of bills of exchange and promissory notes, [5][drawn [6][and payable in India]] and bearing two or more good signatures, one of which shall be that of a scheduled bank [7][or a [8][State] co-operative bank] [9][or any financial institution, which is predominantly engaged in the acceptance or discounting of bills of exchange and promissory notes and which is approved by the Bank in this behalf] and drawn or issued for the purpose of [10][financing agricultural operations] or the marketing of crops, and maturing within [11][fifteen months] from the date of such purchase or rediscount, exclusive of days of grace;

[12][xxx]

[13][(bb) the purchase, sale and rediscount of bills of exchange and promissory notes drawn and payable in India and bearing two or more good signatures, one of which shall be that of a State co-operative bank or a State financial corporation [2][or any financial institution, which is predominantly engaged in the acceptance or discounting of bills of exchange and promissory notes and which is approved by the Bank in this behalf], and drawn or issued for the purpose of financing the production or marketing activities of cottage and small-scale industries approved by the Bank and maturing within twelve months from the date of such purchase or rediscount, exclusive of days of grace, provided that the payment of the principal and interest of such bills of exchange or promissory notes is fully guaranteed by the State Government;]

---

1 Inserted by Act 32 of 1951, w.e.f. 1-11-1951.
2 Inserted by Act 51 of 1974, w.e.f. 13-12-1974.
3 Words "or a Burma scheduled bank" omitted by Act 11 of 1947, w.e.f. 1-4-1947.
4 Substituted for "maturing within ninety days from the date of such purchase or re-discount, exclusive of days of grace" by Act 35 of 1962, w.e.f. 15-9-1962.
5 Substituted for "drawn and payable in India" by MO 1937.
6 Substituted for "either in India or in Burma and payable either in India or in Burma" by Act 11 of 1947, w.e.f. 1-4-1947.
7 Substituted for "a Burma scheduled bank, a provincial co-operative bank, or a Burma co-operative bank" ibid, w.e.f. 1-4-1947.
8 Substituted for "Provincial" by the A.O. 1950.
9 Inserted by Act 51 of 1974, w.e.f. 13-12-1974.
10 Substituted for "financing seasonal agricultural operations", ibid.
11 Substituted for "nine months" by Act 32 of 1951, w.e.f. 1-11-1951.
12 Explanation omitted by Act 23 of 1965, w.e.f. 1-3-1966.
13 Inserted by Act 54 of 1953, w.e.f. 30-12-1953.

(c) the purchase, sale and rediscount of bills of exchange and promissory notes [1][drawn [2][and payable in India]] and bearing the signature of a scheduled bank, [3][xxx] and issued or drawn for the purpose of holding or trading in securities of [4][the Central Government [5][or a [6][State] Government]] [7][xxx] and maturing within ninety days from the date of such purchase or rediscount, exclusive of days of grace;

(3) (a) the purchase from and sale to scheduled banks [8][xxx] of [9][foreign exchange] [10][xxx];

[11][(b) the purchase, sale and rediscount of bills of exchange (including treasury bills) drawn in or on any place in any country outside India which is a member of the International Monetary Fund and maturing,—

(i) in the case of bills of exchange arising out of any *bona fide* transaction relating to the export of goods from India, within one hundred and eighty days, and

(ii) in any other case, within ninety days,

from the date of such purchase or rediscount:

PROVIDED that no such purchase, sale or rediscount shall be made in India except with a scheduled bank or a State co-operative bank;]

[12][xxx]

[13][(3A) the making to any scheduled bank or State co-operative bank, or loans and advances, against promissory notes or such bank, repayable on demand or on the expiry of fixed periods not exceeding one hundred and eighty days:

PROVIDED that the borrowing bank furnishes a declaration in writing, to the effect that—

(i) it holds bills of exchange arising out of any transaction relating to the export of goods from India of a value not less than the amount of such loans or advances,—

(a) drawn in India and no any place in any country outside India which is a member of the International Monetary Fund or in any other country notified in this behalf by the Bank in the Gazette of India, and

[14][(b) maturing not later than one hundred and eighty days from the date of the loan or advance, and it will, so long as any part of such loans and advances remains unpaid, continue to hold such bills of exchange of

---

1 Substituted for "drawn and payable in India" by MO 1937.
2 Substituted for "either in India or Burma and payable either in India or in Burma" by Act 11 of 1947, w.e.f. 1-4-1947.
3 Words "or a Burma scheduled bank" omitted, ibid, w.e.f. 1-4-1947.
4 Substituted for "the Government of India or a L.G." by the M.O. 1937.
5 Substituted for "or a Provincial Government" by Act 11 of 1947, w.e.f. 1-4-1947.
6 Substituted for "Provincial" by the A.O. 1950.
7 Words "or such securities of Part B States as may be specified in this behalf by the Central Government on the recommendation of the Central Board" omitted by Act 32 of 1951, w.e.f. 1-11-1951.
8 Words "and Burma scheduled banks" omitted by Act 11 of 1947, w.e.f. 1-4-1947.
9 Substituted for "sterling" by Act 62 of 1948, w.e.f. 1-1-1949.
10 Words "in amounts of not less than the equivalent of one lakh of rupees" omitted by Act 24 of 1978, w.e.f. 21-7-1978.
11 Substituted by Act 35 of 1962, w.e.f. 15-9-1962.
12 Sub-clause (c) omitted by Act 62 of 1948, w.e.f. 1-1-1949.
13 Inserted by Act 35 of 1962, w.e.f. 15-9-1962.
14 Substituted by Act 58 of 1968, w.e.f. 1-2-1969.

a value not less than the amount of such loans or advances outstanding for the time being; or]

[1][(ii) it has granted a pre-shipment loan or advance to an exporter or any other person in India in order to enable him to export goods from India, the amount of the loan or advance drawn and outstanding at any time being not less than the outstanding amount of the loan or advance obtained by the borrowing bank from the Bank.]]

[2][(3B) the making to any scheduled bank or State co-operative bank or loans and advances repayable on demand or on the expiry of fixed periods not exceeding one hundred and eighty days against promissory notes of such bank:

PROVIDED that the borrowing bank furnishes a declaration in writing to the effect that it has made loans and advances for *bona fide* commercial or trade transactions or for financing agricultural operations or the marketing of crops or for other agricultural purposes as set out in the declaration and the said declaration includes such other particulars as may be required by the Bank;]

(4) the making to [3][xxx] local authorities, scheduled banks [4][, [5][xxx] [6][State] co-operative banks [7][and State Financial Corporations [8][xxx]] or loans and advances, repayable on demand or on the expiry of fixed periods not exceeding ninety days, against the security of—

(a) stocks, funds and securities (other than immovable property) in which a trustee is authorised to invest trust money by any Act of Parliament [9][of the United Kingdom] or by any law for time being in force in [10][India] [11][xxx];

(b) gold or silver or documents of title to the same;

(c) such bills of exchange and promissory notes as are eligible for purchase or rediscount by the Bank [12][or as are fully guaranteed as to the repayment of the principal and payment of interest by a State Government];

(d) promissory notes of any scheduled bank [13][[14][or [6][State]] co-operative bank], supported by documents of title to goods [15][such documents having been transferred], assigned, or pledged to any such bank as security for [16][a loan or advance made] for *bona fide* commercial or trade transactions, or for the purpose of [17][financing agricultural operations] or the marketing of crops:

1 Substituted by Act 58 of 1968, w.e.f. 1-2-1969.
2 Inserted by Act 51 of 1974, w.e.f. 13-12-1974.
3 Words and letter "Part B States" omitted by Act 32 of 1951, w.e.f. 1-11-1951.
4 Substituted for "and Provincial co-operative banks" by the M.O. 1937.
5 The words "Burma scheduled banks" omitted by Act 11 of 1947, w.e.f 1-4-1947.
6 Substituted for "Provincial" by the AO 1950.
7 Substituted by Act 19 of 1957, w.e.f. 8-6-1957.
8 The words and figures "established under the State Financial Corporations Act, 1951" omitted by Act 24 of 1978, w.e.f. 21-7-1978.
9 Inserted by the AO 1950.
10 Substituted for "the States" by Act 32 of 1951, w.e.f. 1-11-1951.
11 Words "or Burma" omitted by Act 11 of 1947, w.e.f. 1-4-1947.
12 Inserted by Act 24 of 1955, w.e.f. 8-5-1955.
13 Substituted for "or a Provincial co-operative bank" by the MO 1937.
14 Substituted for "Burma scheduled bank, provincial co-operative bank or Burma" by Act 11 of 1947, w.e.f. 1-4-1947.
15 Substituted for "which have been transferred" by Act 32 of 1951, w.e.f. 1-11-1951.
16 Substituted for "a cash credit or overdraft granted" by Act 24 of 1955, w.e.f. 8-5-1955.
17 Substituted for "financing seasonal agricultural operations" by Act 51 of 1974, w.e.f. 13-12-1974.

[1][PROVIDED that loans and advances made against the security of bills of exchange and promissory notes arising out of any transaction relating to the export of goods from India shall be repayable on demand or on the expiry of fixed periods not exceeding one hundred and eighty days;]

[2][(4A) the making to any State Financial Corporation [3][xxx], of loans and advances repayable on the expiry of fixed periods not exceeding eighteen months from the date of such loan or advance, against securities of the Central Government or of any State Government, of any maturity, or against bonds and debentures issued by that Corporation and guaranteed by the State Government concerned and maturing within a period not exceeding eighteen months from the date of such loan or advance:

[4][PROVIDED that the previous approval of the State Government shall be obtained for the borrowing by the State Financial Corporation and the amount of loans and advances granted to that Corporation under this clause shall not, at any time, exceed in the aggregate [5][twice the paid-up share capital] thereof;]]

[6][[7][(4AA)] the making of annual contributions to the National Rural Credit (Long Term Operations) Fund and the National Rural Credit (Stabilisation) Fund established under sections 42 and 43, respectively, of the National Bank for Agriculture and Rural Development Act, 1981 (61 of 1981);]

[8][(4B) the making to the Industrial Finance Corporation of India [9][xxx] of loans and advances,—

(a) repayable on demand or on the expiry of fixed periods not exceeding ninety days from the date of such loan or advance, against securities of the Central Government or of any State Government; or

(b) repayable on the expiry of fixed periods not exceeding eighteen months from the date of such loan or advance, against securities of the Central Government of any maturity or against bonds and debentures issued by the Corporation and guaranteed by the Central Government and maturity within a period not exceeding eighteen months from the date of such loan or advance;

[10][xxx]

[11][(4BB) the making to any financial institution notified by the Central Government in this behalf, of loans and advances,—

(a) repayable on demand or on the expiry of fixed periods not exceeding ninety days from the date of such loan or advance, against the securities of the Central Government or of any State Government, or

(b) repayable on the expiry of fixed periods not exceeding eighteen months from the date of such loan or advance, against securities of the Central

1 Inserted by Act 35 of 1962, w.e.f. 15-9-1962.
2 Inserted by Act 14 of 1960, w.e.f. 30-4-1960.
3 Words and figures "established under the State Financial Corporations Act, 1951" omitted by Act 24 of 1978, w.e.f. 21-7-1978.
4 Substituted by Act 51 of 1974, w.e.f. 13-12-1974.
5 Substituted for "ninety per cent. of the paid-up share capital" by Act 81 of 1985, w.e.f. 1-5-1986.
6 Substituted by Act 61 of 1981, w.e.f. 12-7-1982.
7 Clause (4A) renumbered and re-lettered as clause (4AA) thereof by Act 14 of 1960, w.e.f. 30-4-1960.
8 Inserted by Act 54 of 1953, w.e.f. 30-12-1953.
9 Words and figures "established under the Industrial Finance Corporation Act, 1948" omitted by Act 24 of 1978, w.e.f. 21-7-1978.
10 Proviso omitted by Act 66 of 1988, w.e.f. 30-12-1988.
11 Substituted by Act 14 of 1960, w.e.f. 30-4-1960.

Government or of any State Government, of any maturity, or against bonds and debentures issued by that financial institution and guaranteed by the Central Government or any State Government, and maturing within a period not exceeding eighteen months from the date of such loan or advance:

PROVIDED that the amount of loans and advances granted to a financial institution under sub-clause (b) shall not, at any time, exceed in the aggregate sixty per cent.of the paid-up share capital thereof;]

[1][(4BBB) the making to the Unit Trust of loans and advances—

(i) repayable on demand or on the expiry of a fixed period not exceeding ninety days from the date of such loan or advance against the security of stocks, funds and securities (other than immovable property) in which a trustee is authorised to invest trust money by any law for the time being in force in India; [2][xxx]

(ii) repayable on demand or within a period of eighteen months from the date of such loan or advance against the security of the bonds of the Unit Trust issued with the approval of and guaranteed by the Central Government;]

[3][(iii) for the purpose of any scheme other than the first unit scheme under the Unit Trust of India Act, 1963 (52 of 1963) on such terms and conditions and against the security of such other property of the Unit Trust as may be specified in this behalf by the Bank;]

[4][(4C) the making to a Warehousing Corporation established under the Agricultural Produce (Development and Warehousing) Corporations Act, 1956 (28 of 1956) of loans and advances,—

(a) repayable on demand or on the expiry of fixed periods not exceeding ninety days, from the date of such loan or advance, against securities of the Central Government or of any State Government, or

(b) repayable on the expiry of fixed periods not exceeding eighteen months from the date of such loan or advance, against securities of the Central Government or of any State Government, of any maturity, or against bonds and debentures issued by the corporation to which the loan or advance is made, and guaranteed by the Central or a State Government, and maturing within a period not exceeding eighteen months from the date of such loan or advance:

PROVIDED that the amount of loans and advances granted under clause (b) shall not at any time exceed, in the aggregate, three crores of rupees in the case of the Central Warehousing Corporation and fifty lakhs of rupees in the case of a State Warehousing Corporation;]

---

1 Inserted by Act 52 of 1963, w.e.f. 1-2-1964.
2 Word "or" omitted by Act 17 of 1966, w.e.f. 10-6-1966.
3 Inserted, ibid.
4 Inserted by Act 28 of 1956, w.e.f. 1-8-1956.

[1][(4D) the making to the Deposit Insurance Corporation of loans and advances; and generally assisting the Corporation in such manner and on such terms as may be determined by the Central Board;]

[2][(4DD) the making to the National Housing Bank of loans and advances and generally assisting the National Housing Bank in such manner and on such terms as may be determined by the Central Board;]

[3][(4E) the making to the National Bank of loans and advances repayable on demand or on the expiry of fixed period not exceeding eighteen months from the date of making of the loan or advance, either—

(i) against the security of stocks, funds and securities (other than immovable property) in which a trustee is authorised to invest trust money by any law for the time being in force in India; or

(ii) on such other terms and conditions as the Bank may specify;]

[4][(4F) contributing to the initial Capital of the Unit Trust;]

[5][(4G) the making of loans and advances to, and the purchasing of bonds and debentures of, [6][xxx] [7][the Exim Bank] [8][or the Reconstruction Bank] [9][or the Small Industries Bank [10][or the National Bank for Financing Infrastructure and Development or other development financial institution]] out of the National Industrial Credit (Long Term Operations) Fund established under section 46C;]

[2][(4GG) the making of loans and advances to, and the purchasing of bonds and debentures of, the National Housing Bank out of the National Housing Credit (Long Term Operations) Fund established under section 46D;]

(4H) the making to [6][xxx] [9][or the Small Industries Bank] of loans and advances—

(a) repayable on demand or on the expiry of fixed periods not exceeding ninety days from the date of such loan or advance against the security of stocks, funds and securities (other than immovable property) in which a trustee is authorised to invest trust money by any law for the time being in force in India; or

(b) against the security of bills of exchange or promissory notes, arising out of *bona fide* commercial or trade transactions bearing two or more good signatures and maturing within five years from the date of such loan or advance;]

[11][(4-I) the making to scheduled banks, [12][xxx] [7][the Exim Bank] [13][the Reconstruction Bank or the Small Industries Bank] the Industrial Finance Corporation [10][, the National Bank for Financing Infrastructure and Development or other development financial institution] and any other financial institution as may, on the recommendation of the Bank, be approved in this behalf by the Central Government of

---

1 Inserted by Act 47 of 1961, w.e.f. 1-1-1962.
2 Inserted by Act 53 of 1987, w.e.f. 9-7-1988.
3 Substituted by Act 61 of 1981, w.e.f. 12-7-1982.
4 Inserted by Ac 52 of 1963, w.e.f. 1-2-1964.
5 Inserted by Act 18 of 1964, w.e.f. 1-7-1964.
6 Words "the Development Bank or" omitted by Act 53 of 2003, w.e.f. 2-7-2004.
7 Inserted by Act 28 of 1981, w.e.f. 1-1-1982.
8 Inserted by Act 62 of 1984, w.e.f. 20-3-1985.
9 Inserted by Act 39 of 1989, w.e.f. 7-3-1990.
10 Inserted by Act 17 of 2021, w.e.f. 19-4-2021.
11 Inserted by Act 24 of 1978, w.e.f. 21-7-1978.
12 Words "the Development Bank" omitted by Act 53 of 2003, w.e.f. 2-7-2004.
13 Substituted for "or the Reconstruction Bank" by Act 39 of 1989, w.e.f. 7-3-1990.

loans and advances repayable on demand or otherwise and against such security and on such other terms and conditions as may be approved in this behalf by the Central Board for the purpose of enabling such banks, or financial institution, as the case may be, to purchase foreign exchange from the Bank for the purpose of financing the import of capital goods or for such other purposes as may be approved by the Central Government;]

[1][(4J) the making to the Exim Bank of loans and advances—

(a) repayable on demand or on the expiry of a fixed period not exceeding ninety days, from the date of such loan or advance against the security of stocks, funds and securities (other than immovable property) in which a trustee is authorised to invest trust money by any law for the time being in force in India; or

(b) against the security of bills of exchange or promissory notes, arising out of *bona fide* commercial or trade transactions bearing two or more good signatures and maturing within five years from the date of such loan or advance;]

[2][(4K) the making to the Reconstruction Bank of loans and advances—

(a) repayable on demand or on the expiry of a fixed period not exceeding ninety days, from the date of such loan or advance against the security of stocks, funds and securities (other than immovable property) in which a trustee is authorised to invest trust money by any law for the time being in force in India; or

(b) against the security of bills of exchange or promissory notes, arising out of *bona fide* commercial or trade transactions bearing two or more good signatures and maturing within five years from the date of such loan or advance;]

[3][(4L) the making to the National Bank for Financing Infrastructure and Development or other development financial institution of loans and advances—

(a) repayable on demand or on the expiry of a fixed period not exceeding ninety days, from the date of such loan or advance against the security of stocks, funds and securities (other than immovable property) in which a trustee is authorised to invest trust money by any law for the time being in force in India; or

(b) against the security of bills of exchange or promissory notes, arising out of *bona fide* commercial or trade transactions bearing two or more good signatures and maturing within five years from the date of such loan or advance;]

(5) the making to the [4][Central Government] [5][[6][xxx] [7][and [8][State] Governments]] of advances repayable in each case not later than three months from the date of the making of the advance;

---

1 Inserted by Act 28 of 1981, w.e.f. 1-1-1982.
2 Inserted by Act 62 of 1984, w.e.f. 20-3-1985.
3 Inserted by Act 17 of 2021, w.e.f. 19-4-2021.
4 Substituted for "G.G. in C." by the MO 1937.
5 Certain words substituted by ibid.
6 Words "the Federal Railway Authority" omitted by the AO 1948.
7 Substituted for "Provincial Governments, the Government of Burma and the Burma Railway Board" by Act 11 of 1947, w.e.f. 1-4-1947.
8 Substituted for "Provincial" by the AO 1950.

[1][(6) the issue of demand drafts, telegraphic transfers and other kinds of remittances made payable at its own offices or agencies, the purchase of telegraphic transfers, and the making, issue and circulation of bank post bills;]

[2][(6A) dealing in derivatives, and, with the approval of the Central Board, in any other financial instrument.

Explanation: For the purposes of this clause, "derivative" means an instrument, to be settled at a future date, whose value is derived from change in one or a combination of more than one of the following underlying, namely:—

(a) interest rate,

(b) price of securities of the Central Government or a State Government or of such securities of a local authority as may be specified in this behalf by the Central Government,

(c) price of foreign securities,

(d) foreign exchange rate,

(e) index of rates or prices,

(f) credit rating or credit index,

(g) price of gold or silver coins, or gold or silver bullion, or

(h) any other variable of similar nature;]

[3][xxx]

(8) the purchase and sale of securities [4][of the Central [5][Government or a [6][State] Government]] of any maturity or of such securities of a local authority [7][xxx] as may be specified in this behalf by the [8][Central Government] on the recommendation of the Central Board:

PROVIDED that securities fully guaranteed as to principal and interest by [9][any such Government [10][or authority]] shall be deemed for the purposes of this clause to be securities of such Government [10][or authority];

[11][xxx]

[12][(8A) the purchase and sale of shares in, or the capital of [13][the [14][National Bank],] [15][the Deposit Insurance Corporation], [16][xxx], the State Bank [17][or any other bank [18][or financial institution] notified by the Central Government in this behalf];]

1 Substituted by Act 32 of 1951, w.e.f. 1-11-1951.
2 Inserted by Act 26 of 2006, w.e.f. 9-1-2007.
3 Clause (7) repealed by Act 2 of 1948, w.e.f. 5-1-1948.
4 Substituted for "of the G. of I or of a L.G." by the MO 1937.
5 Substituted for "Government, a Provincial Government or the Government of Burma" by Act 11 of 1947, w.e.f. 1-4-197.
6 Substituted for "Provincial" by the AO 1950.
7 Words and letter "or such Part B States" omitted by Act 32 of 1951, w.e.f. 1-11-1951.
8 Substituted for "G.G. in C." by MO 1937.
9 Substituted for "the G. of I., a L.G., a local authority or State in India", ibid.
10 Substituted for "authority or State" by Act 32 of 1951, w.e.f. 1-11-1951.
11 Second proviso omitted, ibid, w.e.f. 1-11-1951.
12 Inserted by Act 23 of 1955, w.e.f. 1-7-1955.
13 Inserted by Act 10 of 1963, w.e.f. 1-5-1963.
14 Substituted for "Agricultural Refinance and Development Corporation" by Act 61 of 1981, w.e.f. 12-7-1982.
15 Inserted by Act 47 of 1961, w.e.f. 1-1-1962.
16 Words "the Development Bank" omitted by Act 53 of 2003, w.e.f. 2-7-2004.
17 Substituted for "or any of its subsidiary banks" by Act 79 of 1956, w.e.f. 22-10-1956.
18 Inserted by Act 19 of 1957, w.e.f. 8-6-1957.

[1][(8AA) the promoting, establishing, supporting or aiding in the promotion, establishment and support of any financial institution, whether as its subsidiary or otherwise;]

[2][(8B) the keeping of deposits with the State Bank for such specific purposes as may be approved by the Central Government in this behalf;]

(9) the custody of monies, securities and other articles of value, and the collection of the proceeds, whether principal, interest or dividends, of any such securities;

(10) the sale realisation of all property, whether movable or immovable, which may in any way come into the possession of the Bank in satisfaction, or part satisfaction, of any of its claims;

(11) the acting as agent for [3][xxx] the [4][Central Government] [5][or any [6][State] Government [7][xxx] or any local authority [8][xxx] [9][or the Industrial Finance Corporation of India [10][xxx] [11][or any other body corporate which is established or constituted by or under any other law] [12][or the Government of any such country outside India or [13][any such person or authority] as may be approved in this behalf by the Central Government] in the transaction of any of the following kinds of business, namely:—

(a) the purchase and sale of gold or silver [14][or foreign exchange];

(b) the purchase, sale, transfer and custody of bills of exchange, securities or shares in any company;

(c) the collection of the proceeds, whether principal, interest or dividends, of any securities or shares;

(d) the remittance of such proceeds, at the risk of the principal, by bills of exchange payable either in India or elsewhere;

(e) the management of public debt;

[15][(f) [16][xxx] the issue and management of [17][xxx] bonds and debentures;]

[18][(11A) the acting as agent for the Central Government,—

[19][(a) in guaranteeing the due performance by any small-scale industrial concern, approved by the Central Government, of its obligations to any bank or other financial institution in respect of loans and advances made, or other credit facilities provided, to it by such bank or other financial institution and the making as such agent of payments in connection with such guarantee, and]

---

1 Inserted by Act 53 of 1987, w.e.f. 9-7-1988.
2 Inserted by Act 38 of 1959, w.e.f. 10-9-1959.
3 Words "the Secretary of State" omitted by the AO 1948.
4 Substituted for "G.G. in C." by MO 1937.
5 Certain words substituted, ibid.
6 Substituted for "Provincial" by the AO 1950.
7 Words "or the Government of Burma" omitted by Act 11 of 1947, w.e.f. 1-4-1947.
8 Words and letter "or any Part B State" omitted by Act 32 of 1951, w.e.f. 1-11-1951.
9 Inserted by Act 44 of 1949.
10 Words "established under the Industrial Finance Corporation Act, 1948 (15 of 1948)" omitted by Act 24 of 1978, w.e.f. 21-7-1978.
11 Inserted by Act 51 of 1974, w.e.f. 13-12-1974.
12 Inserted by Act 32 of 1951, w.e.f. 1-11-1951.
13 Substituted for "any such person" by Act 51 of 1974, w.e.f. 13-12-1974.
14 Inserted by Act 23 of 1947, w.e.f. 18-4-1947.
15 Inserted by Act 44 of 1949.
16 Words "in respect of the aforesaid Corporation" omitted by Act 51 of 1974, w.e.f. 13-12-1974.
17 Word "its" omitted, ibid. w.e.f. 13-12-1974.
18 Substituted by Act 58 of 1968, w.e.f. 1-2-1969.
19 Restored by Act 81 of 1985, w.e.f. 1-5-1986.

(b) in administering any scheme for subsidising the rate of interest or other charges in relation to any loans or advances made, or other credit facilities provided, by banks or other financial institutions for the purpose of financing or facilitating any export from India and the making as such agent of payments on behalf of the Central Government;]

[1][(12) the purchase and sale of gold or silver coins and gold and silver bullion and foreign exchange and the opening of a gold account with the principal currency authority of any foreign country or the Bank for International Settlements or any international or regional bank or financial institution formed by such principal currency authority or authorities or by the Government of any foreign country;]

[2][(12A) the purchase and sale of securities issued by the Government of any country outside India or by any institution or body corporate established outside India and expressed to be payable in a foreign currency or any international or composite currency unit, being in the case of purchase by the Bank securities maturing within a period of ten years from the date of purchase:

PROVIDED that in the case of securities of an institution or body corporate, the repayment of principal and payment of interest in respect of such securities shall be guaranteed by the Government of the country concerned;]

[3][(12AA) lending or borrowing of securities of the Central Government or a State Government or of such securities of a local authority as may be specified in this behalf by the Central Government or foreign securities;

(12AB) dealing in repo or reverse repo:

PROVIDED that lending or borrowing of funds by way of repo or reverse repo shall not be subject to any limitation contained in this section.

Explanation : For the purposes of this clause,—

(a) "repo" means an instrument for borrowing funds by selling securities of the Central Government or a State Government or of such securities of a local authority as may be specified in this behalf by the Central Government or foreign securities, with an agreement to repurchase the said securities on a mutually agreed future date at an agreed price which includes interest for the funds borrowed;

(b) "reverse repo" means an instrument for lending funds by purchasing securities of the Central Government or a State Government or of such securities of a local authority as may be specified in this behalf by the Central Government or foreign securities, with an agreement to resell the said securities on a mutually agreed future date at an agreed price which includes interest for the funds lent;]

[4][(12B) the making of loans and advances in foreign currencies to scheduled banks, [5][xxx] [6][, the Exim Bank], [7][or [8][the Reconstruction Bank or the Small Industries Bank]] the Industrial Finance Corporation [9][the National Bank for Financing Infrastructure and

1 Substituted by Act 24 of 1978, w.e.f. 21-7-1978.
2 Substituted, ibid, w.e.f. 21-7-1978.
3 Inserted by Act 26 of 2006, w.e.f. 9-1-2007.
4 Inserted by Act 24 of 1978, w.e.f. 21-7-1978.
5 Words "the Development Bank" omitted by Act 53 of 2003, w.e.f. 2-7-2004.
6 Inserted by Act 28 of 1981, w.e.f. 1-1-1982.
7 Inserted by Act 62 of 1984, w.e.f. 20-3-1985.
8 Substituted for "the Reconstruction Bank" by Act 39 of 1989, w.e.f. 7-3-1990.
9 Inserted by Act 17 of 2021, w.e.f. 19-4-2021.

Development or other development financial institution,] any State Financial Corporation and any other financial institution as may, on the recommendation of the Bank, be approved by the Central Government and on such terms and conditions as may be specified by the Central Board in this behalf, against promissory notes of such bank or financial institution, as the case may be:

PROVIDED that the borrowing bank or financial institution, as the case may be, furnishes a declaration in writing to the effect that—

(a) it has made loans and advances in foreign currencies for financing international trade or for the import of capital goods or for such other purposes as may be approved by the Central Government; and

(b) that the amount of loans or advances so made and outstanding at any time will not be less than the outstanding amount of the loans or advances obtained by it from the Bank;]

[1][(13) the opening of an account with an office outside India of any bank, including a bank incorporated in India or the making of an agency agreement with, and the acting as an agent or correspondent of, any bank incorporated outside India, or the principal currency authority of any country under the law for the time being in force in that country or any international or regional bank or financial institution formed by such principal currency authorities or foreign governments, and the investing of the funds of the Bank in the shares and securities of any such international or regional bank or financial institution or of any other foreign institution as may be approved by the Central Board in this behalf;]

[2][(13A) participation in any arrangement for the clearing and settlement of any amounts due from, or to, any person or authority on account of the external trade of India with any other country or group of countries or of any remittances to, or from, that country or group of countries, including the advancing, or receiving, of any amount in any currency in connection therewith, and, for that purpose, becoming, with the approval of the Central Government, a member of any international or regional clearing union of central banks monetary or other authorities, or being associated with any such clearing arrangements, or becoming a member of any body or association formed by central banks, monetary or other similar authorities, or being associated with the same in any manner;]

(14) the borrowing of money for a period not exceeding one month for the purposes of the business of the Bank, and the giving of security for money so borrowed:

PROVIDED that no money shall be borrowed under this clause from any person in India [3][xxx] other than a scheduled bank [4][xxx] or from any person outside India [5][xxx] other than a bank which is the principal currency authority of any country under the law for the time being in force in that country:

1 Substituted by Act 24 of 1978, w.e.f. 21-7-1978.
2 Inserted by Act 44 of 1973, w.r.e.f. 15-9-1973.
3 Words "or Burma" omitted by Act 11 of 1947, w.e.f. 1-4-1947.
4 Words "or a Burma scheduled bank" omitted, ibid.
5 Words "and Burma" omitted, ibid.

PROVIDED FURTHER that the total amount of such borrowings from persons in India [1][xxx] shall not at any time exceed the amount of the [2][capital] of the Bank;

[3][xxx]

(15) the making and issue of bank notes subject to the provisions of this Act [4][xxx]; [5][xxx]

[6][(15A) the exercise of powers and functions and the performance of duties entrusted to the Bank under this Act or under any other law for the time being in force;]

[7][15B) the providing of facilities for training in banking and for the promotion of research, where, in the opinion of the Bank, such provision may facilitate the exercise by the Bank of its powers and functions, or the discharge of its duties;]

(16) generally, the doing of all such matters and things as may be incidental to or consequential upon the exercise of its powers or the discharge of its duties under this Act [8][xxx].

18. Power of direct discount

[9][xxx] When, in the opinion of the [10][Bank] [11][xxx], a special occasion has arisen making it necessary or expedient that action should be taken [12][under this section] for the purposes of regulating credit in the interests of Indian [13][xxx] trade, commerce, industry and agricultural, the Bank may, notwithstanding any limitation contained in [14][xxx] section 17,

[15][(1) purchase, sell or discount any bill of exchange or promissory note though such bill or promissory note is not eligible for purchase or discount by the Bank under that section; or]

[16][xxx]

[17][(3) make loans or advances to—

(a) a State co-operative bank, or

(b) on the recommendation of a State co-operative bank, to a cooperative society registered within the area in which the State cooperative bank operates, or

(c) any other person,

repayable on demand or on the expiry of the fixed periods, not exceeding ninety days, on such terms and conditions as the Bank may consider to be sufficient.]

[18][xxx]

[19][xxx]

---

1 Words "and Burma" omitted by Act 11 of 1947, w.e.f. 1-4-1947.
2 Substituted for "share capital" by Act 32 of 1951, w.e.f. 1-11-1951.
3 Clause (14A) omitted by Act 38 of 1959, w.e.f. 1-10-1959.
4 Words "and the making and issue of Burma notes in accordance with the law of Burma" omitted by Act 11 of 1947, w.e.f. 1-4-1947.
5 Word "and" omitted by Ordinance 47 of 1945.
6 Substituted by Act 23 of 1955, w.e.f. 1-7-1955.
7 Inserted by Act 58 of 1968, w.e.f. 1-2-1969.
8 Words "and the law of Burma" omitted by Act 11 of 1947, w.e.f. 1-4-1947.
9 Brackets and figure "(1)" omitted by Act 51 of 1974, w.e.f. 13-12-1974.
10 Substituted for "Central Board" by Act 32 of 1951, w.e.f. 1-11-1951.
11 Certain words omitted by Act 62 of 1948, w.e.f. 1-1-1949.
12 Substituted for "under this sub-section" by Act 51 of 1974, w.e.f. 13-12-1974.
13 The words "or Burman" omitted by Act 11 of 1947, w.e.f. 1-4-1947.
14 Words, brackets, letters and figures "sub-clauses (a) and (b) of clause (2) or sub-clause (a) or (b) of clause (3) or clause (4) of" omitted by Act 51 of 1974, w.e.f. 13-12-1974.
15 Substituted, ibid, w.e.f. 13-12-1974.
16 Clause (2) omitted by Act 24 of 1978, w.e.f. 21-7-1978.
17 Substituted by Act 51 of 1974, w.e.f. 13-12-1974.
18 The proviso omitted by Act 62 of 1948, w.e.f. 1-1-1949.
19 Sub-section (2) omitted by Act 51 of 1974, w.e.f. 13-12-1974.

[1][18A. Validity of loan or advance not to be questioned

Notwithstanding anything to the contrary contained in any other law for the time being in force,—

(a) the validity of any loan or advance granted by the Bank in pursuance of the provisions of this Act shall not be called in question merely on the ground of non-compliance with the requirements of such other law as aforesaid or of any resolution, contract, memorandum, articles of association or other instrument:

PROVIDED that nothing in this clause shall render valid any loan or advance obtained by any company or co-operative society where such company or co-operative society is not empowered by its memorandum to obtain loans or advances;

(b) where a loan or advance has been granted under clause (3A) or under clause (3B) of section 17 or a loan or advance granted under clause (3) of section 18 by the Bank to any person has been applied by such person, wholly or in part, in making a loan or advance to any borrower, any sum received—

(i) by the borrowing bank on account of bills of exchange in respect of which the declaration under clause (i) of the proviso to clause (3A) of section 17 has been furnished or in repayment or realisation of the outstanding loans and advances referred to in clause (ii) of the said proviso or in the proviso to clause (3B) of the said section, or

(ii) by the borrowing bank or any other person in repayment or realisation of loans and advances granted to a borrower out of funds obtained by it or by him from the Bank under section 18,

shall be utilised only for the repayment by the borrowing bank or other person, as the case may be, of the amounts due to be repaid by it or by him to the Bank, and shall be held by it or by him in trust for the Bank, until such time as the amounts are so repaid.]

19. Business which the Bank may not transact

Save as otherwise provided in sections 17, 18, [2][42] and 45, the Bank may not—

(1) engage in trade or otherwise have a direct interest in any commercial, industrial or other undertaking except such interest as it may in any way acquire in the course of the satisfaction of any of its claims:

PROVIDED that all such interests shall be disposed of at the earliest possible moment;

[3][(2) purchase the shares of any banking company or of any other company, or grant loans upon the security of any such shares;]

(3) advance money on mortgage of, or otherwise on the security of, immovable property or documents of title relating thereto, or become the owner of immovable property, except so far as is necessary for its own business premises and residences for its officers and servants;

(4) make loans or advances;

(5) draw or accept bills payable otherwise than on demand;

(6) allow interest on deposits or current accounts.

---

1 Inserted by Act 51 of 1974, w.e.f. 13-12-1974.
2 Inserted by Act 38 of 1956, w.e.f. 6-10-1956.
3 Substituted by Act 32 of 1951, w.e.f. 1-1-1951.

CHAPTER III
CENTRAL BANKING FUNCTIONS

20. Obligation of the Bank to transact Government business

The Bank shall undertake to accept monies for account of [1][[2]xxx] the Central Government [3][xxx] and to make payments up to the amount standing to the credit of [4][its account], and to carry out [5][its exchange], remittance and other banking operations, including the management of the public debt [6][of the Union].

[7][xxx]

21. Bank to have the right to transact Government business in India

(1) The [8][Central Government] [9][xxx] shall entrust the Bank, on such conditions as may be agreed upon, with all [10][its] money, remittance, exchange and banking transactions in India, and, in particular, shall deposit free of interest all [10][its] cash balances with the Bank:

PROVIDED that nothing in this sub-section shall prevent the [8][Central Government] [11][xxx] from carrying on money transactions at places where the Bank has no branches or agencies, and the [8][Central Government] [9][xxx] may hold at such places such balances as [12][it] may require.

(2) The [8][Central Government] [13][xxx] shall entrust the Bank, on such conditions as may be agreed upon, with the management of the public debt and with the issue of any new loans.

(3) In the event of any failure to reach agreement on the conditions referred to in this section the [8][Central Government] shall decide what the conditions shall be.

[14][(4) Any agreement made under this section shall be laid, as soon as may be after it is made, before Parliament.]

[15][xxx]

[16][21A. Bank to transact Government business of States on agreement

(1) The Bank may by agreement with the Government of any [17][xxx] State [18][xxx] undertake—

(a) all its money, remittance, exchange and banking transactions in India, including in particular, the deposit, free of interest, of all its cash balances with the Bank; and

1 Certain words substituted by the M.O. 1937.
2 The words "the Secretary of State" omitted by the AO 1950.
3 The words and letter "and the Governments of Part A States" omitted by Act 37 of 1956, w.e.f. 1-11-1956.
4 Substituted for "their accounts respectively", ibid.
5 Substituted for "their exchange", ibid.
6 Inserted, ibid.
7 Section 20A omitted to the repeal of the Ordinance by Act 11 of 1947 which was earlier temporarily inserted by Ordinance 19 of 1945.
8 Substituted for "G.G. in C." by MO 1937.
9 Words "and the State Governments" omitted by Act 37 of 1956, w.e.f. 1-11-1956.
10 Substituted for "their", ibid.
11 Words "or any State Government" omitted, ibid.
12 Substituted for "they", ibid.
13 Words "and each State Government" omitted, ibid.
14 Substituted, ibid.
15 Sub-section (5) omitted, ibid.
16 Inserted by Act 32 of 1951, w.e.f. 1-11-1951.
17 Word and letter "Part B" omitted by Act 37 of 1956, w.e.f. 1-11-1956.
18 Words "(including the autonomous State of Meghalaya)" omitted by Act 81 of 1971, w.e.f. 21-1-1972.

(b) the management of the public debt of, and the issue of any new loans by, that State.

(2) Any Agreement made under this section shall be laid, as soon as may be after it is made, before Parliament.]

[1][21B. **Effect of agreements made between the Bank and certain States before the 1st November, 1956**

(1) Any agreement made under section 21 or section 21A between the Bank and the Government of a State specified in the *Explanation* below and in force immediately before the 1st day of November, 1956, shall, as from that day have effect as if it were an agreement made on that day under section 21A between the Bank and the Government of the corresponding State subject to such modifications, if any, being of a character not affecting the general operation of the agreement, as may be agreed upon between the Bank and the Government of the corresponding State, or in default of such agreement, as may be made therein by order of the Central Government.

Explanation : In this sub-section "corresponding State" means,—

(a) in relation to the agreement between the Bank and the State of Andhra, the State of Andhra Pradesh;

(b) in relation to the agreement between the Bank and any other Part A State as it existed before the 1st day of November, 1956, the State with the same name; and

(c) in relation to the agreement between the Bank and the Part B State of Mysore or Travancore-Cochin as it existed before the 1st day of November, 1956, the State of Mysore of Kerala respectively.

(2) Any agreement made under section 21A between the Bank and the Government of the Part B State of Hyderabad, Madhya Bharat or Saurashtra shall be deemed to have terminated on the 31st day of October, 1956.]

22. Right to issue bank notes

(1) The Bank shall have the sole right to issue bank notes in [2][India], and may, for a period which shall be fixed by the [3][Central Government] on the recommendation of the Central Board, issue currency notes of the Government of India supplied to it by the [3][Central Government], and the provisions of this Act applicable to bank notes shall, unless a contrary intention appears, apply to all currency notes of the Government of India issued either by the [3][Central Government] or by the Bank in like manner as if such currency notes were bank notes, and references in this Act to bank notes shall be construed accordingly.

(2) On and from the date on which this Chapter comes into force the [3][Central Government] shall not issue any currency notes.

[4][**22A. Non-applicability of certain provisions of digital form of bank notes**

Nothing contained in sections 24, 25, 27, 28 and 39 shall apply to the bank notes issued in digital form by the Bank.]

23. Issue Department

(1) The issue of bank notes shall be conducted by the Bank in an Issue Department which shall be separated and kept wholly distinct from the Banking Department, and

1 Inserted by Act 37 of 1956, w.e.f. 1-11-1956.
2 Substituted for "the States" by Act 32 of 1951, w.e.f. 1-11-1951.
3 Substituted for "G.G. in C." by MO 1937.
4 Inserted by Finance Act, 2022 (No. 6 of 2022), dt. 30-3-2022.

the assets of the Issue Department shall not be subject to any liability other than the liabilities of the Issue Department as hereinafter defined in section 34.

(2) The Issue Department shall not issue bank notes to the Banking Department or to any other person except in exchange for other bank notes or for such coin, bullion or securities as are permitted by this Act to form part of the Reserve.

[1][xxx]

[2][24. Denominations of notes

(1) Subject to the provisions of sub-section (2) bank notes shall be of the denominational value to two rupees, five rupees, ten rupees, twenty rupees, fifty rupees, one hundred rupees, five hundred rupees, one thousand rupees, five thousand rupees and ten thousand rupees or of such other denominational values, not exceeding ten thousand rupees, as the Central Government may, on the recommendation of the Central Board, specify in this behalf.

(2) The Central Government may, on the recommendation of the Central Board, direct the non-issue or the discontinuance of issue of bank notes of such denominational values as it may specify in this behalf.]

25. Form of bank notes

The design, form the material of bank notes shall be such as may be approved by the [3][Central Government] after consideration of the recommendations made by the Central Board.

26. Legal tender character of notes

(1) Subject to the provisions of sub-section (2), every bank note shall be legal tender at any place in [4][India] in payment, or on account for the amount expressed therein, and shall be guaranteed by the [3][Central Government].

(2) On recommendation of the Central Board the [3][Central Government] may, by notification in the Gazette of India, declare that, with effect from such date as may be specified in the notification, any series of bank notes of any denomination shall cease to be legal tender [5][save at such office or agency of the Bank and to such extent as may be specified in the notification].

[6][xxx]

[7][26A. Certain bank notes to cease to be legal tender

Notwithstanding anything contained in section 26, no bank note of the denominational value of five hundred rupees, one thousand rupees or ten thousand rupees issued before the 13th day of January, 1946, shall be legal tender in payment or on account for the amount expressed therein.]

27. Re-issue notes

The Bank shall not re-issue bank notes which are torn, defaced or excessively spoiled.

---

1 Sub-section (3) omitted by Act 11 of 1947, w.e.f. 1-4-1947.
2 Substituted by Act 58 of 1968, w.e.f. 1-2-1969.
3 Substituted for "G.G. in C." by MO 1937.
4 Substituted for "the States" by Act 32 of 1951, w.e.f. 1-11-1951.
5 Substituted for "save at an office or agency of the Bank" by Act 32 of 1951, w.e.f. 1-11-1951.
6 Sub-section (3) omitted by Act 11 of 1947, w.e.f. 1-4-1947.
7 Inserted by Act 62 of 1956, w.e.f. 1-11-1956.

28. Recovery of notes lost, stolen, mutilated or imperfect

[1][xxx] Notwithstanding anything contained in any enactment or rule of law to the contrary, no person shall of right be entitled to recover from the [2][Central Government] or the Bank, the value of any lost, stolen, mutilated or imperfect currency note of the Government of India or bank note:

PROVIDED that the Bank may, with the previous sanction of the [1][Central Government], prescribed the circumstances in and the conditions and limitations subject to which the value of such currency notes or bank notes may be refunded as of grace and the rules made under this proviso shall be laid on the table [3][xxx] of [4][Parliament].

[5][xxx]

[6]**[28A. Issue of special bank notes and special one rupee notes in certain cases**

(1) For the purpose of controlling the circulation of bank notes without India, the Bank may, notwithstanding anything contained in any other provision of this Act, issue bank notes of such design, form and material as may be approved under sub-section (3) (hereinafter in this section referred to as special bank notes) of the denominational values of five rupees, ten rupees and one hundred rupees.

(2) For the purpose of controlling the circulation of Government of India one rupee notes without India, the Central Government may, notwithstanding anything contained in any other provision of this Act or in the Currency Ordinance, 1940 (Ord. 4 of 1940) issue Government of India notes of the denominational value of one rupee of such design, form and material as may be adopted under sub-section (3) (hereinafter in this section referred to as special one rupee notes).

(3) The design, form and material of the special bank notes shall be such as may be approved by the Central Government after consideration of the recommendations made by the Governor and of the special one rupee notes shall be such as the Central Government may think fit to adopt.

(4) Neither the special bank notes nor the special one rupee notes shall be legal tender in India.

(5) The special one rupee note shall be deemed to be included in the expression "rupee coin" for all the purposes of this Act except section 39, but shall be deemed not to be a currency note for any of the purposes of this Act.

(6) Where a special bank note is on its face expressed to be payable at a specified office or branch of the Bank, the obligation imposed by section 39 shall be only on the specified office or branch and, further, shall be subject to such regulations as may be made under this section.

(7) The Bank may, with the previous sanction of the Central Government, make regulations to provide for all matters for which provision is necessary or convenient for the purpose of giving effect to the provisions of this section, and, in particular, the manner in which, and the conditions or limitations subject to which—

(i) bank notes and one rupee notes in circulation in any country outside India may be replaced by special notes issued under this section;

(ii) any such special notes may be exchanged for any other bank notes or one rupee notes.]

---

1 Brackets and figure "(1)" omitted by Act 11 of 1947, w.e.f. 1-4-1947.
2 Substituted for "G.G. in C." by the MO 1937.
3 Words "of both Houses" omitted by the AO 1948.
4 Substituted for "the Central Legislature" by the A.O. 1950.
5 Sub-section (2) omitted by Act 11 of 1947, w.e.f. 1-4-1947.
6 Inserted by Act 14 of 1959, w.e.f. 1-5-1959.

29. Bank exempt from stamp duty on bank notes

The Bank shall not be liable to the payment of any stamp duty under the Indian Stamp Act, 1899 (2 of 1899) in respect of bank notes [1][xxx] issued by it.

30. Powers of Central Government to supersede Central Board

(1) If in the opinion of the [2][Central Government] the Bank fails to carry out any of the obligations imposed on it by or under this Act [3][xxx] [4][the Central Government] may, by notification in the Gazette of India, declare the Central Board to be superseded, and thereafter the general superintendence and direction of the affairs of the Bank shall be entrusted to such agency as the [2][Central Government] may determine, and such agency may exercise the powers and do all acts and things which may be exercised or done by the Central Board under this Act.

(2) When action is taken under this section the [2][Central Government] shall cause a full report of the circumstances leading to such action and of the action taken to be laid before [5][Parliament] at the earliest possible opportunity and in any case within three months from the issue of the notification superseding the Board.

31. Issue of demand bills and notes

[6][(1)] No person in [7][India] other than the Bank, or, as expressly authorised by this Act the [2][Central Government] shall draw, accept, make or issue any bill of exchange, hundi, promissory note or engagement for the payment of money payable to bearer on demand, or borrow, owe or take up any sum or sums of money on the bills, hundis or notes payable to bearer on demand of any such person:

PROVIDED that cheques or drafts, including hundis, payable to bearer on demand or otherwise may be drawn on a person's account with a banker, shroff or agent.

[8][(2) Notwithstanding anything contained in the Negotiable Instruments Act, 1881, (26 of 1881) no person in [7][India] other than the Bank or, as expressly authorised by this Act, the Central Government shall make or issue any promissory note expressed to be payable to the bearer of the instrument.]

[9][(3) Notwithstanding anything contained in this section, the Central Government may authorise any scheduled bank to issue electoral bond.

Explanation : For the purposes of this sub-section, "electroal bond" means a bond issued by any scheduled bank under the scheme as may be notified by the Central Government.]

[10]**[xxx]**

33. Assets of the Issue Department

(1) The assets of the Issue Department shall consist of gold coin, gold bullion, [11][foreign securities], rupee coin and rupee securities to such aggregate amount as is not less than the total of the liabilities of the Issue Department as hereinafter defined.

---

1 The words "or Burma notes" omitted by Act 11 of 1947, w.e.f. 1-4-1947.
2 Substituted for "G.G. in C." by the MO 1937.
3 Words "or by or under the law of Burma" omitted by Act 11 of 1947, w.e.f. 1-4-1947.
4 Substituted for "he" by the MO 1937.
5 Substituted for "the Central Legislature" by the AO 1950.
6 Section 31 renumbered as sub-section (1) thereof by Act 23 of 1946, w.e.f. 10-11-1946.
7 Substituted for "the States" by Act 32 of 1951, w.e.f. 1-11-1951.
8 Inserted by Act 23 of 1946, w.e.f. 10-11-1946.
9 Inserted by Act 7 of 2017, w.e.f. 1-4-2017.
10 Section 32 omitted by the Reserve Bank of India (Amendment) Act, 1974 (51 of 1974), w.e.f. 13-12-1974.
11 Substituted for "sterling securities" by Act 62 of 1948, w.e.f. 1-1-1949.

[1][(2) The aggregate value of the gold coin, gold bullion and foreign securities held as assets and the aggregate value of the gold coin and gold bullion so held shall not at any time be less than two hundred crores of rupees and one hundred and fifteen crores of rupees, respectively.]

[2][(3) The remainder of the assets shall be held in rupee coin, Government of India rupee securities of any maturity, promissory notes drawn by the National Bank for any loans or advances under clause (4E) of section 17 and such bills of exchange and promissory notes payable in India as are eligible for purchase by the Bank under sub-clause (a) or sub-clause (b) or sub-clause (bb) of clause (2) of section 17 or under clause (1) of section 18.]

(4) For the purposes of this section, gold coin the gold bullion shall be valued at [3][a price not exceeding the international market price for the time being obtaining], rupee coin shall be valued at its face value, and securities shall be valued [4][at rates not exceeding the market rates] for the time being obtaining.

(5) Of the gold coin and gold bullion held as assets, not less than seventeen-twentieths shall be held in [5][India], and all gold coin and gold bullion held as assets shall be held in the custody of the Bank or its agencies:

PROVIDED that gold belonging to the Bank which is in any other bank or in any mint or treasury or in transit may be reckoned as part of the assets.

[6][(6) For the purposes of this section, the foreign securities which may be held as part of the assets shall be—

(i) securities of the following kinds payable in the currency of any foreign country which is a member of the International Monetary Fund, namely:—

(a) balances with the bank which is the principal currency authority of that foreign country and any other balances or securities in foreign currency maintained with or issued by the International Monetary Fund, the International Bank for Reconstruction and Development, the International Development Association or the International Finance Corporation [7][or Asian Development Bank] or the Bank for International Settlements or [8][any banking or financial institution [9][approved] by the Central Government] in this behalf provided that they are repayable within a [10][period of ten years];

(b) bills of exchange bearing two or more good signatures and drawn on and payable at any place in that foreign country and having a maturity not exceeding ninety days; and

(c) Government securities of that foreign country maturing [11][within ten years];

---

1 Substituted by Act 48 of 1957, w.e.f. 31-10-1957.
2 Substituted by Act 61 of 1981, w.e.f. 12-7-1982.
3 Substituted. for "0.118489 grammes of fine gold per rupee" by Act 8 of 1991, w.e.f. 15-10-1990.
4 Substituted for "at the market rate" by Act 58 of 1968, w.e.f. 1-2-1969.
5 Substituted for "the States" by Act 32 of 1951, w.e.f. 1-11-1951.
6 Substituted by Act 51 of 1974, w.e.f. 13-12-1974.
7 Inserted by Act 24 of 1978, w.e.f. 21-7-1978.
8 Substituted for "any commercial bank notified by the Central Government", ibid, w.e.f. 21-7-1978).
9 Substituted for "notified" by Act 1 of 1984, w.e.f. 15-2-1984.
10 Substituted for "period of five years" by Act 24 of 1978, w.e.f. 21-7-198.
11 Substituted for "within five years", ibid.

(ii) any drawing rights representing a liability of the International Monetary Fund.]

34. Liabilities of Issue Department

(1) The liabilities of the Issue Department shall be an amount equal to the total of the amount of the currency notes of the Government of India and bank notes for the time being in circulation.

[1][xxx]

[2][xxx

[3][xxx]

[4][xxx]

[5][37. Suspension of assets requirements as to foreign securities

Notwithstanding anything contained in the foregoing provisions, the Bank may, with the previous sanction of the Central Government, for periods not exceeding six months in the first instance, which may, with the like sanction, be extended from time to time by period not exceeding three months at a time, hold as assets foreign securities of less amount in value than that required by sub-section (2) of section 33.

[6][xxx]

38. Obligations of Government and the Bank in respect of rupee coin

The [7][Central Government] shall undertake not [8][xxx] to put into circulation any rupees, except through the Bank, [9][xxx] and the Bank shall undertake not to dispose of rupee coin otherwise than for the purposes of circulation [10][xxx].

39. Obligation to supply different forms of currency

(1) The Bank shall issue rupee coin on demand in exchange for bank notes and currency notes of the Government of India and shall issue currency notes or bank notes on demand in exchange for coin which is legal tender under the Indian Coinage Act, 1906 (3 of 1906).

(2) The Bank shall, in exchange for currency notes or bank notes of [11][two] rupees or upwards, supply currency notes or bank notes of lower value or other coins which are legal tender under the Indian Coinage Act, 1906 (3 of 1906), in such quantities as may, in the opinion of the Bank, be required for circulation; and the [7][Central Government] shall supply such coins to the Bank on demand. If the [7][Central Government] at any time fails to supply such coins, the Bank shall be released from its obligations to supply them to the public.

---

1 Sub-section (2) omitted by Act 55 of 1963, w.e.f. 1-2-1964.
2 Sub-section (3) omitted, ibid.
3 Section 35 omitted by the Reserve Bank (Transfer to Public Ownership) Act, 1948 (62 of 1948), w.e.f. 1-1-1949.
4 Section 36 omitted by the Banking Laws (Miscellaneous Provisions) Act, 1963 (55 of 1963), w.e.f. 1-2-1964.
5 Substituted by Act 38 of 1956, w.e.f. 6-10-1956.
6 Proviso omitted by Act 48 of 1957, w.e.f. 31-10-1957.
7 Substituted for "G.G. in C" by the M.O. 1937.
8 Words and figures "to re-issue any rupee coin delivered under section 36 nor" omitted by Act 55 of 1963, w.e.f. 1-2-1964.
9 Words "and as provided in that section" omitted by Ordinance 4 of 1940.
10 The words "or by delivery to the Central Government under that sections" omitted by Act 55 of 1963, w.e.f. 1-2-1964.
11 Substituted for "five" by Act 62 of 1948, w.e.f. 1-1-1949.

[1][40. **Transactions in foreign exchange**

The Bank shall sell to or buy from any authorised person who makes a demand in that behalf at its office in Bombay, Calcutta, Delhi or Madras [2][or at such or its branches as the Central Government may, by order determine], foreign exchange at such rates of exchange and on such conditions as the Central Government may from time to time by general or special order determine, having regard so far as rates of exchange are concerned to its obligations to the International Monetary Fund:

PROVIDED that no person shall be entitled to demand to buy or sell foreign exchange of a value less than two lakhs of rupees.

Explanation : In the section "authorised person" means a person who is entitled by or under the [3][Foreign Exchange Regulation Act, 1973 (46 of 1973)], to buy, or as the case may be, sell, the foreign exchange to which his demand relates.]

[4]**[xxx]**

42. Cash reserves of scheduled banks to be kept with the Bank

[5][(1) Every bank included in the Second Schedule shall maintain with the Bank an average daily balance the amount of which shall not be less than [6][such per cent. of the total of the demand and time liabilities in India of such bank as shown in the return referred to in sub-section (2), as the Bank may from time to time, having regard to the needs of securing the monetary stability in the country, notify in the Gazette of India]:

[7][xxx]

Explanation : For the purposes of this section,—

(a) "average daily balance" shall mean the average of the balances held at the close of business of each day [8][of a fortnight];

[9][(b) "fortnight" shall mean the period from Saturday to the second following Friday, both days inclusive;]

[10][(c) "liabilities" shall not include—

(i) the paid-up capital or the reserves or any credit balance in the profit and loss account of the bank;

(ii) the amount of any loan taken from the Bank [11][xxx] [12][or from the Exim Bank] [13][or from the Reconstruction Bank] [14][or from the National Housing Bank] or from the [15][National Bank] [16][or from the Small Industries Bank [17][or from the National Bank for Financing

---

1 Substituted. by Act 23 of 1947, w.e.f. 18-4-1947.
2 Inserted by Act 54 of 1953, w.e.f. 30-12-1953.
3 Substituted for "Foreign Exchange Regulation Act, 1947 (7 of 1947)" by Act 1 of 1984, w.e.f. 15-2-1984.
4 Section 41A omitted by the Reserve Bank of India (Amendment) Act, 1947 (11 of 1947), w.e.f. 1-4-1947.
5 Substituted by Act 38 of 1956, w.e.f. 6-10-1956.
6 Substituted for "three per cent. of the total of the demand and time liabilities in India of such bank as shown in the return referred to in sub-section (2)" by Act 26 of 2006, w.e.f. 1-4-2007.
7 Proviso omitted, ibid, w.e.f. 1-4-2007.
8 Substituted for "of a week" by Act 1 of 1984, w.e.f. 29-3-1985.
9 Substituted, ibid, w.e.f. 29-3-1985.
10 Substituted by Act 23 of 1965, w.e.f. 1-3-1966.
11 Words "or from the Development Bank" omitted by Act 53 of 2003, w.e.f. 2-7-2004.
12 Inserted by Act 28 of 1981, w.e.f. 1-1-1982.
13 Inserted by Act 62 of 1984, w.e.f. 20-3-1985.
14 Inserted by Act 53 of 1987, w.e.f. 9-7-1988.
15 Substituted for "Agricultural Refinance and Development Corporation" by Act 61 of 1981, w.e.f. 12-7-1982.
16 Inserted by Act 39 of 1989, w.e.f. 7-3-1990.
17 Inserted by Act 17 of 2021, w.e.f. 19-4-2021.

Infrastructure and Development or from the other development financial institution]] [1][xxx];

(iii) in the case of a State co-operative bank, also any loan taken by such bank from a State Government [2][or from the National Co-operative Development Corporation established under the National Co-operative Development Corporation Act, 1962 (26 of 1962)] and any deposit of money with such bank representing the reserve fund or any part thereof [3][xxx] maintained with it by any co-operative society within its area of operation;]

[4][(iv) in the case of a State co-operative bank, which has granted an advance against any balance maintained with it, such balance to the extent of the amount outstanding in respect of such advance;]

[2][(v) in the case a Regional Rural Bank, also any loan taken by such bank from its Sponsor Bank;]

(d) the aggregate of the "liabilities" of a Scheduled bank which is not a State co-operative bank, to,—

(i) the State Bank;

(ii) a subsidiary bank as defined in section 2 of the State Bank of India (Subsidiary Banks) Act, 1959 (38 of 1959);

(iii) a corresponding new bank constituted by section 3 of the Banking Companies (Acquisition and Transfer of Undertakings) Act, 1970 (5 of 1970);

[2][(iiia) a corresponding new bank constituted by section 3 of the Banking Companies (Acquisition and Transfer of Undertakings) Act, 1980 (40 of 1980);]

(iv) a banking company as defined in clause (c) of section 5 of the Banking Regulation Act, 1949 (10 of 1949);

(v) a co-operative bank; or

(vi) any other financial institution notified by the Central Government in this behalf,

shall be reduced by the aggregate of the liabilities of all such banks and institutions to the scheduled bank;

(e) the aggregate of the "liabilities" of a scheduled bank which is a State co-operative bank, to,—

(i) the State Bank;

(ii) a subsidiary bank as defined in section 2 of the State Bank of India (Subsidiary Banks) Act, 1959 (38 of 1959);

(iii) a corresponding new bank constituted by section 3 of the Banking Companies (Acquisition and Transfer of Undertakings) Act, 1970 (5 of 1970);

---

1 Words "or from the State Bank or from any other bank notified by the Central Government in this behalf, and" omitted by Act 51 of 1974, w.e.f. 13-12-1974.
2 Inserted by Act 1 of 1984, w.e.f. 29-3-1985.
3 Words "required to be" omitted by Act 51 of 1974, w.e.f. 13-12-1974.
4 Inserted, ibid.

[1][(iiia) a corresponding new bank constituted by section 3 of the Banking Companies (Acquisition and Transfer of Undertakings) Act, 1980 (40 of 1980);]

(iv) a banking company as defined in clause (c) of section 5 of the Banking Regulation Act, 1949 (10 of 1949); or

(v) any other financial institution notified by the Central Government in this behalf,

shall be reduced by the aggregate of the liabilities of all such banks and institutions to the State co-operative bank.]

(1A) Notwithstanding anything contained in sub-section (1), the Bank may, by notification in the Gazette of India, direct that every scheduled bank shall, with effect from such date as may be specified in the notification, maintain with the Bank, in addition to the balance prescribed by or under sub-section (1), an additional average daily balance the amount of which shall not be less than the [2][rate specified in the notification, such additional balance being calculated with reference to the excess of the total of the demand and time liabilities of the bank as shown in the return referred to in sub-section (2) over the total of its demand and time liabilities] at the close of business on the date specified in the notification as shown by such return so however, that the additional balance shall, in no case, be more than such excess:

[1][PROVIDED that the Bank may, by a separate notification in the Gazette of India, specify different dates in respect of a Bank subsequently included in the Second Schedule].

[3][xxx]

[1][1C) The Bank may, for the purposes of this section, specify from time to time with reference to any transaction or class of transactions that such transaction or transactions shall be regarded as liability in India of a scheduled bank, and if any question arises as to whether any transaction or class of transactions shall be regarded, for the purposes of this section, as liability in India of a scheduled bank, the decision of the Bank thereon shall be final.]

[4][(2) Every scheduled bank shall send to the Bank a return signed by two responsible officers of such bank showing—

(a) the amount of its demand and time liabilities and the amount of its borrowings from banks in India, [5][classifying them into demand and time liabilities],

[6][xxx]

(b) the total amount of legal tender notes and coins held by it in India,

(c) the balance held by it at the Bank in India,

(d) the balances held by it at other banks in current account and the money at call and short notice in India,

---

1 Inserted by Act 1 of 1984, w.e.f. 29-3-1985.
2 Substituted by Act 35 of 1962, w.e.f. 15-9-1962.
3 Sub-sections (1AA) and (1B) omitted by Act 26 of 2006, w.e.f. 1-4-2007.
4 Substituted by Act 32 of 1951, w.e.f. 1-11-1951.
5 Substituted for "other than the State Bank and any other bank notified by the Central Government in this behalf" by Act 51 of 1974, w.e.f. 13-12-1974.
6 Clause (aa) omitted by Act 51 of 1974, w.e.f. 13-12-1974.

(e) the investments (at book value) in Central and State Government securities including treasury bills and treasury deposit receipts,

(f) the amount of advances in India,

(g) the inland bills purchased and discounted in India [1][and foreign bills purchased and discounted],

[2][at the close of business on each alternate Friday, and every such return shall be sent not later than seven days after the date to which it relates]:

[3][PROVIDED that the Bank may, by notification in the Gazette of India, delete or modify or add to any of the particulars specified in the foregoing clauses:

PROVIDED FURTHER that] where [4][such alternate] Friday is a public holiday under the Negotiable Instruments Act, 1881 (26 of 1881), for one or more offices of a scheduled bank the return shall give the preceding working days figures in respect of such office or offices, but shall nevertheless be deemed to relate to that Friday:

[5][PROVIDED ALSO that where the Bank is satisfied that the furnishing of a fortnightly return under this sub-section is impracticable in the case of any scheduled bank by reason of the geographical position of the bank and its branches, the Bank may allow such bank—

(i) to furnish a provisional return for the fortnight within the period aforesaid to be followed by a final return not later than twenty days after the date to which it relates, or

(ii) to furnish in lieu of a fortnightly return a monthly return to be sent not later than twenty days after the end of the month to which it relates giving the details specified in this sub-section in respect of such bank at the close of business for the month.]]

[4][(2A) Where the last Friday of a month is not an alternate Friday for the purpose of sub-section(2), every scheduled bank shall send to the Bank, a special return giving the details specified in sub-section (2) as at the close of business on such last Friday or where such last Friday is a public holiday under the Negotiable Instruments Act, 1881 (26 of 1881), as at the close of business on the preceding working day and such return shall be sent not later than seven days after the date to which it relates.]

[6][(3) If the average daily balance held at the Bank by a scheduled bank during any [7][fortnight] is below the minimum prescribed by or under sub-section (1) or sub-section (1A), such scheduled bank shall be liable to pay to the Bank in respect of that [7][fortnight] penal interest at a rate of three per cent. above the bank rate on the amount by which such balance with the Bank falls short of the prescribed minimum, and if during the next succeeding [7][fortnight], such average daily balance is still below the prescribed minimum, the rates of penal interest shall be increased to a rate of five per cent, above the bank rate in respect of that [7][fortnight] and each subsequent [7][fortnight] during which the default continues on the amount by which such balance at the Bank falls short of the prescribed minimum.]

---

1 Inserted by Act 54 of 1953, w.e.f. 30-12-1953.

2 Substituted "at the close of business on each Friday, and every such return shall be sent not later than five days after the date to which it relates" by Act 1 of 1984, w.e.f. 29-3-1985.

3 Substituted for "Provided that" by Act 51 of 1974, w.e.f. 13-12-1974.

4 Inserted by Act 1 of 1984, w.e.f. 29-3-1985.

5 Substituted, ibid.

6 Substituted by Act 38 of 1956, w.e.f. 6-10-1956.

7 Substituted for "week" by Act 1 of 1984, w.e.f. 29-3-1985.

[1][(3A) When under the provisions of sub-section (3) penal interest at the increased rate of five per cent, above the bank rate has become payable by a scheduled bank, [2][if thereafter the average daily balance held at the Bank during the next succeeding [3][fortnight] is still below the prescribed minimum,

(a) every director, manager or secretary of the scheduled bank, who is knowingly and wilfully a party to the default, shall be punishable with fine which may extend to five hundred rupees and with a further fine which may extend to five hundred rupees for each subsequent [3][fortnight] during which the default continues, and

(b) the Bank may prohibit the scheduled bank from receiving after the said [3][fortnight] any fresh deposit,]

and, if default is made by the scheduled bank in complying with the prohibition referred to in clause (b), every director and officer of the scheduled bank who is knowingly and wilfully a party to such default or who through negligence or otherwise contributes to such default shall in respect of each such default be punishable with fine which may extend to five hundred rupees and with a further fine which may extend to five hundred rupees for each day after the first on which a deposit received in contravention of such prohibition is retained by the scheduled bank.

Explanation : In this sub-section "officer" includes a [4][xxx] manager, secretary, branch manager, and branch secretary.]

(4) Any scheduled bank failing to comply with the provisions of sub-section (2) [5][shall be liable to pay to the Bank] a penalty of one hundred rupees for each day during which the failure continues.

[6][(5) (a) The penalties imposed by sub-sections (3) and (4) shall be payable within a period of fourteen days from the date on which a notice issued by the Bank demanding the payment of the same is served on the scheduled bank, and in the event of failure of the scheduled bank to pay the same within such period, may be levied by a direction of the principal civil court having jurisdiction in the area where an office of the defaulting bank is situated, such direction to be made only upon an application made in this behalf to the court by the Bank;

(b) when the court makes a direction under clause (a), it shall issue a certificate specifying the sum payable by the scheduled bank and every such certificate shall be enforceable in the same manner as if it were a decree made by the court in a suit;

(c) notwithstanding anything contained in this section, if the Bank is satisfied that the defaulting bank and sufficient cause for its failure to comply with the provisions of sub-section (1), (1A) or (2), it may not demand the payment of the penal interest of the penalty, as the case may be.]

[7][(6) The Bank shall, save as hereinafter provided, by notification in the Gazette of India,—

---

1 Inserted by Act 38 of 1940, w.e.f. 27-22-1940.
2 Substituted by Act 38 of 1956, w.e.f. 6-10-1956.
3 Substituted for "week" by Act 1 of 1984, w.e.f. 29-3-1985.
4 Words "managing agent" omitted by Act 32 of 1951, w.e.f. 1-11-1951.
5 Substituted for "shall be liable to pay to the Central Government or to the Bank, as the case may be, or to each,", ibid, w.e.f. 1-11-1951.
6 Substituted by Act 35 of 1962, w.e.f. 15-9-1962.
7 Substituted by Act 10 of 1949, w.e.f. 16-3-1949.

(a) direct the inclusion in the Second Schedule of any bank not already so included which carries on the business of banking [1][in India] and which—

(i) has a paid-up capital and reserve of an aggregate value of not less than five lakhs of rupees, and

(ii) satisfies and Bank that its affairs are not being conducted in a manner detrimental to the interests of its depositors, and

(iii) [2][is a State co-operative bank or a company] as defined in [3][section 3 of the Companies Act, 1956 (1 of 1956), or an institution notified by the Central Government in this behalf] or a corporation or a company incorporated by or under any law in force in any place [4][outside India];

(b) direct the exclusion from that Schedule of any scheduled bank,—

(i) the aggregate value of whose paid-up capital and reserves becomes at any time less than five lakhs of rupees, or

(ii) which is, in the opinion of the Bank after making an inspection under section 35 of the [5][Banking Regulation Act, 1949 (10 of 1949)], conducting its affairs to the detriment of the interests of its depositors, or

(iii) which goes into liquidation or otherwise ceases to carry on banking business:

PROVIDED that the Bank may, on application of the scheduled bank concerned and subject to such conditions, if any, as it may impose, defer the making of a direction under sub-clause (i) or sub-clause (ii) of clause (b) for such period as the Bank considers reasonable to give the scheduled bank an opportunity of increasing the aggregate value of its paid-up capital and reserves to not less than five lakhs of rupees or, as the case may be, of removing the defects in the conduct of its affairs;

(c) alter the description in that Schedule whenever any scheduled bank changes its name.

Explanation : In this sub-section, the expression "value" means the real or exchangeable value and not the nominal value which may be shown in the books of the bank concerned; and if any dispute arises in computing the aggregate value of the paid-up capital and reserves of a bank, a determination thereof by the Bank shall be final for the purposes of this sub-section.]

[6][(6A) In considering whether a State co-operative bank or a regional rural bank should be included in or excluded from the Second Schedule, it shall be competent for the Bank to act on a certificate from the National Bank on the question whether or not a State co-operative bank or a regional rural bank, as the case may be, satisfies the requirements as to paid-up capital and reserves or whether its affairs are not being conducted in a manner detrimental to the interests of its depositors.]

1 Substituted for "in any State of India" by Act 32 of 1951, w.e.f. 1-11-1951.
2 Substituted for "is a company" by Act 23 of 1965, w.e.f. 1-3-1966.
3 Substituted for "clause (2) of section 2 of the Indian Companies Act, 1913 (7 of 1913)" by Act 19 of 1957, w.e.f. 8-6-1957.
4 Substituted for "outside the States of India" by Act 32 of 1951, w.e.f. 1-11-1951.
5 Substituted for "Banking Companies Act, 1949" by Act 51 of 1974, w.e.f. 13-12-1974.
6 Inserted by Act 61 of 1981, w.e.f. 12-7-1982.

[1][(7) The Bank may, for such period and subject to such conditions as may be specified, grant to any scheduled bank such exemptions from the provisions of this section as it thinks fit with reference to all or any of its offices or with reference to the whole or any part of its assets and liabilities.]

[2]**[43. Publication of consolidated statement by the Bank**

The Bank shall cause to be published each [3][fortnight] a consolidated statement showing the aggregate liabilities and assets of all the scheduled banks together, based on the returns and information received under this Act or any other law for the time being in force.]

[4]**[43A. Protection of action taken in good faith**

(1) No suit or other legal proceeding shall lie against the Bank or any of its officers for anything which is in good faith done or intended to be done in pursuance of section 42 or section 43 [5][or in pursuance of the provisions of Chapter IIIA].

(2) No suit or other legal proceeding shall lie against the Bank or any of its officers for any damage caused or likely to be caused by anything which is in good faith done or intended to be done in pursuance of section 42 or section 43 [5][or in pursuance of the provisions of Chapter IIIA].]

[6]**[xxx]**

[7]**[45. Appointment of agents**

(1) Unless otherwise directed by the Central Government with reference to any place, the Bank may, having regard to public interest, convenience of banking, banking development and such other factors which in its opinion are relevant in this regard, appoint the National Bank, or the State Bank, or a corresponding new bank constituted under section 3 of the Banking Companies (Acquisition and Transfer of Undertakings) Act, 1970 (5 of 1970), or a corresponding new bank constituted under section 3 of the Banking Companies (Acquisition and Transfer of Undertakings) Act, 1980 (40 of 1980), or any subsidiary bank as defined in the State Bank of India (Subsidiary Banks) Act, 1959 (38 of 1959), as its agent at all places, or at any place in India for such purposes as the Bank may specify.

(2) When any bank is appointed by the Bank as its agent under sub-section (1) to receive on behalf of the Bank any payment required to be made into the Bank, or any bill, hundies or other securities required to be delivered into the Bank, under any law or rule, regulations or other instructions having the force of law, the same may be paid or delivered into the bank so appointed as the agent of the Bank.]

---

1 Inserted by Act 32 of 1951, w.e.f. 1-11-1951.
2 Substituted by Act 51 of 1974, w.e.f. 13-12-1974.
3 Substituted for "week" by Act 1 of 1984, w.e.f. 29-3-1985.
4 Inserted by Act 54 of 1953, w.e.f. 30-12-1953.
5 Inserted by Act 35 of 1962, w.e.f. 15-9-1962.
6 Section 44 omitted by the Banking Laws (Application to Co-operative Societies) Act, 1965 (23 of 1965), w.e.f. 1-3-1966.
7 Substituted by Act 61 of 1981, w.e.f. 12-7-1982.

[1][CHAPTER IIIA

COLLECTION AND FURNISHING OF CREDIT INFORMATION

45A. Definitions

In this Chapter, unless the context otherwise requires,—

(a) "banking company" means a banking company as defined in section 5 of the [2][Banking Regulation Act, 1949 (10 of 1949)] and includes the State Bank of India, [3][any subsidiary bank as defined in the State Bank of India (Subsidiary Banks) Act, 1959 (38 of 1959), any corresponding new bank constituted by section 3 of the Banking Companies (Acquisition and Transfer of Undertakings) Act, 1970 (5 of 1970), and any other financial institution notified by the Central Government in this behalf];

(b) "borrower" means any person to whom any credit limit has been sanctioned by any banking company, whether availed of or not, and includes—

(i) in the case of a company or corporation, its subsidiaries;

(ii) in the case of a Hindu undivided family, any member thereof or any firm in which such member is a partner;

(iii) in the case of a firm, any partner thereof or any other firm in which such partner is a partner; and

(iv) in the case of an individual, any firm in which such individual is a partner;

(c) "credit information" means any information relating to—

(i) the amounts and the nature of loans or advances and other credit facilities granted by a banking company to any borrower or class of borrowers;

(ii) the nature of security taken from any borrower [4][or class of borrowers] for credit facilities [5][granted to him or to such class;]

(iii) the guarantee furnished by a banking company for any of its customers [4][or any class of its customers];

[6][(iv) the means, antecedents, history of financial transactions and the creditworthiness of any borrower or class of borrowers;

(v) any other information which the Bank may consider to be relevant for the more orderly regulation of credit or credit policy.]

45B. Power of Bank to collect credit information

The Bank may—

(a) collect, in such manner as it may think fit, credit information from banking companies; and

(b) furnish such information to any banking company in accordance with the provisions of section 45D.

---

1 Inserted by Act 35 of 1962, w.e.f. 1-9-1962.
2 Substituted for "Banking Companies Act, 1949" by Act 51 of 1974, w.e.f. 13-12-1974.
3 Substituted for "or any other banking or financial institution notified by the Central Government in this behalf", ibid.
4 Inserted, ibid.
5 Substituted for "granted to him; and", ibid.
6 Inserted by Act 51 of 1974, w.e.f. 13-12-1974.

45C. Power to call for returns containing credit information

(1) For the purpose of enabling the Bank to discharge its functions under this Chapter, it may at any time direct any banking company to submit to it such statements relating to such credit information and in such form and within such time as may be specified by the Bank from time to time.

(2) A banking company shall, notwithstanding anything to the contrary contained in any law for the time being in force on in any instrument regulating the constitution thereof or in any agreement executed by it, relating to the secrecy of its dealings with its constituents, be bound to comply with any direction issued under sub-section (1).

45D. Procedure for furnishing credit information to banking companies

(1) A banking company may, in connection with any financial arrangement entered into or proposed to be entered into by it, with any person, make an application to the Bank in such form as the Bank may specify requesting it to furnish the applicant with such credit information as may be specified in the application.

(2) On receipt of an application under sub-section (1), the Bank shall, as soon as may be, furnish the applicant with such credit information relating to the matters specified in the application, as may be in its possession:

PROVIDED that the information so furnished shall not disclose the names of the banking companies which have submitted such information to the Bank.

(3) The Bank may in respect of each application levy such fees, not exceeding twenty-five rupees, as it may deem fit for furnishing credit information.

45E. Disclosure of information prohibited

(1) Any credit information contained in any statement submitted by a banking company under section 45C or furnished by the Bank to any banking company under section 45D, shall be treated as confidential and shall not, except for the purposes of this Chapter, be published or otherwise disclosed.

(2) Nothing in this section shall apply to—

(a) the disclosure by any banking company, with the previous permission of the Bank, of any information furnished to the Bank under section 45C;

(b) the publication by the Bank, if it considers necessary in the public interest so to do, of any information collected by it under section 45C, in such consolidated form as it may think fit without disclosing the name of any banking company or its borrowers;

[1][(c) the disclosure or publication by the banking company or by the Bank of any credit information to any other banking company or in accordance with the practice and usage customary among bankers or as permitted or required under any other law;

[2][(d) the disclosures of any credit information under the Credit Information Companies (Regulation) Act, 2005 (30 of 2005):]

PROVIDED that any credit information received by a banking company under this clause shall not be published except in accordance with the practice and usage customary among bankers or as permitted or required under any other law.]

---

1 Inserted by Act 51 of 1974, w.e.f. 13-12-1974.
2 Inserted by Act 30 of 2005, w.e.f. 14-12-2006.

(3) Notwithstanding anything contained in any law for the time being in force, no court, tribunal or other authority shall compel the Bank or any banking company to produce or to give inspection of any statement submitted by that banking company under section 45C or to disclose any credit information furnished by the Bank to that banking company under section 45D.

45F. Certain claims for compensation barred

No person shall have any right, whether in contract or otherwise, to any compensation for any loss incurred by reason of the operation of any of the provisions of this Chapter.

[1]**[xxx]**

[2][CHAPTER IIIB

PROVISIONS RELATING TO NON-BANKING INSTITUTIONS RECEIVING DEPOSITS AND FINANCIAL INSTITUTIONS

45H. Chapter IIIB not to apply in certain cases

The provisions of this Chapter shall not apply to the State Bank or a banking company as defined in section 5 of the [3][Banking Regulation Act, 1949 (10 of 1949)] or [4][a corresponding new bank as defined in clause (da) of section 5 of that Act or a subsidiary bank as defined in the State Bank of India (Subsidiary Banks) Act, 1959 (38 of 1959)] or [5][a Regional Rural Bank or a co-operative bank] or a primary agricultural credit society or a primary credit society]:

PROVIDED that for the purposes of this Chapter, the [6][Tamil Nadu Industrial Investment Corporation Limited] shall not be deemed to be a banking company.

45-I. Definitions

In this Chapter, unless the context otherwise requires,—

[7][(a) "business of a non-banking financial institution" means carrying on the business of a financial institution referred to in clause (c) and includes business of a non-banking financial company referred to in clause (f);]

[8][(aa)] "company" means a company as defined in section 3 of the Companies Act, 1956 (1 of 1956), and includes a foreign company within the meaning of section 591 of that Act;

(b) "corporation" means a corporation incorporated by an Act of any legislature;

[9][(bb) "deposit" includes and shall be deemed always to have included any receipt of money by way of deposit or loan or in any other form, but does not include,—

(i) amounts raised by way of share capital;

(ii) amounts contributed as capital by partners of a firm;

---

1 Section 45G omitted by the Reserve Bank of India (Amendment) Act, 1974 (51 of 1974), w.e.f. 13-12-1974.
2 Inserted by Act 55 of 1963, w.e.f. 1-2-1964.
3 Substituted for "Banking Companies Act, 1949" by Act 51 of 1974, w.e.f. 13-12-1974.
4 Substituted for "a banking institution notified under section 51 of that Act" by Act 1 of 1984, w.e.f. 15-2-1984.
5 Substituted for "a co-operative bank" by Act 21 of 1976, w.e.f. 26-9-1975.
6 Substituted for "Madras Industrial Investment Corporation Limited" by Act 51 of 1974, w.e.f. 13-12-1974..
7 Inserted by Act 23 of 1997, w.e.f. 9-1-1997.
8 Clause (a) renumbered as clause (aa) thereof, ibid, w.e.f. 9-1-1997.
9 Substituted by Act 1 of 1984, w.e.f. 15-2-1984.

(iii) amounts received from a scheduled bank or a co-operative bank or any other banking company as defined in clause (c) of section 5 of a Banking Regulation Act, 1949 (10 of 1949);

(iv) any amount received from,—

[1][xxx]

(b) a State Financial Corporation,

(c) any financial institution specified in or under section 6A of the Industrial Development Bank of India Act, 1964 (18 of 1964), or

(d) any other institution that may be specified by the Bank in this behalf;

(v) amounts received in the ordinary course of business, by way of—

(a) security deposit,

(b) dealership deposit,

(c) earnest money, or

(d) advance against orders for goods, properties or services;

(vi) any amount received from an individual or a firm or an association of individuals not being a body corporate, registered under any enactment relating to money lending which is for the time being in force in any State; and

(vii) any amount received by way of subscriptions in respect of a chit.

Explanation I : "Chit" has the meaning assigned to it in clause (b) of section 2 of the Chit Funds Act, 1982 (40 of 1982).

Explanation II : Any credit given by a seller to a buyer on the sale of any property (whether movable or immovable) shall not be deemed to be deposit for the purposes of this clause;]

[2][*Explanation III* : The amounts accepted by a co-operative society from the members or shareholders, by whatever name called, but excluding the amounts received as share capital, shall be deemed to be deposits for the purposes of this clause, if such members or shareholders are nominal or associate members, by whatever name called, who do not have full voting rights in the meetings of such co-operative society.]

[3][(c) "financial institution" means any non-banking institution which carries on as its business or part of its business any of the following activities, namely:—

(i) the financing, whether by way of making loans or advances or otherwise, of any activity other than its own;

(ii) the acquisition of shares, stock, bonds, debentures or securities issued by a Government or local authority or other marketable securities of a like nature;

(iii) letting or delivering of any goods to a hirer under a hire-purchase agreement as defined in clause (c) of section 2 of the Hire-Purchase Act, 1972 (26 of 1972);

---

1 Item (a) omitted by Act 53 of 2003, w.e.f. 2-7-2004.
2 Inserted by Act 21 of 2019, w.e.f. 21-2-2019.
3 Substituted by Act 51 of 1974, w.e.f. 13-12-1974.

(iv) the carrying on of any class of insurance business;

(v) managing, conducting or supervising, as foreman, agent or in any other capacity, of chits or kuries as defined in any law which is for the time being in force in any State, or any business, which is similar thereto;

(vi) collecting, for any purpose or under any scheme or arrangement by whatever name called, monies in lump sum or otherwise, by way of subscriptions or by sale of units, or other instruments or in any other manner and awarding prizes or gifts, whether in cash or kind, or disbursing monies in any other way, to persons from whom monies are collected or to any other person,

[1][but does not include any institution, which carries on as its principal business,—

(a) agricultural operations; or

(aa) industrial activity; or]

(b) the purchase, or sale of any goods (other than securities) or the providing of any services; or

(c) the purchase, construction or sale of immovable property, so, however, that no portion of the income of the institution is derived from the financing of purchases, constructions or sales of immovable property by other persons;]

[2][*Explanation*: For the purposes of this clause, "industrial activity" means any activity specified in sub-clauses (i) to (xviii) of clause (c) of section 2 of the Industrial Development Bank of India Act, 1964 (18 of 1964);]

(d) "firm" means a firm as defined in the Indian Partnership Act, 1932 (9 of 1932) [3][xxx];

(e) "non-banking institution" means a company, corporation [4][or co-operative society];

[1][(f) "non-banking financial company" means—

(i) a financial institution which is a company;

(ii) a non-banking institution which is a company and which has as its principal business the receiving of deposits, under any scheme or arrangement or in any other manner, or lending in any manner;

(iii) such other non-banking institution or class of such institutions, as the Bank may, with the previous approval of the Central Government and by notification in the Official Gazette, specify.]

COMMENTS

Sub-cls. (i) to (xvii) of cl. (c) of s. 2 of the Industrial Development Bank of India Act, 1964 enumerates industrial concerns as any concern engaged or to be engaged in the manufacture, preservation or processing of goods, shipping, mining including development of mines, the hotel industry, the transport of passengers or goods by road or by water or by air or by ropeway or by lift, the generation, storage or distribution of electricity or any other form of energy, the maintenance, repair, testing or servicing of machinery or equipment of any description or vehicles or vessels or motor boats or trailers or tractors, assembling, repairing or packing any article with the aid of

1 Substituted by Act 23 of 1997, w.e.f. 9-1-1997.

2 Inserted by Act 23 of 1997, w.e.f. 9-1-1997.

3 The words ", of which the capital subscribed by its partners exceeds one lakh of rupees" omitted by Act 1 of 1984, w.e.f. 15-2-1984.

4 Substituted for ", co-operative society or firm", ibid, w.e.f. 15-2-1984.

machinery or power, the setting up of, or development of, an industrial area or an industrial estate, fishing or providing shore facilities for fishing or maintenance thereof, providing special or technical knowledge or other services for the promotion of industrial growth, or providing engineering, technical, financial management, marketing or other services or facilities for industry, service industry such as altering, ornamenting, polishing, finishing, oiling, washing, cleaning or otherwise treating or adapting any article or substance with a view to its use, sale, transport, delivery or disposal, providing medical, health or other allied services, providing services relating to information technology, telecommunication or electronics, leasing, sub-leasing or giving on hire or hire-purchase of industrial plants, equipments, machinery or other assets including vehicles, ships and aircraft, such other activity as the Central Government may, having regard to the objects of this Act, by notification in the Official Gazette, specify in this behalf, or the research and development of any concept, technology, design, process or product whether in relation to any of the matters aforesaid, including any activities specified under sub-cl. (xvii), or any other matter.

The expression "processing of goods" includes any art or process for producing, preparing or making an article by subjecting any material to a manual, mechanical, chemical, electrical or any other like operation.

[1][45-IA. Requirement of registration and net owned fund

(1) Notwithstanding anything contained in this Chapter or in any other law for the time being in force, no non-banking financial company shall commence or carry on the business of a non-banking financial institution without—

(a) obtaining a certificate of registration issued under this Chapter; and

[2][(b) having the net owned fund of twenty-five lakh rupees or such other amount, not exceeding hundred crore rupees, as the Bank may, by notification in the Official Gazette, specify:

PROVIDED that the Bank may notify different amounts of net owned fund for different categories of non-banking financial companies.]

(2) Every non-banking financial company shall make an application for registration to the Bank in such form as the Bank may specify:

PROVIDED that a non-banking financial company in existence on the commencement of the Reserve Bank of India (Amendment) Act, 1997 (23 of 1997) shall make an application for registration to the Bank before the expiry of six months from such commencement and notwithstanding anything contained in sub-section (1) may continue to carry on the business of a non-banking financial institution until a certificate of registration is issued to it or rejection of application for registration is communicated to it.

(3) Notwithstanding anything contained in sub-section (1), a non-banking financial company in existence on the commencement of the Reserve Bank of India (Amendment) Act, 1997 (23 of 1997) and having a net owned fund of less than twenty-five lakh rupees may, for the purpose of enabling such company to fulfil the requirement of the net owned fund, continue to carry on the business of a non-banking financial institution—

(i) for a period of there years from such commencement; or

(ii) for such further period as the Bank may, after recording the reasons in writing for so doing, extend,

subject to the condition that such company shall, within three months of fulfilling the requirement of the net owned fund, inform the Bank about such fulfillment:

---

1 Inserted by Act 23 of 1997, w.e.f. 9-1-1997.

2 Substituted by Act 23 of 2019, w.e.f. 9-8-2019.

PROVIDED that the period allowed to continue business under this sub-section shall in no case exceed six years in the aggregate.

(4) The Bank, for the purpose of considering the application for registration, may require to be satisfied by an inspection of the books of the non-banking financial company or otherwise that the following conditions are fulfilled:—

(a) that the non-banking financial company is or shall be in a position to pay its present or future depositors in full as and when their claims accrue;

(b) that the affairs of the non-banking financial company are not being or are not likely to be conducted in a manner detrimental to the interest of its present or future depositors;

(c) that the general character of the management or the proposed management of the non-banking financial company shall not be prejudicial to the public interest or the interests of its depositors;

(d) that the non-banking financial company has adequate capital structure and earning prospects;

(e) that the public interest shall be served by the grant of certificate of registration to the non-banking financial company to commence or to carry on the business of India;

(f) that the grant of certificate of registration shall not be prejudicial to the operation and consolidation of the financial sector consistent with monetary stability, and economic growth considering such other relevant factors which the Bank may, by notification in the Official Gazette, specify; and

(g) any other condition, fulfilment of which in the opinion of the Bank, shall be necessary to ensure that the commencement of or carrying on of the business in India by a non-banking financial company shall not be prejudicial to the public interest or in the interests of the depositors.

(5) The Bank may, after being satisfied that the conditions specified in sub-section (4) are fulfilled, grant a certificate of registration subject to such conditions which it may consider fit to impose.

(6) The Bank may cancel a certificate of registration granted to a non-banking financial company under this section if such company—

(i) ceases to carry on the business of a non-banking financial institution in India; or

(ii) has failed to comply with any condition subject to which the certificate of registration had been issued to it; or

(iii) at any time fails to fulfil any of the conditions referred to in clauses (d) to (g) of sub-section (4); or

(iv) fails—

(a) to comply with any direction issued by the Bank under the provisions of this Chapter; or

(b) to maintain accounts in accordance with the requirements of any law or any direction or order issued by the Bank under the provisions of this Chapter; or

(c) to submit or offer for inspection its books of account and other relevant documents when so demanded by an inspecting authority of the Bank; or

(v) has been prohibited from accepting deposit by an order made by the Bank under the provisions of this Chapter and such order has been in force for a period of not less than three months:

PROVIDED that before cancelling a certificate of registration on the ground that the non-banking financial company has failed to comply with the provisions of clause (ii) or has failed to fulfil any of the conditions referred to in clause (iii) the Bank, unless it is of the opinion that the delay in cancelling the certificate of registration shall be prejudicial to public interest or the interest of the depositors or the non-banking financial company, shall give an opportunity to such company on such term as the Bank may specify for taking necessary steps to comply with such provision or fulfilment of such condition:

PROVIDED FURTHER that before making any order of cancellation of certificate of registration, such company shall be given a reasonable opportunity of being heard.

(7) A company aggrieved by the order of rejection of application for registration or cancellation of certificate of registration may prefer an Appeal, within a period of thirty days from the date on which such order of rejection or cancellation is communicated to it, to the Central Government and the decision of the Central Government where an appeal has been preferred to it, or of the Bank where no appeal has been preferred, shall be final:

PROVIDED that before making any order of rejection of appeal, such company shall be given a reasonable opportunity of being heard.

Explanations : For the purposes of this section,—

(I) "net owned fund" means—

(a) the aggregate of the paid-up equity capital and free reserves as disclosed in the latest balance-sheet of the company after deducting therefrom—

(i) accumulated balance of loss;

(ii) deferred revenue expenditure; and

(iii) other intangible assets; and

(b) further reduced by the amounts representing—

(1) investments of such company in shares of—

(i) its subsidiaries;

(ii) companies in the same group;

(iii) all other non-banking financial companies; and

(2) the book value of debentures, bonds, outstanding loans and advances (including hire-purchase and lease finance) made to, and deposits with,—

(i) subsidiaries of such company; and

(ii) companies in the same group,

to the extent such book value exceeds ten per cent. of (a) above.

(II) "subsidiaries" and "companies in the same group" shall have the same meanings assigned to them in the Companies Act, 1956 (1 of 1956).]

COMMENTS

A subsidiary company or subsidiary within the meaning of s. 2(47) of the Companies Act, 1956 (now refer section 2(87) of Companies Act, 2013 (18 of 2013) (means a subsidiary company within the meaning of s. 4 of that Act. Sec. 4 of the Companies Act says : For the purposes of this

Act, a company shall, subject to the provisions of sub-s. (3), be deemed to be a subsidiary of another if, but only if that other controls the composition of its board of directors or that other where the first-mentioned company is an existing company in respect of which the holders of preference shares issued before the commencement of this Act have the same voting rights in all respects as the holders of equity shares, exercises or controls more than half of the total voting power of such company; where the first-mentioned company is any other company, holds more than half in nominal value of its equity share capital; or the first-mentioned company is a subsidiary of any company which is the other's subsidiary. In determining whether one company is a subsidiary of another, any shares held or power exercisable by that other company in a fiduciary capacity shall be treated as not held or exercisable by it; subject to the provisions of cls. (c) and (d), any shares held or power exercisable by any person as a nominee for that other company (except where that other is concerned only in a fiduciary capacity; or by, or by a nominee for, a subsidiary of that other company, not being a subsidiary which is concerned only in a fiduciary capacity; shall be treated as held or exercisable by that other company; any shares held or power exercisable by any person by virtue of the provisions of any debentures of the first-mentioned company or of a trust deed for securing any issue of such debentures shall be disregarded; any shares held or power exercisable by, or by a nominee for, that other or its subsidiary not being held or exercisable as mentioned in cl. (c) shall be treated as not held or exercisable by that other, if the ordinary business of that other or its subsidiary, as the case may be, includes the lending of money and the shares are held or the power is exercisable as aforesaid by way of security only for the purposes of a transaction entered into in the ordinary course of that business.

45-IB. Maintenance of percentage of assets

(1) Every non-banking financial company shall invest and continue to invest in India in unencumbered approved securities, valued at a price not exceeding the current market price of such securities, an amount which, at the close of business on any day, shall not be less than five per cent. or such higher percentage not exceeding twenty-five per cent. as the Bank may, from time to time and by notification in the Official Gazette, specify, of the deposits outstanding at the close of business on the last working day of the second preceding quarter:

PROVIDED that the Bank may specify different percentages of investment in respect of different classes of non-banking financial companies.

(2) For the purpose of ensuring compliance with the provisions of this section, the Bank may require every non-banking financial company to furnish a return to it in such form, in such manner and for such period as may be specified by the Bank.

(3) If the amount invested by a non-banking financial company at the close of business on any day falls below the rate specified under sub-section (1), such company shall be liable to pay to the Bank, in respect of such shortfall, a penal interest at a rate of three per cent.per annum above the bank rate on such amount by which the amount actually invested falls short of the specified percentage, and where the shortfall continues in the subsequent quarters, the rate of penal interest shall be five per cent.per annum above the bank rate on such shortfall for each subsequent quarter.

(4)(a) The penal interest payable under sub-section (3) shall be payable within a period of fourteen days from the date on which a notice issued by the Bank demanding payment of the same is served on the non-banking financial company and, in the event of a failure of the non-banking financial company to pay the same within such period, penalty may be levied by a direction of the principal civil court having jurisdiction in the area where an office of the defaulting non-banking financial company is situated and such direction shall be made only upon an application made in this behalf to the court by the Bank; and

(b) when the court makes a direction under clause (a), it shall issue a certificate specifying the sum payable by the non-banking financial company and every such certificate shall be enforceable in the same manner as if it were a decree made by the court in a suit.

(5) Notwithstanding anything contained in this section, if the Bank is satisfied that the defaulting non-banking financial company had sufficient cause for its failure to comply with the provisions of sub-section (1), it may not demand the payment of the penal interest.

Explanation : For the purpose of this section,—

(i) "approved securities" means securities of any State Government or of the Central Government and such bonds, both the principal whereof and the interest whereon shall have been fully and unconditionally guaranteed by any such Government;

(ii) "unencumbered approved securities" includes the approved securities lodged by the non-banking financial company with another institution for an advance or any other arrangement to the extent to which such securities have not been drawn against or availed of or encumbered in any manner;

(iii) "quarter" means the period of three months ending on the last day of March, June, September or December.

45-IC. Reserve fund

(1) Every non-banking financial company shall create a reserve fund the transfer therein a sum not less than twenty per cent.of its net profit every year as disclosed in the profit and loss account and before any dividend is declared.

(2) No appropriation of any sum from the reserve fund shall be made by the non-banking financial company except for the purpose as may be specified by the Bank from time to time and every such appropriation shall be reported to the Bank within twenty-one days from the date of such withdrawal:

PROVIDED that the Bank may, in any particular case and for sufficient cause being shown, extend the period of twenty-one days by such further period as it thinks fit or condone any delay in making such report.

(3) Notwithstanding anything contained in sub-section (1), the Central Government may, on the recommendation of the Bank and having regard to the adequacy of the paid-up capital and reserves of a non-banking financial company in relation to its deposit liabilities, declare by order in writing that the provisions of sub-section (1) shall not be applicable to the non-banking financial company for such period as may be specified in the order:

PROVIDED that no such order shall be made unless the amount in the reserve fund under sub-section (1) together with the amount in the share premium account is not less than the paid-up capital of the non-banking financial company.]

[1]**[45-ID. Power of Bank to remove directors from office**

(1) Where the Bank is satisfied that in the public interest or to prevent the affairs of a non-banking financial company being conducted in a manner detrimental to the interest of the depositors or creditors, or financial stability or for securing the proper management of such company, it is necessary so to do, the Bank may, by order and for reasons to be recorded in writing, remove from office, a director (by whatever name

1 Inserted by Act 23 of 2019, w.e.f. 9-8-2019.

called) of such company, other than Government owned non-banking financial company with effect from such date as may be specified in the said order.

(2) No order under sub-section (1) shall be made unless the director concerned has been given a reasonable opportunity of making a representation to the Bank against the proposed order:

PROVIDED that if, in the opinion of the Bank, any delay will be detrimental to the interest of the said company or its depositors, the Bank may, at the time of giving the aforesaid opportunity or at any time thereafter, by order direct that, pending the consideration of the representation, if any, the director, shall not, with effect from the date of such order—

(a) act as such director of that company;

(b) in any way, whether directly or indirectly, be concerned with or take part in the management of that company.

(3) Where any order is made in respect of a director of a company under sub-section (1), he shall cease to be a director of that non-banking financial company and shall not, in any way, whether directly or indirectly, be concerned with, or take part in the management of any non-banking financial company for such period not exceeding five years at a time as may be specified in the order.

(4) Where an order under sub-section (1) has been made, the Bank may, by order in writing, appoint a suitable person in place of the director, who has been so removed from his office, with effect from such date as may be specified in such order.

(5) Any person appointed under sub-section (4) shall,—

(a) hold office during the pleasure of the Bank and subject thereto for a period not exceeding three years or such further periods not exceeding three years at a time;

(b) not incur any obligation or liability by reason only of his being a director for anything done or omitted to be done in good faith in the execution of the duties of his office or in relation thereto.

(6) Notwithstanding anything contained in any other law for the time being in force or in any contract, memorandum or articles of association, on the removal of a director from office under this section, such director shall not be entitled to claim any compensation for the loss or termination from office.

45-IE. Supersession of Board of directors of non-banking financial company (other than Government Company)

(1) Where the Bank is satisfied that in the public interest or to prevent the affairs of a non-banking financial company being conducted in a manner detrimental to the interest of the depositors or creditors, or of the non-banking financial company (other than Government Company), or for securing the proper management of such company or for financial stability, it is necessary so to do, the Bank may, for reasons to be recorded in writing, by order, supersede the Board of Directors of such company for a period not exceeding five years as may be specified in the order, which may be extended from time to time, so, however, that the total period shall not exceed five years.

(2) The Bank may, on supersession of the Board of Directors of the non-banking financial company under sub-section (1), appoint a suitable person as the Administrator for such period as it may determine.

(3) The Bank may issue such directions to the Administrator as it may deem appropriate and the Administrator shall be bound to follow such directions.

(4) Upon making the order of supersession of the Board of Directors of a non-banking financial company,—

(a) the chairman, managing director and other directors shall from the date of supersession of the Board of Directors vacate their offices;

(b) all the powers, functions and duties, which may, by or under the provisions of this Act or any other law for the time being in force, be exercised and discharged by or on behalf of the Board of Directors of such non-banking financial company or by a resolution passed in general meeting of such non-banking financial company, shall, until the Board of Directors of such company is reconstituted, be exercised and discharged by the Administrator referred to in sub-section (2).

(5) (a) The Bank may constitute a committee consisting of three or more members who have experience in law, finance, banking, administration or accountancy to assist the Administrator in discharge of his duties.

(b) The committee shall meet at such times and places and observe such rules of procedure as may be specified by the Bank.

(6) The salary and allowances payable to the Administrator and the members of the committee constituted by the Bank shall be such as may be specified by the Bank and be paid by the concerned non-banking financial company.

(7) On or before the expiration of the period of supersession of the Board of Directors as specified in the order issued under sub-section (1), the Administrator of the non-banking financial company shall facilitate reconstitution of the Board of Directors of the non-banking financial company.

(8) Notwithstanding anything contained in any other law for the time being in force or in any contract, no person shall be entitled to claim any compensation for the loss or termination of his office.

(9) The Administrator referred to in sub-section (2) shall vacate office immediately after the Board of Directors of the non-banking financial company has been reconstituted.]

45J. Bank to regulate or prohibit issue of prospectus or advertisement soliciting deposits of money

The Bank may, if it considers necessary in the public interest so to do, by general or special order,—

(a) regulate or prohibit the issue by any non-banking institution of any prospectus or advertisement soliciting deposits of money from the public, and

(b) specify the conditions subject to which any such prospectus or advertisement, if not prohibited, may be issued.

[1][**45JA. Power of Bank to determine policy and issue directions**

(1) If the Bank is satisfied that, in the public interest or to regulate the financial system of the country to its advantage or to prevent the affairs of any non-banking financial company being conducted in manner detrimental to the interest of the depositors or in a manner prejudicial to the interest of the non-banking financial company, it is necessary or expedient so to do, it may determine the policy and give directions to all or any of the non-banking financial companies relating to income

1 Inserted by Act 23 of 1997, w.e.f. 9-1-1997.

recognition, accounting standards, making of proper provision for bad and doubtful debts, capital adequacy based on risk weights for assets and credit conversion factors for off balance-sheet items and also relating to deployment of funds by a non-banking financial company or a class of non-banking financial companies or non-banking financial companies generally, as the case may be, and such non-banking financial companies shall be bound to follow the policy so determined and the direction so issued.

(2) Without prejudice to the generality of the powers vested under sub-section (1), the Bank may give directions to non-banking financial companies generally or to a class of non-banking financial companies or to any non-banking financial company in particular as to—

(a) the purpose for which advances or other fund based or non-fund based accommodation may not be made; and

(b) the maximum amount of advances of other financial accommodation or investment in shares and other securities which, having regard to the paid-up capital, reserves and deposits of the non-banking financial company and other relevant considerations, may be made by that non-banking financial company to any person or a company or to a group of companies.]

45K. Power of Bank to collect information from non-banking institutions as to deposits and to give directions

(1) The Bank may at any time direct that every non-banking institution shall furnish to the Bank, in such form, at such intervals and within such time, such statements information or particulars relating to or connected with deposits received by the non-banking institution, as may be specified by the Bank by general or special order.

(2) Without prejudice to the generality of the power vested in the Bank under sub-section (1), the statements, information or particulars to be furnished under sub-section (1), may relate to all or any of the following matters, namely, the amount of the deposits, the purposes and periods for which, and the rates of interest and other terms and conditions on which, they are received.

(3) The Bank may, if it considers necessary in the public interest so to do, give directions to non-banking institutions either generally or to any non-banking institution or group of non-banking institutions in particular, in respect of any matters relating to or connected with the receipt of deposits, including the rates of interest payable on such deposits, and the periods for which deposits may be received.

(4) If any non-banking institution fails to comply with any direction given by the Bank under sub-section (3), the Bank may prohibit the acceptance of deposits by that non-banking institution.

[1][xxx]

(6) Every non-banking institution receiving deposits shall, if so required by the Bank and within such time as the Bank may specify, cause to be sent at the cost of the non-banking institution a copy of its annual balance-sheet and profit and loss account or other annual accounts to every person from whom the non-banking institution holds, as on the last day of the year to which the accounts relate, deposits higher than such sum as may be specified by the Bank.

---

1 Sub-section (5) omitted by Act 51 of 1974, w.e.f. 13-12-1974.

45L. Power of Bank to call for information from financial institutions and to give directions

(1) If the Bank is satisfied for the purpose of enabling it to regulate the credit system of the country to its advantage it is necessary so to do, it may—

(a) require financial institutions either generally or any group of financial institutions or financial institution in particular, to furnish to the Bank in such form, at such intervals and within such time, such statements, information or particulars relating to the business of such financial institutions or institution, as may be specified by the Bank by general or special order;

(b) give to such institutions either generally or to any such institution in particular, directions relating to the conduct of business by them or by it as financial institutions or institution.

(2) Without prejudice to the generality of the power vested in the Bank under clause (a) of sub-section (1), the statements, information or particulars to be furnished by a financial institution may relate to all or any of the following matters, namely, the paid-up capital, reserves or other liabilities, the investments whether in Government securities or otherwise, the persons to whom, and the purposes and periods for which, finance is provided and the terms and conditions, including the rates of interest, on which it is provided.

(3) In issuing directions to any financial institution under clause (b) of sub-section (1), the Bank shall have due regard to the conditions in which, and the objects for which, the institution has been established, its statutory responsibilities, if any, and the effect the business of such financial institution is likely to have on trends in the money and capital markets.

45M. Duty of non-banking institutions to furnish statements, etc., required by Bank

It shall be the duty or every non-banking institution to furnish the statements, information or particulars called for, and to comply with any direction given to it, under the provisions of this Chapter.

[1][**45MA. Powers and duties of auditors**

(1) It shall be the duty of an auditor of a non-banking institution to inquire whether or not the non-banking institution has furnished to the Bank such statements, information or particulars relating to or connected with deposits received by it, as are required to be furnished under this Chapter, and the auditor shall, except where he is satisfied on such inquiry that the non-banking institution has furnished such statements, information or particulars, make a report to the Bank giving the aggregate amount of such deposits held by the non-banking institution.

[2][(1A) The Bank may, on being satisfied that it is necessary so to do, in the public interest or in the interest of the depositors or for the purpose of proper assessment of the books of accounts, issue directions to any non-banking financial company or any class of non-banking financial companies or non-banking financial companies generally or to the auditors of such non-banking financial company or companies relating to balance-sheet, profit and loss account, disclosure of liabilities in the books of accounts or any matter relating thereto.]

1 Inserted by Act 51 of 1974, w.e.f. 13-12-1974.
2 Inserted by Act 23 of 1997, w.e.f. 9-1-1997.

(2) Where, in the case of [1][a non-banking financial company], the auditor has made, or intends to make, a report to the Bank under sub-section (1), he shall include in his report under sub-section (2) of section 227 of the Companies Act, 1956 (1 of 1956), the contents of the report which he has made or intends to make, to the Bank.]

[2][(3) Where the bank is of the opinion that it is necessary so to do in the public interest or in the interest of the non-banking financial company or in the interest of depositors of such company it may at any time by order direct that a special audit of the accounts of the non-banking financial company in relation to any such transaction or class of transactions or for such period or periods, as may be specified in the order, shall be conducted and the Bank may appoint an auditor or auditors to conduct such special audit and direct the auditor or the auditors to submit the report to it.

(4) The remuneration of the auditors as may be fixed by the Bank, having regard to the nature and volume of work involved in the audit and the expenses of or incidental to the audit, shall be borne by the non-banking financial company so audited.]

[3][45MAA. Power to take action against auditors

Where any auditor fails to comply with any direction given or order made by the Bank under section 45MA, the Bank, may, if satisfied, remove or debar the auditor from exercising the duties as auditor of any of the Bank regulated entities for a maximum period of three years, at a time.]

[2][45MB. Power of Bank to prohibit acceptance of deposit and alienation of assets

(1) If any non-banking financial company violates the provisions of any section or fails to comply with any direction or order given by the Bank under any of the provisions of this Chapter, the Bank may prohibit the non-banking financial company from accepting any deposit.

(2) Notwithstanding anything to the contrary contained in any agreement or instruments or any law for the time being in force, the Bank, on being satisfied that it is necessary so to do in the public interest or in the interest of the depositors, may direct, the non-banking financial company against which an order prohibiting from accepting deposit has been issued, not to sell, transfer, create, charge or mortgage or deal in any manner with its property and assets without prior written permission of the Bank for such period not exceeding six months from the date of the order.

[3][45MBA. Resolution of non-banking financial company

(1) Without prejudice to any other provision of this Act or any other law for the time being in force, the Bank may, if it is satisfied, upon an inspection of the Books of a non-banking financial company that it is in the public interest or in the interest of financial stability so to do for enabling the continuance of the activities critical to the functioning of the financial system, frame schemes which may provide for any one or more of the following, namely:—

(a) amalgamation with any other non-banking institution;

(b) reconstruction of the non-banking financial company;

(c) splitting the non-banking financial company into different units or institutions and vesting viable and non-viable businesses in separate units or institutions to preserve the continuity of the activities of that non-banking

1 Substituted for "a non-banking institution, being a company" by Act 23 of 1997, w.e.f. 9-1-1997.
2 Inserted by Act 23 of 1997, w.e.f. 9-1-1997.
3 Inserted by Act 23 of 2019, w.e.f. 9-8-2019.

financial company that are critical to the functioning of the financial system and for such purpose establish institutions called "Bridge Institutions".

Explanation : For the purposes of this sub-section, "Bridge Institutions" mean temporary institutional arrangement made under the scheme referred to in this sub-section, to preserve the continuity of the activities of a non-banking financial company that are critical to the functioning of the financial system.

(2) Without prejudice to the generality of the foregoing provisions, the scheme referred to in sub-section (1) may provide for—

(a) reduction of the pay and allowances of the chief executive officer, managing director, chairman or any officer in the senior management of the non-banking financial company;

(b) cancellation of all or some of the shares of the non-banking financial company held by the chief executive officer, managing director, chairman or any officer in the senior management of the non-banking financial company or their relatives;

(c) sale of any of the assets of the non-banking financial company.

(3) The chief executive officer, managing director, chairman or any officer in the senior management of the non-banking financial company whose pay and allowances are reduced or the shareholders whose shares are cancelled under the scheme shall not be entitled to any compensation.]

45MC. Power of Bank to file winding up petition

(1) The Bank, on being satisfied that a non-banking financial company—

(a) is unable to pay its debt; or

(b) has by virtue of the provisions of section 45-IA become disqualified to carry on the business of a non-banking financial institution; or

(c) has been prohibited by the Bank from receiving deposit by an order and such order has been in force for a period of not less than three months; or

(d) the continuance of the non-banking financial company is detrimental to the public interest or to the interest of depositors of the company,

may file an application for winding up of such non-banking financial company under the Companies Act, 1956 (1 of 1956).

(2) A non-banking financial company shall be deemed to be unable to pay its debt if it has refused or has failed to meet within five working days any lawful demand made at any to its offices or branches and the Bank certifies in writing that such company is unable to pay its debt.

(3) A copy of every application made by the Bank under sub-section (1) shall be sent to the Registrar of Companies.

(4) All the provisions of the Companies Act, 1956 (1 of 1956) relating to winding up of a company shall apply to a winding up proceeding initiated on the application made by the Bank under this provision.]

45N. Inspection

[1][(1) The Bank may, at any time, cause an inspection to be made by one or more of its officers or employees or other persons (hereafter in this section referred to as the inspecting authority)—

1 Substituted by Act 51 of 1974, w.e.f. 13-12-1974.

(i) of any non-banking institution, including a financial institution, for the purposes of verifying the correctness or completeness of any statement, information or particulars furnished to the Bank or for the purpose of obtaining any information or particulars which the non-banking institution has failed to furnish on being called upon to do so; or

(ii) of any non-banking institution being a financial institution, if the Bank considers it necessary or expedient to inspect that institution.]

(2) It shall be the duly of every director or member of any committee or other body for the time being vested with the management of the affairs of the non-banking institution or other officer or employee thereof to produce to the inspecting authority all such books, accounts and other documents in his custody or power and to furnish that authority with any statements and information relating to the business of the institution as that authority may require of him, within such time as may be specified by that authority.

(3) The inspecting authority may examine on oath any director or member of any committee or body for the time being vested with the management of the affairs of the non-banking institution or other officer or employee thereof, in relation to its business and may administer an oath accordingly.

[1][**45NA. Deposits not to be solicited by unauthorised person**

No person shall solicit on behalf of any non-banking institution either by publishing or causing to be published any prospectus or advertisement or in any other manner deposits of money from the public unless—

(a) he has been authorised in writing by the said non-banking institution to do so and specifies the name of the institution which has so authorised him, and

(b) the prospectus or advertisement complies with any order made by the Bank under section 45J and with any other provision of law for the time being in force, applicable to the publication of such prospectus or advertisement.]

[2][**45NAA. Power in respect of group companies**

(1) The Bank may, at any time, direct a non-banking financial company to annex to its financial statements or furnish separately, within such time and at such intervals as may be specified by the Bank, such statements and information relating to the business or affairs of any group company of the non-banking financial company as the Bank may consider necessary or expedient to obtain for the purposes of this Act.

(2) Notwithstanding anything to the contrary contained in the Companies Act, 2013 (18 of 2013), the Bank may, at any time, cause an inspection or audit to be made of any group company of a non-banking financial company and its books of account.

Explanation : For the purposes of this section,—

(a) "group company" shall mean an arrangement involving two or more entities related to each other through any of the following relationships, namely:—

(i) subsidiary–parent (as may be notified by the Bank in accordance with Accounting Standards);

---

1 Inserted by Act 51 of 1974, w.e.f. 13-12-1974.

2 Inserted by Act 23 of 2019, w.e.f. 9-8-2019.

(ii) joint venture (as may be notified by the Bank in accordance with Accounting Standards);

(iii) associate (as may be notified by the Bank in accordance with Accounting Standards);

(iv) promoter-promotee (under the Securities and Exchange Board of India Act, 1992 (15 of 1992) or the rules or regulations made thereunder for listed companies);

(v) related party;

(vi) common brand name (that is usage of a registered brand name of an entity by another entity for business purposes); and

(vii) investment in equity shares of twenty per cent. and above in the entity;

(b) "Accounting Standards" means the Accounting Standards notified by the Central Government under section 133, read with section 469 of the Companies Act, 2013 (18 of 2013) and sub-section (1) of section 210A of the Companies Act, 1956 (1 of 1956).]

[1][45NB. Disclosure of information

(1) Any information relating to a non-banking financial company,—

(i) contained in any statement or return submitted by such company under the provisions of this chapter; or

(ii) obtained through audit or inspection or otherwise by the Bank,

shall be treated as confidential and shall not, except otherwise provided in this section, be disclosed.

(2) Nothing in this section shall apply to—

(a) the disclosure by any non-banking financial company, with the previous permission of the Bank, of any information furnished to the Bank under sub-section (1);

(b) the publication by the Bank, if it considers necessary in the public interest so to do, of any information collected by it under sub-section (1) in such consolidated form as it may think fit without disclosing the name of any non-banking financial company or its borrowers;

(c) the disclosure or publication by the non-banking financial company or by the Bank of any such information to any other non-banking financial company or in accordance with the practice and usage customary amongst such companies or as permitted or required under any other law:

PROVIDED that any such information received by a non-banking financial company under this clause shall not be published except in accordance with the practice and usage customary amongst companies or as permitted or required under any other law.

(3) Notwithstanding anything contained in this Act or in any other law for the time being in force, the Bank, if it is satisfied that, in the public interest or in the interest of the depositors or the non-banking financial company or to prevent the affairs of any non-banking financial company being conducted in a manner detrimental to the interest of the depositors, it is expedient so to do, may, either on its own motion or on being

1 Inserted by Act 23 of 1997, w.e.f. 9-1-1997.

requested, furnish or communicate any information relating to the conduct of business by any non-banking financial company to any authority constituted under any law.

(4) Notwithstanding anything contained in any law for the time being in force, no court or tribunal or other authority shall compel the Bank to produce or to give inspection of any statement or other material obtained by the Bank under any provisions of this chapter.]

45NC. Power of Bank to exempt

The Bank, on being satisfied that it is necessary so to do, may declare by notification in the Official Gazette that any or all of the provisions of this Chapter shall not apply to a non-banking institution or a class of non-banking institutions or a non-banking financial company or to any class or non-banking financial companies either generally or for such period as may be specified, subject to such conditions, limitations or restrictions as it may think fit to impose.]

[1]**[xxx]**

45Q. Chapter IIIB to override other laws

The provisions of this Chapter shall have effect notwithstanding anything inconsistent therewith contained in any other law for the time being in force or any instrument having effect by virtue of any such law.]

[2]**[45QA. Power of Company Law Board to offer repayment of deposit**

(1) Every deposit accepted by a non-banking financial company, unless renewed, shall be repaid in accordance with the terms and condition of such deposit.

(2) Where a non-banking financial company has failed to repay and deposit or part thereof in accordance with the terms and conditions of such deposit, the Company Law Board constituted under section 10E of the Companies Act, 1956 (1 of 1956), may, if it is satisfied, either on its own motion or on an application of the depositor, that it is necessary so to do to safeguard the interests of the company, the depositors or in the public interest, direct, by order, the non-banking financial company to make repayment of such deposit or part thereof forthwith or within such time and subject to such conditions as may be specified in the order:

PROVIDED that the Company Law Board may, before making any order under this sub-section, give a reasonable opportunity of being heard to the non-banking financial company and the other persons interested in the matter.

45QB. Nomination by depositors

(1) Where a deposit is held by a non-banking financial institution to the credit of one or more persons, the depositor or, as the case may be, all the depositors together may nominate, in the manner prescribed by rules made by the Central Government under section 45ZA of the Banking Regulation Act, 1949 (10 of 1949), one person to whom in the event of the death of the sole depositor or the death of all the depositors, the amount of deposit may be returned by the non-banking financial institution.

(2) Notwithstanding anything contained in any other law for the time being in force, or in any disposition, whether testamentary or otherwise, in respect of such deposit, where a nomination made purports to confer on any person the right to receive the amount of deposit from the non-banking financial institution, the nominee shall, on the death of the sole depositor or, as the case may be, on the death of all the depositors,

1 Sections 45-O and 45P omitted by the Reserve Bank of India (Amendment) Act, 1974, (51 of 1974), w.e.f. 13-12-1974.

2 Inserted by Act 23 of 1997, w.e.f. 9-1-1997.

become entitled to all the rights of the sole depositor or, as the case may be, of the depositors, in relation to such deposit to the exclusion of all other persons, unless the nomination is varied or cancelled in the manner prescribed by rules made by the Central Government under section 45ZA of the Banking Regulation Act, 1949 (10 of 1949).

(3) Where the nominee is a minor, it shall be lawful for the depositor making the nomination to appoint, in the manner prescribed by rules made by the Central Government under section 45ZA of the Banking Regulation Act, 1949 (10 of 1949), any person to receive the amount of deposit in the event of his death during the minority of the nominee.

(4) Payment by a non-banking institution in accordance with the provisions of this section shall constitute a full discharge to the non-banking institution of its liability in respect of the deposit:

PROVIDED that nothing contained in this sub-section shall effect the right or claim which any person may have against the person to whom any payment is made under this section.

(5) No notice of the claim of any person, other than the person or persons in whose name a deposit is held by a non-banking institution, shall be receivable by the non-banking institution, nor shall the non-banking institution be bound by any such notice even though expressly given to it:

PROVIDED that where any decree order, certificate or other authority from a court of competent jurisdiction relating to such deposit is produced before a non-banking institution, the non-banking institution shall take due note of such decree, order, certificate or other authority.]

[1][CHAPTER IIIC
PROHINITION OF ACCEPTANCE OF DEPOSITS BY UNINCORPORATED BODIES

45R. Interpretation

The words and expressions used in this Chapter and defined in Chapter IIIB shall have the meanings respectively assigned to them therein.

[2][45S. Deposits not to be accepted in certain cases

(1) No person, being an individual or a firm or an unincorporated association of individuals shall, accept any deposit—

(i) if his or its business wholly or partly includes any of the activities specified in clause (c) of section 45-1; or

(ii) if his or its principal business is that of receiving of deposits under any scheme or arrangement or in any other manner or lending in any manner:

PROVIDED that nothing contained in this sub-section shall apply to the receipt of money by an individual by way of loan from any of his relatives or to the receipt of money by a firm by way of loan from the relative or relatives of any of the partners.

(2) Where any person referred to in sub-section (1) holds any deposit on the 1st day of April, 1997 which is not in accordance with sub-section (1), such deposit shall be repaid by that person immediately after such deposit becomes due for repayment or within three years from the date of such commencement, whichever is earlier:

1 Inserted by Act 1 of 1984, w.e.f. 15-2-1984.
2 Substituted by Act 23 of 1997, w.e.f. 1-4-1997.

PROVIDED that if the Bank is satisfied on an application made by any person to the Bank that such person is unable to repay a part of the deposits for reasons beyond his control or such repayment shall cause extreme hardship to him, it may, by an order in writing, extend such period by a period not exceeding one year subject to such conditions as may be specified in the order.

(3) On and from the 1st day of April, 1997, no person referred to in sub-section (1) shall issue or cause to be issued any advertisement in any form for soliciting deposit.

Explanation : For the purposes of this section, a person shall be deemed to be a relative of another if, and only if,—

(i) they are members of a Hindu undivided family; or

(ii) they are husband and wife; or

(iii) the one is related to the other in the manner indicated in the List of Relatives below:

List of Relatives

1. Father, 2. Mother (including step-mother), 3. Son (including step-son), 4. Son's wife, 5. Daughter (including step-daughter), 6. Father's father, 7. Father's mother, 8. Mother's mother, 9. Mother's father, 10. Son's son, 11. Son's son's wife, 12. Son's Daughter 13. Son's Daughter's husband, 14. Daughter's husband, 15. Daughter's son, 16. Daughter's son's wife, 17. Daughter's daughter, 18. Daughter's daughter's husband. 19. Brother (including step-brother), 20. Brother's wife, 21. Sister (including step-sister), 22. Sister's husband].

45T. Power to issue search warrants

(1) Any court having jurisdiction to issue a search warrant under the Code of Criminal Procedure, 1973 (2 of 1974), may, on an application by an officer of the bank or of the State Government authorised in this behalf stating his belief that certain documents relating to acceptance of deposits in contravention of the provisions of section 45S are secreted in any place within the local limits of the jurisdiction of such court, issue a warrant to search for such documents.

(2) A warrant issued under sub-section (1) shall be executed in the same manner and shall have the same effect as a search warrant issued under the Code of Criminal Procedure, 1973 (2 of 1974).]

[1][CHAPTER IIID

REGULATION OF TRANSACTIONS IN DERIVATIVES, MONEY MARKET INSTRUMENTS, SECURITIES, ETC.

45U. Definitions

For the purposes of this Chapter—

(a) "derivative" means an instrument, to be settled at a future date, whose value is derived from change in interest rate, foreign exchange rate, credit rating or credit index, price of securities (also called "underlying"), or a combination of more than one of them and includes interest rate swaps, forward rate agreements, foreign currency swaps, foreign currency-rupee swaps, foreign currency options, foreign currency-rupee options or such other instruments as may be specified by the Bank from time to time;

1 Inserted by Act 26 of 2006, w.e.f. 9-1-2007.

(b) "money market instruments" include call or notice money, term money, repo, reverse repo, certificate of deposit, commercial usance bill, commercial paper and such other debt instrument of original or initial maturity up to one year as the Bank may specify from time to time;

(c) "repo" means an instrument for borrowing funds by selling securities with an agreement to repurchase the securities on a mutually agreed future date at an agreed price which includes interest for the funds borrowed;

(d) "reverse repo" means an instrument for lending funds by purchasing securities with an agreement to resell the securities on a mutually agreed future date at an agreed price which includes interest for the funds lent;

(e) "securities" means securities of the Central Government or a State Government or such securities of a local authority as may be specified in this behalf by the Central Government and, for the purposes of "repo" or "reverse repo", include corporate bonds and debentures.

45V. Transactions in derivatives

(1) Notwithstanding anything contained in the Securities Contracts (Regulation) Act, 1956 (42 of 1956) or any other law for the time being in force, transactions in such derivatives, as may be specified by the Bank from time to time, shall be valid, if at least one of the parties to the transaction is the Bank, a scheduled bank, or such other agency falling under the regulatory purview of the Bank under the Act, the Banking Regulation Act, 1949 (10 of 1949), the Foreign Exchange Management Act, 1999 (42 of 1999), or any other Act or instrument having the force of law, as may be specified by the Bank from time to time.

(2) Transactions in such derivatives, as had been specified by the Bank from time to time, shall be deemed always to have been valid, as if the provisions of sub-section (1) were in force at all material times.

45W. Power to regulate transactions in derivatives, money market instruments, etc.

(1) The Bank may, in public interest, or to regulate the financial system of the country to its advantage, determine the policy relating to interest rates or interest rate products and give directions in that behalf to all agencies or any of them, dealing in securities, money market instruments, foreign exchange, derivatives, or other instruments of like nature as the Bank may specify from time to time:

PROVIDED that the directions issued under this sub-section shall not relate to the procedure for execution or settlement of the trades in respect of the transactions mentioned therein, on the Stock Exchanges recognised under section 4 of the Securities Contracts (Regulation) Act, 1956(42 of 1956).

(2) The Bank may, for the purpose of enabling it to regulate agencies referred to in sub-section (1), call for any information, statement or other particulars from them, or cause an inspection of such agencies to be made.

45X. Duty to comply with directions and furnish information

It shall be the duty of every director or member or other body for the time being vested with the management of the affairs of the agencies referred to in section 45W to comply with the directions given by the Bank and to submit the information or statement or particulars called for under that section.]

[1][CHAPTER IIIE
JOINT MECHANISM

45Y. Joint Mechanism

(1) Notwithstanding anything contained in this Act or the Securities and Exchange Board of India Act, 1992 (15 of 1992) or any other law for the time being in force, if any difference of opinion arises as to whether—

(i) any instrument, being derivative referred to in clause (a) or money market instrument referred to in clause (b) or repo referred to in clause (c) or reverse repo referred to in clause (d) or securities referred to in clause (e) of section 45U of this Act; or

(ii) any instrument, being policy of life insurance under the Insurance Act, 1938(4 of 1938), or the rules or regulations made thereunder, or, scrips or any other securities referred to in sub-clauses (i), (ia), (ib), (ic), (id), (ie), (ii), (iia) and (iii) of clause (h) of section 2 of the Securities Contracts (Regulation) Act, 1956 (42 of 1956),

is hybrid or composite instrument, having a component of money market investment or securities market instrument or a component of insurance or any other instrument referred to in clause (i) or clause (ii) and falls within the jurisdiction of the Reserve Bank of India or the Securities and Exchange Board of India established under section 3 of the Securities and Exchange Board of India Act, 1992 (15 of 1992) or the Insurance Regulatory and Development Authority established under section 3 of the Insurance Regulatory and Development Authority Act, 1999 (41 of 1999) or the Pension Fund Regulatory and Development Authority constituted by the Resolution of the Government of India number F.No. 1(6)2007-PR, dated the 14th November, 2008, such difference of opinion shall be referred to a Joint Committee consisting of the following, namely:—

(a) the Union Finance Minister *ex officio* Chairperson;

(b) the Governor, Reserve Bank of India *ex officio* Vice-Chairperson;

(c) the Secretary, Department of Economic Affairs in the Ministry of Finance, Government of India *ex officio* Member;

(d) the Secretary, Department of Financial Services in the Ministry of Finance, Government of India *ex officio* Member;

(e) the Chairperson, Insurance Regulatory and Development Authority *ex officio* Member;

(f) the Chairman, Securities and Exchange Board of India *ex officio* Member;

(g) the Chairperson, Pension Fund Regulatory and Development Authority *ex officio* Member.

(2) The Secretary, Department of Financial Services in the Ministry of Finance, Government of India shall be the convener of the meetings of the Joint Committee referred to in sub-section (1).

(3) In case of any difference of opinion referred to in sub-section (1), any Member of the Joint Committee referred to in clauses (b), (e), (f) or (g) of that sub-section may make a reference to the Joint Committee.

(4) The Joint Committee shall follow such procedure as it may consider expedient and give, within a period of three months from the date of reference made under sub-section (3), its decisions thereon to the Central Government.

---

1 Inserted by Act 26 of 2010, w.e.f. 18-6-2010.

(5) The decision of the Joint Committee shall be binding on the Reserve Bank of India, the Securities and Exchange Board of India, the Insurance Regulatory and Development Authority and the Pension Fund Regulatory and Development Authority.]

[1][CHAPTER IIIF
MONETARY POLICY

45Z. Provisions of this Chapter to override other provisions of Act

The provisions of this Chapter shall have effect, notwithstanding anything inconsistent therewith contained in any other provisions of this Act.

45ZA. Inflation target

(1) The Central Government shall, in consultation with the Bank, determine the inflation target in terms of the Consumer Price Index, once in every five years.

(2) The Central Government shall, upon such determination, notify the inflation target in the Official Gazette.

45ZB. Constitution of Monetary Policy Committee

(1) The Central Government may, by notification in the Official Gazette, constitute a Committee to be called the Monetary Policy Committee of the Bank.

(2) The Monetary Policy Committee shall consist of the following Members, namely:—

(a) the Governor of the Bank—Chairperson, *ex officio*;

(b) Deputy Governor of the Bank, in charge of Monetary Policy—Member, *ex officio*;

(c) one officer of the Bank to be nominated by the Central Board—Member, *ex officio*; and

(d) three persons to be appointed by the Central Government—Members.

(3) The Monetary Policy Committee shall determine the Policy Rate required to achieve the inflation target.

(4) The decision of the Monetary Policy Committee shall be binding on the Bank.

45ZC. Eligibility and selection of Members appointed by Central Government

(1) The Members of the Monetary Policy Committee referred to in clause (d) of sub-section (2) of section 45ZB shall be appointed by the Central Government from amongst persons of ability, integrity and standing, having knowledge and experience in the field of economics or banking or finance or monetary policy:

PROVIDED that no person shall be appointed as a Member, in case such person—

(i) has completed the age of seventy years on the date of appointment as Member;

(ii) is a Member of any Board or Committee of the Bank;

(iii) is an employee of the Bank;

(iv) is a public servant as defined under section 21 of the Indian Penal Code (45 of 1860);

(v) is a Member of Parliament or any State Legislature;

(vi) has been at any time, adjudged as an insolvent;

---

1 Inserted by Act 28 of 2016, w.e.f. 27-6-2016.

(vii) has been convicted of an offence which is punishable with an imprisonment for a term of one hundred and eighty days or more;

(viii) is physically or mentally incapable of discharging the duties of a Member of the Monetary Policy Committee; or

(ix) has a material conflict of interest with the Bank and is unable to resolve such conflict.

(2) The Members of the Monetary Policy Committee referred to in clause (d) of sub-section (2) of section 45ZB shall be appointed by the Central Government on the recommendations made by Search-cum-Selection Committee consisting of the following members, namely:—

(a) Cabinet Secretary—Chairperson;

(b) Governor of the Reserve Bank of India or his representative (not below the rank of Deputy Governor)—Member;

(c) Secretary, Department of Economic Affairs—Member;

(d) three experts in the field of economics or banking or finance or Monetary policy to be nominated by the Central Government—Members.

(3) While selecting the Members of the Monetary Policy Committee, the Search-cum-Selection Committee shall follow such procedure as may be prescribed by the Central Government.

45ZD. Terms and conditions of appointment of Members of Monetary Policy Committee

(1) The Members of the Monetary Policy Committee appointed under clause (d) of sub-section (2) of section 45ZB shall hold office for a period of four years and shall not be eligible for re-appointment.

(2) The terms and conditions of appointment of Members of the Monetary Policy Committee shall be such as may be prescribed by the Central Government and the remuneration and other allowances payable to such Members shall be such as may be specified by the regulations made by the Central Board.

(3) A Member may resign from the Monetary Policy Committee, at any time before the expiry of his tenure under sub-section (1), by giving to the Central Government, a written notice of not less than six weeks, and on the acceptance of the resignation by the Central Government, he shall cease to be a Member of the Monetary Policy Committee.

45ZE. Removal of Members of Monetary Policy Committee

(1) The Central Government may remove from office any Member of the Monetary Policy Committee appointed under clause (d) of sub-section (2) of section 45ZB, who—

(a) is, or at any time has been, adjudged as an insolvent; or

(b) has become physically or mentally incapable of acting as a Member; or

(c) has been convicted of an offence which, in the opinion of the Central Government, involves moral turpitude; or

(d) has failed to adequately disclose any material conflict of interest at the time of his appointment; or

(e) does not attend three consecutive meetings of the Monetary Policy Committee without obtaining prior leave; or

(f) has acquired such financial or other interest as is likely to affect prejudicially his functions as a Member; or

(g) has acquired any post referred to in clauses (ii), (iii), (iv) and clause (v) of the proviso to sub-section (1) of section 45ZC; or

(h) has, in the opinion of the Central Government, so abused his position as to render his continuance in office detrimental to the public interest.

(2) No Member appointed under clause (d) of sub-section (2) of section 45ZB shall be removed under clause (d) or clause (e) or clause (f) or clause (g) or clause (h) of sub-section (1) unless he has been given a reasonable opportunity of being heard in the matter.

45ZF. Vacancies, etc., not to invalidate proceedings of Monetary Policy Committee

No act or proceeding of the Monetary Policy Committee shall be invalid merely by reason of—

(a) any vacancy in, or any defect in the constitution of the Monetary Policy Committee; or

(b) any defect in the appointment of a person acting as a Member of the Monetary Policy Committee; or

(c) any irregularity in the procedure of the Monetary Policy Committee not affecting the merits of the case.

45ZG. Secretary to Monetary Policy Committee

(1) The Bank shall appoint a Secretary to the Monetary Policy Committee to provide secretariat support to the said Committee.

(2) The Secretary shall perform such functions and in such manner as may be specified by the regulations made by the Central Board.

45ZH. Information for Monetary Policy Committee Members

(1) The Bank shall provide all information to the Members of the Monetary Policy Committee that may be relevant to achieve the inflation target.

(2) In addition to information provided by the Bank under sub-section (1), any Member of the Monetary Policy Committee may, at any time, request the Bank for additional information, including any data, models or analysis.

(3) The Bank shall provide the information, as referred to in sub-section (2), to the Member of the Monetary Policy Committee, within reasonable time, unless—

(a) the information pertains to an entity or person and is not publicly available; or

(b) the information allows an entity or person to be identified and the information is not publicly available.

(4) Any information provided by the Bank to a Member of the Monetary Policy Committee shall be provided to all the Members of the Monetary Policy Committee.

45Z-I. Meetings of Monetary Policy Committee

(1) The Bank shall organise at least four meetings of the Monetary Policy Committee in a year.

(2) The meeting schedule of the Monetary Policy Committee for a year shall be published by the Bank at least one week before the first meeting in that year.

(3) The meeting schedule may be changed only—

(a) by way of a decision taken at a prior meeting of the Monetary Policy Committee; or

(b) if, in the opinion of the Governor, an additional meeting is required or a meeting is required to be rescheduled due to administrative exigencies.

(4) Any change in meeting schedule shall be published by the Bank as soon as practicable.

(5) The quorum for a meeting of the Monetary Policy Committee shall be four Members, at least one of whom shall be the Governor and in his absence, the Deputy Governor who is the Member of the Monetary Policy Committee.

(6) The meetings of the Monetary Policy Committee shall be presided over by the Governor, and in his absence by the Deputy Governor who is a Member of the Monetary Policy Committee.

(7) Each Member of the Monetary Policy Committee shall have one vote.

(8) All questions which come up before any meeting of the Monetary Policy Committee shall be decided by a majority of votes by the Members present and voting, and in the event of an equality of votes, the Governor shall have a second or casting vote.

(9) The Central Government may, if it considers necessary, convey its views in writing to the Monetary Policy Committee from time to time.

(10) The vote of each Member of the Monetary Policy Committee for a proposed resolution shall be recorded against such Member.

(11) Each Member of the Monetary Policy Committee shall write a statement specifying the reasons for voting in favour of, or against the proposed resolution.

(12) The procedure, conduct code of confidentiality and any other incidental matter for the functioning of the Monetary Policy Committee shall be such as may be specified by the regulations made by the Central Board.

(13) The proceeding of the Monetary Policy Committee shall be confidential.

45ZJ. Steps to be taken to implement decision of Monetary Policy Committee

(1) The Bank shall publish a document explaining the steps to be taken by it to implement the decisions of the Monetary Policy Committee, including any changes thereto.

(2) The particulars to be included in such document and the frequency of publications of such document shall be such as may be specified by the regulations made by the Central Board.

45ZK. Publication of decisions

The Bank shall publish, after the conclusion of every meeting of the Monetary Policy Committee, the resolution adopted by the said Committee.

45ZL. Publication of proceedings of meeting of Monetary Policy Committee

The Bank shall publish, on the fourteenth day after every meeting of the Monetary Policy Committee, the minutes of the proceedings of the meeting which shall include the following, namely:—

(a) the resolution adopted at the meeting of the Monetary Policy Committee;

(b) the vote of each member of the Monetary Policy Committee, ascribed to such member, on resolutions adopted in the said meeting; and

(c) the statement of each member of the Monetary Policy Committee under sub-section (11) of section 45ZL on the resolutions adopted in the said meeting.

45ZM. Monetary Policy Report

(1) The Bank shall, once in every six months, publish a document to be called the Monetary Policy Report, explaining—

(a) the sources of inflation; and

(b) the forecasts of inflation for the period between six to eighteen months from the date of publication of the document.

(2) The form and contents of the Monetary Policy Report shall be such as may be specified by the regulations made by the Central Board.

45ZN. Failure to maintain inflation target

Where the Bank fails to meet the inflation target, it shall set out in a report to the Central Government—

(a) the reasons for failure to achieve the inflation target;

(b) remedial actions proposed to be taken by the Bank; and

(c) an estimate of the time-period within which the inflation target shall be achieved pursuant to timely implementation of proposed remedial actions.

Explanation : For the purposes of this section, the factors that constitute failure shall be such as may be notified by the Central Government in the Official Gazette, within three months from the date of the commencement of Part I of Chapter XII of the Finance Act, 2016.

45ZO.Power to make rules

(1) The Central Government may, by notification in the Official Gazette, make rules for the purpose of carrying out the provisions of this Chapter.

(2) In particular and without prejudice to the generality of the foregoing power, such rules may provide for—

(a) the procedure of functioning of the Search-cum-Selection Committee under sub-section (3) of section 45ZC;

(b) the terms and conditions of appointment (other than the remuneration and other allowances), of Members of the Monetary Policy Committee under sub-section (2) of section 45ZD; and

(c) any other matter which is to be, or may be, prescribed by the Central Government by rules.]

CHAPTER IV

GENERAL PROVISIONS

46. Contribution by Central Government to the Reserve Fund

The [1][Central Government] shall transfer to the Bank rupee securities to the value of five crores of rupees to be allocated by the Bank to the Reserve Fund.

[2]**[46A. Contribution to National Rural Credit (Long Term Operations) Fund and National Rural Credit (Stabilisation) Fund**

The Bank shall contribute every year such sums of money as it may consider necessary and feasible to do so, to the National Rural Credit (Long Term Operations) Fund and the National Rural Credit (Stabilisation) Fund established and maintained by the National Bank under sections 42 and 43, respectively, of the National Bank for Agriculture and Rural Development Act, 1981 (61 of 1981).]

1 Substituted for "G.G. in C." by the M.O. 1937.

2 Substituted for existing sections 46A and 46B by Act 61 of 1981, w.e.f. 12-7-1982.

[1][46C. National Industrial Credit (Long Term Operations) Fund

(1) The Bank shall establish and maintain a Fund to be known as the National Industrial Credit (Long Term Operations) Fund to which shall be credited—

(a) an initial sum of ten crores of rupees by the Bank;

(b) such further sums of money as the Bank may contribute every year:

PROVIDED that the annual contribution during each of the five years commencing with the year ending on the 30th day of June, 1965 shall not be less than five crores of rupees:

PROVIDED FURTHER that the Central Government may, if the circumstances so require, authorise the Bank to reduce the said sum of five crores of rupees in any year.

(2) The amount in the said fund shall be applied by the Bank only to the following objects, namely:—

[2][xxx]

[3][(c) the making to the Exim Bank [4][or the Reconstruction Bank [5][or the Small Industries Bank [6][or the National Bank for Financing Infrastructure and Development or the other development financial institution]], as the case may be] of loans and advances for the purposes of any business of the Exim Bank [4][or the Reconstruction Bank [5][or the Small Industries Bank [6][or the National Bank for Financing Infrastructure and Development or the other development financial institution,]] as the case may be];

(d) the purchasing of bonds and debentures issued by the Exim Bank [4][or the Reconstruction Bank [5][or the Small Industries Bank [6][or the National Bank for Financing Infrastructure and Development or the other development financial institution,]] as the case may be].]

[7][46D. National Housing Credit (Long Term Operations) Fund

(1) The Bank shall establish and maintain a Fund to be known as the National Housing Credit (Long Term Operations) Fund to which shall be credited every year such sums of money as it may consider necessary.

(2) The amount in the said Fund shall be applied by the Bank only to the following objects, namely:—

(a) the making to the National Housing Bank of loans and advances for the purpose of any business of the National Housing Bank;

(b) the purchasing of bonds and debentures issued by the National Housing Bank.]

[8][47. Allocation of surplus profits

After making provision for bad and doubtful debts, depreciation in assets, contributions to staff and superannuation fund [9][and for all other matters for which provision is to be made by or under this Act or which] are usually provided for by bankers, the balance, of the profits shall be paid to the Central Government.]

---

1 Inserted by Act 18 of 1964, w.e.f. 1-7-1964.
2 Clauses (a) and (b) omitted by Act 53 of 2003, w.e.f. 2-7-2004.
3 Inserted by Act 28 of 1981, w.e.f. 1-1-1982.
4 Inserted by Act 62 of 1984, w.e.f. 20-3-1985.
5 Inserted by Act 39 of 1989, w.e.f. 7-3-1990.
6 Inserted by Act 17 of 2021, w.e.f. 19-4-2021.
7 Inserted by Act 53 of 1987, w.e.f. 9-7-1988.
8 Substituted by Act 62 of 1948, w.e.f. 1-1-1949.
9 Substituted for "and such other contingencies as" by Act 24 of 1955, w.e.f. 8-5-1955.

48. Exemption of Banks from income-tax and super-tax

(1) Notwithstanding anything contained in [1][the Income-tax Act, 1961 (43 of 1961)] or any other enactment for the time being in force relating to income-tax or super-tax, the bank shall not be liable to pay income-tax or super-tax on any of its income, profits or gains.

[2][xxx]

[3][xxx]

49. Publication of Bank rate

The Bank shall make public from time to time the standard rate at which it is prepared to buy or re-discount bills of exchange or other commercial paper eligible for purchase under this Act.

[4]**[50. Auditors**

(1) Not less than two auditors shall be appointed, and their remuneration fixed, by the Central Government.

(2) The auditors shall hold office for such term not exceeding one year as the Central Government may fix while appointing them, and shall be eligible for re-appointment.]

51. Appointment of special auditors by Government

Without prejudice to anything contained in section 50, the [5][Central Government] may at any time appoint the [6][Comptroller and Auditor-General] [7][xxx] to examine and report upon the accounts of the Bank.

52. Powers and duties of auditors

(1) Every auditor shall be supplied with a copy of the annual balance-sheet, and it shall be his duty to examine the same, together with the accounts and vouchers relating thereto; and every auditor shall have a list delivered to him of all books kept by the Bank, and shall at all reasonable time have access to the books, accounts and other documents of the Bank, and may at the expense of the Bank [8][xxx] employ accountants or other person to assist him in investigating such accounts, and may, in relation to such accounts, examine any Director or officer of the Bank.

(2) The auditors shall make a report [9][xxx] to the [5][Central Government] [10][xxx] upon the annual balance-sheet and accounts, and in every such report they shall state whether, in their opinion, the balance-sheet is a full and fair balance-sheet containing all necessary particulars and properly drawn up so as to exhibit a true and correct view of the state of the Bank's affairs, and, in case they have called for any explanation or information from the Central Board, whether it has been given and whether it is satisfactory. [11][xxx].

---

1 Substituted for "Indian Income-tax Act, 1922" by Act 24 of 1978, w.e.f. 21-7-1978.
2 Proviso omitted by Act 62 of 1948, w.e.f. 1-1-1949.
3 Sub-section (2) omitted, ibid, w.e.f. 1-1-1949.
4 Substituted by Act 62 of 1948, w.e.f. 1-1-1949.
5 Substituted for "G.G. in C." by the MO 1937.
6 Substituted for "Auditor General" by Act 32 of 1951, w.e.f. 1-11-1951.
7 Words "or such auditors as it thinks fit" omitted by Act 62 of 1948, w.e.f. 1-1-1949.
8 Words "if appointed by it or at the expense of the Central Government if appointed by that Government" omitted by Act 24 of 1955, w.e.f. 8-5-1955.
9 Words "to the shareholders or" omitted by Act 62 of 1948, w.e.f. 1-1-1949.
10 Words "as the case may be" omitted, ibid, w.e.f. 1-1-1949.
11 Words "Any such report made to the shareholders shall be read, together with the report of the Central Board, at the annual general meeting" omitted, ibid, w.e.f. 1-1-1949.

53. Returns

(1) The Bank shall prepare and transmit to the [1][Central Government] a weekly account of the Issue Department and of the Banking Department in [2][such] form as the [1][Central Government] may, by notification in the Gazette of India, prescribe. The [1][Central Government] shall cause these accounts to be [3][published in the Gazette of India at such intervals and in such modified form as it may deem fit].

(2) The Bank shall also, within two months from the date on which the annual accounts of the Bank are closed, transmit to the [1][Central Government] a copy of the annual accounts signed by the Governor, the Deputy Governors and the Chief Accounting Officer of the Bank, and certified by the auditors, together with a report by the Central Board on the working of the Bank throughout the year, and the [1][Central Government] shall cause such accounts and report to be published in the Gazette of India.

[4][xxx]

[5][54. Rural Credit and Development

The Bank may maintain expert staff to study various aspects of rural credit and development and in particular it may:—

(a) tender expert guidance and assistance to the National Bank;

(b) conduct special studies in such areas as it may consider necessary to do so for promoting integrated rural development.]

[6][54A. Delegation of powers

(1) The Governor may, by general or special order, delegate to a Deputy Governor, subjects to such conditions and limitations, if any, as may be specified in the order, such of the powers and functions exercisable by him [7][xxx] under this Act or under any other law for the time being in force as he may deem necessary for the efficient administration of the functions of the Bank.

(2) The fact that a Deputy Governor exercises any power or does any act or thing in pursuance of this Act shall be conclusive proof of his authority to do so.]

[8][54AA. Power of Bank to depute its employees to other institutions

[9][(1) The Bank may, notwithstanding anything contained in any law, or in any agreement, for the time being in force, depute any member of its staff for such period as it may think fit,—

(a) to any institution which is wholly or substantially owned by the Bank;

(b) to the Development Bank, so, however, that no such deputation shall continue after the expiration of thirty months from the commencement of section 5 of the Public Financial Institutions Laws (Amendment) Act, 1975 (52 of 1975);

(c) to the Unit Trust, so, however, that no such deputation shall continue after the expiration of thirty months from the date notified by the Central

1 Substituted for "G.G. in C." by the MO 1937.
2 Substituted by the MO 1937.
3 Substituted for "published weekly in the Government of India" by Act 24 of 1978, w.e.f. 21-7-1978.
4 Sub-section (3) omitted by Act 62 of 1948, w.e.f. 1-1-1949.
5 Substituted by Act 61 of 1981, w.e.f. 12-7-1982.
6 Inserted by Act 24 of 1955, w.e.f. 8-5-1955.
7 Words "by or" omitted by Act 58 of 1960, w.e.f. 26-12-1960.
8 Inserted by Act 58 of 1968, w.e.f. 1-2-1969.
9 Substituted by Act 52 of 1975, w.e.f. 16-2-1976.

Government under sub-section (1) of section 4A of the Unit Trust of India Act, 1963 (52 of 1963);

and thereupon the person so deputed shall, during the period of his deputation, render such service to the institution to which he is so deputed as that institution may require.]

(2) Where a person has been deputed to an institution under sub-section (1), he shall not be entitled to claim any salary, emoluments and other terms and conditions of service which he would not have been entitled to claim if he had not been so deputed.

(3) Nothing contained in this section shall empower the Bank to depute any member of its staff to any institution on any salary, emoluments or other terms and conditions which is or are less favourable to him than that or those to which he is entitled immediately before such deputation.

(4) For the purposes of this section, an institution shall be deemed to be substantially owned by the Bank if in the capital of the institution the Bank has not less than forty per cent, share.

Explanation : The word "capital" means, in relation to the Unit Trust, the initial capital of the Trust.]

[1]**[xxx]**

57. Liquidation of the Bank

(1) Nothing in the [2][Companies Act, 1956 (1 of 1956)] shall apply to the Bank and the Bank shall not be placed in liquidation save by order of the [3][Central Government] and in such manner as [4][it may direct].

[5][xxx]

[6][57A. Powers of Bank not to apply to International Financial Services Centre

Notwithstanding anything contained in any other law for the time being in force, the powers exercisable by the Bank under this Act,—

(a) shall not extend to an International Financial Services Centre set up under sub-section (1) of section 18 of the Special Economic Zones Act, 2005 (28 of 2005);

(b) shall be exercisable by the International Financial Services Centres Authority established under sub-section (1) of section 4 of the International Financial Services Centres Authority Act, 2019,

insofar as regulation of financial products, financial services and financial institutions that are permitted in the International Financial Services Centres are concerned.]

58. Power of the Central Board to make regulations

(1) The Central Board may, with the previous sanction of the [3][Central Government], [7][by notification in the Official Gazette,] make regulations consistent with this Act to provide for all matters for which provision is necessary or convenient for the purpose of giving effect to the provisions of this Act.

(2) In particular without prejudice to the generality of the foregoing provision, such regulations may provide for all or any of the following matters, namely:—

---

1 Sections 55 and 56 omitted by the Reserve Bank (Transfer to Public Ownership) Act, 1948 (62 of 1948), w.e.f. 1-1-1949.
2 Substituted for "Indian Companies Act, 1913 (7 of 1913)" by Act 19 of 1957, w.e.f. 8-6-1957.
3 Substituted for "G.G. in C." by the MO 1937.
4 Substituted for "he may direct" ibid.
5 Sub-section (2) omitted by Act 62 of 1948, w.e.f. 1-1-1949.
6 Inserted by Act 50 of 2019, w.e.f. 1-10-2020.
7 Inserted by Act 66 of 1988, w.e.f. 30-12-1988.

[1][xxx]

(f) the manner in which the business of the Central Board shall be transacted, and the procedure to be followed at meetings thereof;

(g) the conduct of business of Local Boards and the delegation to such Boards of powers and functions;

(h) the delegation of powers and functions of the Central Board [2][xxx] to Deputy Governors, Directors or officers of the Bank;

(i) the formation of Committees of the Central Board, the delegation of powers and functions of the Central Board to such Committees, and the conduct of business in such Committees;

(j) the constitution and management of staff and superannuation funds for the officers and servants of the Bank;

(k) the manner and form in which contracts binding on the Bank may be executed;

(l) the provision of an official seal of the Bank and the manner and effect of its use;

(m) the manner and form in which the balance-sheet of the Bank shall be drawn up and in which the accounts shall be maintained;

(n) the remuneration of Directors of the Bank;

(o) the relations of the scheduled banks with the Bank and the returns to be submitted by the scheduled banks to the Bank;

(p) the regulation of clearing-houses for the [3][banks (including post office savings banks)];

[4][(pp) the regulation of fund transfer through electronic means between the banks or between the banks and other financial institutions referred to in clause (c) of section 45-I, including the laying down of the conditions subject to which banks and other financial institutions shall participate in such fund transfers, the manner of such fund transfers and the rights and obligations of the participants in such fund transfers;]

(q) the circumstances in which, and the conditions and limitations subject to which, the value of any lost, stolen, mutilated or imperfect currency note of the Government of India or bank note may be refunded;

[5][(qa) the remuneration and other allowances payable to Members of the Monetary Policy Committee under sub-section (2) of section 45ZD;

(qb) the functions of the Secretary under sub-section (2) of section 45ZG;

(qc) the procedure, manner of conducting of meetings and related matters of the Monetary Policy Committee under sub-section (12) of section 45ZI;

(qd) the particulars and the frequency of publication of document under sub-section (2) of section 45ZJ;

(qe) the form and contents of the Monetary Policy Report to be published under sub-section (2) of section 45ZM;] and

---

1 Clauses (a) to (e) omitted by Act 62 of 1948, w.e.f. 1-1-1949.
2 Words "to the Governor, or" omitted by Act 54 of 1953, w.e.f. 30-12-1953.
3 Substituted for "the scheduled banks" by Act 66 of 1988, w.e.f. 30-12-1988.
4 Inserted by Act 21 of 2000, w.e.f. 9-6-2000.
5 Inserted by Act 28 of 2016, w.e.f. 27-6-2016.

(r) generally, for the efficient conduct of the business of the Bank.

[1][(3) Any regulation made under this section shall have effect from such earlier or later date as may be specified in the regulation.

(4) Every regulation shall, as soon as may be after it is made by the Central Board, be, forwarded to the Central Government and that Government shall cause a copy of the same to be laid before each House of Parliament, while it is in session, for a total period of thirty days which may be comprised in one session or in two or more successive sessions, and if, before the expiry of the session immediately following the session or the successive sessions aforesaid, both Houses agree in making any modification in the regulation, or both Houses agree that the regulation should not be made, the regulation shall, thereafter, have effect only in such modified form or be of no effect, as the case may be; so, however, that any such modification or annulment shall be without prejudice to the validity of anything previously done under that regulation.]

[2][(5)] Copies of all regulations made under this section shall be available to the public on payment.

[3][58A. Protection of action taken in good faith

(1) No suit, prosecution or other legal proceeding shall lie against the Central Government or the Bank or any other person in respect of anything which is in good faith done or intended to be done under this Act or in pursuance of any order, regulation or direction made or given thereunder.

(2) No suit or other legal proceeding shall lie against the Central Government or the Bank for any damage caused or likely to be caused by anything which is in good faith done or intended to be done under this Act or in pursuance of any order, regulation or direction made or given thereunder.]

[4][CHAPTER V
PENALTIES

58B. Penalties

(1) Whoever in any application, declaration, return, statement, information or particulars made, required or furnished by or under or for the purposes of any provisions of this Act, or any order, regulation or direction made or given thereunder or in any prospectus or advertisement issued for or in connection with the invitation by any person, of deposits of money from the public wilfully makes a statement which is false in any material particular knowing it to be false or willfully omits to make a material statement shall be punishable with imprisonment for a term which may extend to three years and shall also be liable to fine.

(2) If any person fails to produce any book, account or other document or to furnish any statement, information or particulars which, under this Act or any order, regulation or direction made or given thereunder, it is his duty to produce or furnish or to answer any question put to him in pursuance of the provisions of this Act or of any order, regulation or direction made or given thereunder, he shall be punishable with fine which may extend to [5][one lakh rupees] in respect of each offence and if he persists in such failure or refusal, with further fine which may extend to [6][five thousand rupees] for every day, after the first during which the offence continues.

1 Inserted by Act 51 of 1974, w.e.f. 13-12-1974.
2 Sub-section (3) renumbered as sub-section (5) thereof, ibid, w.e.f. 13-12-1974.
3 Inserted, ibid.
4 Inserted, ibid.
5 Substituted for "two thousand rupees" by Act 23 of 2019, w.e.f. 9-8-2019.
6 Substituted for "one hundred rupees" by Act 23 of 2019, w.e.f. 9-8-2019.

(3) If any person contravenes the provisions of section 31, he shall be punishable with fine which may extend to the amount of the bill of exchange, *hundi*, promissory note or engagement for payment of money in respect whereof the offence is committed.

(4) If any person discloses any credit information, the disclosure of which is prohibited under section 45E, he shall be punishable with imprisonment for a term which may extend to six mounts, or with fine which may extend to one thousand rupees, or with both.

[1][(4A) If any person contravenes the provisions of sub-section (1) of section 45-IA, he shall be punishable with imprisonment for a term which shall not be less than one year but which may extend to five years and with fine which shall not be less than one lakh rupees but which may extend to [2][twenty-five lakh rupees].

(4AA) If any auditor fails to comply with any direction given or order made by the Bank under section 45MA, he shall be punishable with fine which may extend to [3][ten lakh rupees].

(4AAA) Whoever fails to comply with any order made by the Company Law Board under sub-section (2) of section 45QA, shall be punishable with imprisonment for a term which may extend to three years and shall also be liable to a fine of not less than [4][five thousand rupees] for every day during which such non-compliance continues.]

(5) If any person [1][other than an auditor]—

(a) receives [5][any deposit without being authorised so to do or] in contravention of any direction given or order made under Chapter IIIB; or

[1][(aa) fails to comply with any direction given or order made by the Bank under any of the provisions of Chapter IIIB; or]

(b) issues any prospectus or advertisement otherwise than in accordance with [6][section 45J] or any order made under section 45], as the case may be,

he shall be punishable with imprisonment for a term which may extend to three years and shall also be liable to fine which may extend,—

(i) in the case of a contravention falling under clause (a), to twice the amount of the deposit received; and

(ii) in the case of a contravention falling under clause (b), to twice the amount of the deposit called for by the prospectus or advertisement.

[7][(5A) If any person contravenes any provision of section 45S, he shall be punishable with imprisonment for a term which may extend to two years, or with fine which may extend to twice the amount of deposit received by such person in contravention of that section, or two thousand rupees, whichever is more, or with both:

PROVIDED that in the absence of special and adequate reasons to the contrary to be mentioned in the judgment of the court, the imprisonment shall not be less than one year and the fine shall not be less than one thousand rupees.

(5B) Notwithstanding anything contained in section 29 of the Code of Criminal Procedure, 1973 (2 of 1974), it shall be lawful for Metropolitan Magistrate or a Judicial

---

1 Inserted by Act 23 of 1997, w.e.f. 9-1-1997.
2 Substituted for "five lakh rupees" by Act 23 of 2019, w.e.f. 9-8-2019.
3 Substituted for "five thousand rupee", ibid.
4 Substituted for "rupees fifty", ibid, w.e.f. 9-8-2019.
5 Substituted for "any deposit" by Act 23 of 2019, w.e.f. 9-8-2019.
6 Substituted for "section 45NA", ibid.
7 Inserted by Act 1 of 1984, w.e.f. 15-2-1984.

Magistrate of the first class to impose a sentence of the fine in excess of the limit specified in that section on any person convicted under sub-section (5A).]

(6) If any other provision of this Act is contravened or if any default is made in complying with any other requirement of this Act or of any order, regulation or direction made or given or condition imposed thereunder, any person guilty of such contravention or default shall be punishable with fine which may extend to [1][one lakh rupees] and where a contravention or default is a continuing one, with further fine which may extend to [2][ten thousand rupees] for every day, after the first, during which the contravention or default continues.

58C. Offences by companies

(1) Where a person committing a contravention or default referred to in section 58B is a company, every person who, at the time the contravention or default was committed, was in charge of, and was responsible to, the company for the conduct of the business of the company, as well as the company, shall be deemed to be guilty of the contravention or default and shall be liable to be proceeded against and punished accordingly:

PROVIDED that nothing contained in this sub-section shall render any such person liable to punishment if he proves that the contravention or default was committed without his knowledge or that he had exercised all due diligence to prevent the contravention or default.

(2) Notwithstanding anything contained in sub-section (1), where an offence under this Act has been committed by a company and it is proved that the same was committed with the consent or connivance of, or is attributable to any neglect on the part of, any director, manager, secretary, or other officer or employee of the company, such director, manager, secretary, other officer or employee shall also be deemed to be guilty of the offence and shall be liable to be proceeded against and punished accordingly.

Explanation 1 : Any offence punishable under this Act shall be deemed to have been committed at the place where the registered office or the principal place of business, as the case may be, in India, of the company is situated.

Explanation 2 : For the purpose of this section,—

(a) "a company" means any body corporate and includes a corporation, a non-banking institution, a firm, a co-operative society or other association of individuals;

(b) "director", in relation to a firm, means a partner in the firm.

58D. Application of section 58B barred

Nothing contained in section 58B shall apply to, or in respect of, any matter dealt with in section 42.

58E. Cognizance of offences

(1) No court shall take cognizance of any offence punishable under this Act except upon a complaint in writing made by an officer of the Bank, generally or specially authorised in writing in this behalf by the Bank, and no court other than that of a Metropolitan Magistrate or a Judicial Magistrate of the first class or a court superior thereto shall try any such offence:

[3][PROVIDED that in respect of any offence punishable under sub-section (5A) of section 58B, a complaint in writing may also be made by an officer of the State

1 Substituted for "two thousand rupees" by Act 23 of 2019, w.e.f. 9-8-2019.
2 Substituted for "one hundred rupees", ibid.
3 Inserted by Act 1 of 1984, w.e.f. 15-2-1984.

Government, generally or specially authorised in writing in this behalf by that Government.]

(2) Notwithstanding anything contained in the Code of Criminal Procedure, 1973 (2 of 1974), a Magistrate may, if he sees reason so to do, dispense with the personal attendance of the officer of the Bank filing the complaint, but the Magistrate may in his discretion, at any stage of the proceedings, direct the personal attendance of the complainant.

58F. Application of fine

A Court imposing any fine under this Act may direct that the whole or any part thereof shall be applied in, or towards payment of, the costs of the proceedings.]

[1][**58G. Power of Bank to impose fine**

(1) Notwithstanding anything contained in section 58B, if the contravention or default of the nature referred to in section 58B is committed by a non-banking financial company, the Bank may impose on such non-banking financial company—

(a) a penalty not exceeding [2][twenty-five thousand]; or

(b) where the contravention or default is under sub-section (4A) or clause (a) or clause (aa) of sub-section (5) of section 58B, a penalty of [3][ten lakh] rupees or twice the amount involved in such contravention or default, where the amount is quantifiable, whichever is more; and where such contravention or default is a continuing one, further penalty which may extend to [4][one lakh] rupees for every day, after the first, during which the contravention or default continues.

(2) For the purpose of imposing penalty under sub-section (1), the Bank shall serve a notice on the non-banking financial company requiring it to show cause why the amount specified in the notice should not be imposed as a penalty and a reasonable opportunity of being heard shall also be given to such non-banking financial company.

(3) Any penalty imposed by the Bank under this section shall be payable within a period of thirty days from the date on which notice issued by the Bank demanding payment of the sum is served on the non-banking financial company and, in the event of failure of the non-banking financial company to pay the sum within such period, may be levied on a direction made by the principal civil court having jurisdiction in the area where the registered office or the head office of the non-banking financial company is situated:

PROVIDED that no such direction shall be made, except on an application made by an officer of the Bank authorised in this behalf, to by the principal civil court.

(4) The court which makes a direction under sub-section (4), shall issue a certificate specifying the sum payable by the non-banking financial company and every such certificate shall be enforceable in the same manner as if it were a decree made by the court in a civil suit.

(5) No complaint shall be filed against any non-banking financial company in any court of law pertaining to any contravention or default in respect of which any penalty has been imposed by the Bank under this section.

---

1 Inserted by Act 23 of 1997, w.e.f. 9-1-1997.
2 Substituted for "five thousand" by Act 23 of 2019, w.e.f. 9-8-2019.
3 Substituted for "five lakh", ibid.
4 Substituted for "twenty-five thousand", ibid.

(6) Where any complaint has been filed against a non-banking financial company in a court in respect of contravention or default of the nature referred to in section 58B, no proceedings for imposition of penalty against that non-banking financial company shall be taken under this section.]

59. [1][*Repealed*]

60. [1][*Repealed*]

61. [1][*Repealed*]

[2][THE FIRST SCHEDULE

[See section 9]

[3][1. The Western Area shall consist of the States of Goa, Gujarat, Madhya Pradesh and Maharashtra and the Union territories of Dadra and Nagar Haveli, and Daman and Diu.

2. The Eastern Area shall consist of the States of Arunachal Pradesh, Assam, Bihar, Manipur, Meghalaya, Mizoram, Nagaland, Orissa, Sikkim, Tripura and West Bengal and the Union territories of Andaman and Nicobar Islands.]

3. The Northern Area shall consist of the States of Jammu and Kashmir[4], [5][Punjab, Haryana,] [6][Himachal Pradesh], Rajasthan and Uttar Pradesh and the Union territories of [7][Chandigarh] [8][and Delhi].

4. The Southern area shall consist of the States of Andhra Pradesh, [9][Karnataka], [10][Tamil Nadu] and Kerala and the [11][Union territories of Pondicherry and [12][Lakshadweep]].]

1 Repealed by the Repealing and Amending Act, 1937 (20 of 1937), w.e.f. 14-4-1937.
2 Substituted by the Adaptation of Laws (No. 3) Order, 1956.
3 Substituted for items 1 and 2 by Act 23 of 1997, w.e.f. 9-1-1997.
4 Now the Union territory of Jammu and Kashmir and the Union territory of Ladakh, w.e.f. 31-10-2019.
5 Substituted for "Punjab" by the Punjab Reorganisation and Delhi High Court (Adaptation of Laws on Union Subjects) Order, 1968, w.e.f. 1-11-1956.
6 Inserted by the State of Himachal Pradesh (Adaptation of Laws on Union Subjects) Order, 1973, w.e.f. 25-1-1971.
7 Inserted by the Punjab Reorganisation and Delhi High Court (Adaptation of Laws on Union Subjects) Order, 1968, w.e.f. 1-11-1966.
8 Substituted for "Himachal Pradesh and Delhi" by the State of Himachal Pradesh (Adaptation of Laws on Union Subjects) Order, 1973, w.e.f. 25-1-1971.
9 Substituted for "Mysore" by the Mysore State (Alteration of Name) (Adaptation of Laws on Union Subjects) Order, 1974, w.e.f. 1-11-1973.
10 Substituted for "Madras" by the Madras State (Alteration of Name) Adaptation of Laws on Union Subjects) Order, 1970, w.e.f. 14-1-1969.
11 Substituted. for "Union territory of Laccadive, Minicoy and Admindivi Islands" by Regulation 7 of 1963.
12 Substituted for "Laccadive, Minicoy and Amindivi Islands." by the Laccadive, Minicoy and Amindivi Islands (Alteration of Name) Adaptation of Laws Order, 1974, w.e.f. 1-11-1973.

[1]THE SECOND SCHEDULE

[See section 42 and section 2(e)]

SCHEDULED BANKS

[2][AB Bank PLC]

Abhyudaya Co-operative Bank Ltd., Bombay.

[3][xxx].

Ahmednagar Sahakari Bank Ltd., Mumbai (1998)

Ajodhia Bank, Fyzabad.

[4][xxx].

Akola Janta Commercial Co-operative Bank Ltd., Akola (Maharashtra). (w.e.f. 22-5-1999).

Akola Urban Co-operative Bank Ltd., Akola (Maharashtra).

[5][xxx].

Algemene Bank Nederland N.V.

[6][xxx].

[7][xxx]

[8][xxx].

[9][Allahabad UP Gramin Bank Uttar Pradesh.]

[10][xxx].

Amahath Co-operative Bank Ltd., Bangalore (Karnataka) (w.e.f. 29-1-2002).

[11][xxx].

[12][xxx].

[13][American Express Banking Corp.]

American Express International Banking Corporation.

ANZ Grindlays Bank Limited (6-8-1996).

[14][xxx]

---

1 This Schedule was amended by the India and Burma (Burma Monetary Arrangements) Order, 1937; Act 23 of 1955; Act 79 of 1956 and Act 38 of 1959 and by notifications under section 42(6) of this Act from time to time.

2 Substituted for "AB Bank Limited" by Noti. No. DoR/LIC No. 6222/23.13.048/2023-24, dt. 25-1-2024.

3 "Adhiyaman Grama Bank, Dharampuri, Tamil Nadu" excluded by RBI Noti. No. RPCD.CO. RRB. No. 3230/03.05100/2008-09, dt. 22-9-2008.

4 "Akola Gramin Bank, Akola, Maharashtra" excluded by RBI Noti. No. RPCD.CO. RRB. No. 7431/03.05.100/2008-09, dt. 27-1-2009.

5 "Alaknanda Gramin Bank, Pauri (Uttar Pradesh)" excluded by RBI Noti. No. RPCD.CO. RRB. No. 3230/03.05.100/2008-09, dt. 22-9-2008.

6 "Aligarh Gramin Bank, Aligarh (Uttar Pradesh)" excluded by RBI Noti. No. RPCD.CO. RRB. No. 3230/03.05.100/2008-09, dt. 22-9-2008.

7 "Allahabad Bank" excluded vide Noti. DOR.No. Ret.BC. 54/12.01.001/2019-20, dt. 27-3-2020, w.e.f. 1-4-2020.

8 "Allahabad Kshetriya Gramin Bank, Allahabad, Uttar Pradesh" excluded by RBI Noti. No. RPCD.CO. RRB. No. 7431/03.05.100/2008-09, dt. 27-1-2009.

9 Included by RBI Noti. No. RPCD.CO.RRB. No. 11377/3.5.100/2010-11, dt. 31-3-2011.

10 "Alwar Bharatpur Anchalik Gramin Bank, Bharatpur (Rajasthan)" excluded by RBI Noti. No. RPCD.CO.RRB. No. 3230/03.05.100/2008-09, dt. 22-9-2008.

11 "Ambala-Kurukshetra Gramin Bank LTD., Ambala (Haryana)" excluded by RBI Noti. No. RPCD.CO. RRB. No. 3230/03.05.100/2008-09, dt.. 22-9-2008.

12 "American Express Bank Ltd." excluded by RBI Noti. No. DBOD.IBD. No. 2095/ 23.13.019/2007-08, dt. 5-3-2008.

13 Included by RBI Noti. No. DBOD.IBD. No. 8739/23.03.018/2008-09, dt. 4-12-2008.

14 "Andhra Bank" excluded vide Noti. DOR. No. Ret.BC.55/12-01.001/2019-20, dt. 27-3-2020, w.e.f. 1-4-2020.

[1][Andhra Pradesh Grameena Vikas Bank, Warangal (Andhra Pradesh)]

Andhra Pradesh State Co-operative Bank Ltd., Hyderabad.

[1][Andhra PragathiGrameena Bank, Kadape (Andhra Pradesh)]

Arab Bangladesh Bank Limited (10-6-1996).

[2][xxx]

Arunachal Pradesh Rural Bank, Pasighat (Arunachal Pradesh).

[3][xxx]

[4][Assam Gramin Vikash Bank, Guwahati, Assam]

[5][xxx]

[6][Av Small Finance Bank Limited, Jaipur (Rajasthan)]

[7][Australia and New Zealand Banking Group Limited]

[8][xxx]

Avaroli Kshetriya Gramin Bank Sawai Madhopur (Rajasthan) (1981)

[9][Axis Bank Ltd.]

[10][xxx]

[11][xxx]

[12][xxx]

[13][xxx]

[14][Bandhan Bank Limited]

[15][Bangiya Gramin Vikas Bank, Berhampore (West Bengal)]

[16][xxx]

Bank International, Indonesia (18-4-1996).

[17][xxx]

Bank of America National Association.

---

1 Included by RBI Noti. No. RPCD.CO. RRB. No. 3231/03.05.100/2008-09, dt. 22-9-2008.

2 "Aravali Kshetriya Gramin Bank, Swai Madhopur (Rajasthan)" excluded by RBI Noti. No. RPCD.CO.RRB. No. 7812-B/03-05.100/2009-10, dt. 21-1-2010.

3 "Aryavart Gramin Bank, Lucknow, Uttar Pradesh" excluded by RBI Noti. No. RPCD.CO.RRB. No. 56/03.05.100/2013-14, dt. 14-11-2013.

4 Included by RBI Noti. No. RPCD.CO.RRB. No. 7430/03.05.100/2008-09, dt. 27-1-2009.

5 "Aurangabad Jalna Kshetriya Gramin Bank, Aurangabad (Maharashtra)" excluded by RBI Noti. No. RPCD.CO.RRB. No. 7431/03.05.100/2008-09, dt. 27-1-2009.

6 Included vide Noti. No. DBR.NBD. (SFB-AFL), No. 2689/16.13 216/2017-18, dt. 18-9-2017.

7 Included by RBI Noti. No. DBOD.IBD. No. 19042/23.03.024/2010-11, dt. 7-6-2011.

8 "Avadh Gramin Bank, Hardoi (Uttar Pradesh)" excluded by RBI Noti. No. RPCD.CO.RRB. No. 3230/03.05.100/2008-09, dt. 22-9-2008.

9 Name of "UTI Bank LTD." changed to "Axis Bank LTD." by Noti. DBOD. No. PSBD.1174/1601.127/2007-08, dt. 2-8-2007, w.e.f. 30-7-2007.

10 "Baitarani Gramya Bank, Baripada (Odisha)" excluded by RBI Noti. No. RPCD.CO.RRB. No. 47/03.05.100/2013-14, dt. 22-10-2011.

11 "Balasore Gramya Bank, Balasore (Orissa)" excluded by RBI Noti. No. RPCD.CO.RRB.BC. No. 95/03.05.100/2013-14, dt. 9-4-2014.

12 "Ballia-Etawah Gramin Bank, Uttar Pradesh" excluded by RBI Noti. No. RPCD.CO.RRB. No. 47/03.05.100/2013-14, dt. 22-10-2013.

13 "Ballia Kshetriya Gramin Bank, Ballia (Uttar Pradesh)" excluded by RBI Noti. No. RPCD.CO.RRB. No. 11379/3.5.100/2010-11, dt. 31-3-2011.

14 Included by RBI Noti. No. DBR.PSBD. No. 3427/16.01.0145/2015-16, dt. 3-9-2015.

15 Included by RBI Noti. No. RPCD.CO.RRB. No. 7812-A/03.05.100/2009-10, dt. 21-1-2010.

16 "Banaskantha Mehsana Gramin Bank, Patan (Gujarat)" excluded by RBI Noti. No. RPCD.CO.RRB. No. 3230/03.05.100/2008-09, dt. 22-9-2008.

17 "Bank Muscat" excluded by Noti. No. Ret. BC. No. 73/12.06.115/2003-04, dt. 2-4-2004.

Bank of Bahrain and Kuwait BSC (1986).
Bank of Baroda.
Bank of China, Calcutta.
[1][Bank of China Limited]
Bank of Cochin Ltd., Ernakulam.
Bank of Credit and Commerce International (Overseas) Ltd.
Bank of Cylon (30-12-1995).
Bank of India
Bank of Karad Ltd., Karad.
Bank of Karnataka, Hubli.
Bank of Kerala Ltd.
Bank of Madura Ltd., Madurai.
Bank of Maharashtra.
Bank of Nova Scotia.
Bank of Oman Ltd.
[2][xxx]
[3][xxx]
Bank of Tamilnadu Ltd.
Bank of Thanjavur Ltd.
[4][Bank of Tokyo Mitsubishi UFG Ltd.]
Banque Indosuez.
Banque Nationale de Paris.
[5][xxx]
[6][xxx]
Bareilly Corporation Bank Ltd., Bareilly.
[7][xxx]
[8][Baroda Gujarat Gramin Bank, Bharuch (Gujarat).]
[9][Baroda Rajasthan Kshetriya Gramin Bank, Ajmer, Rajasthan].
[10][xxx]
[11][Baroda UP Bank, Gorakhpur, Uttar Pradesh]

---

1 Included vide Noti. No. DBR.IBD. No. 10585/23.03.005/2018-19, dt. 19-6-2019.
2 Bank of Punjab Ltd." excluded by Noti. DBOD. No. PSBD 353/16.01.130/2005-06, dt. 7-10-2005, w.e.f. 1-10-2005.
3 "Bank of Rajasthan Ltd." excluded by RBI Noti. No. DBOD. No. PSBD/2866/16.01.056/2010-11, dt. 18-8-2010, w.e.f. 13-8-2010.
4 Substituted for "The Bank of Tokyo Mitsubishi Ltd." vide Noti. No. DBOD. No. IBD. No. 937/23.03-007/2005-2006, dt.26-12-2005.
5 "Bara Banki Gramin Bank, Bara Banki (Uttar Pradesh)" excluded by RBI Noti. No. RPCD.CO. RRB. No. 3230/03.05.100/2008-09, dt. 22-9-2008.
6 "Bardhaman Gramin Bank, Burdwan (West Bengal)" excluded by RBI Noti. No. RPCD.CO.RRB.BC. No. 95/03.05.100/2013-14, dt. 9-4-2014.
7 "Bareilly Kshetriya Gramin Bank, Bareilly, Uttar Pradesh" excluded by RBI Noti. No. RPCD.CO. RRB. No. 7431/03.05.100/2008-09, dt. 27-1-2009.
8 Included by RBI Noti. No. RPCD.CO. RRB. No. 3231/03.05.100/2008-09, dt. 22-9-2008.
9 Included by RBI Noti. No. RPCD.CO. RRB. No. 55/03.05.100/2013-14, dt. 14-11-2013.
10 "Baroda Rajasthan Gramin Bank, Ajmer, Rajasthan" excluded by RBI Noti. No. RPCD.CO. RRB. No. 56/03.05.100/2013-14, dt. 14-11-2013.
11 Included in place of "Baroda Uttar Pradesh Gramin Bank" vide Noti. DOR.1765/31.04.002/2021-22, dt. 12-10-2021.

[1][xxx]

[2][xxx]

[3][xxx]

[4][xxx]

[5][xxx]

[6][xxx]

[7][xxx]

[8][Bharat Co-operative Bank (Mumbai) Ltd., Mumbai.]

Bharat Overseas Bank Ltd., Madras.

Bharati Sahakari Bank Ltd., Pune-411030 (Maharashtra) (w.e.f. 1-6-2002).

[9][xxx]

[10][xxx]

[11][xxx]

Bidur Gramin Bank, Bijnor (U.P.) (1983).

[12][Bihar Gramin Bank, Bagusarai, Bihar.]

[13][xxx]

Bihar State Co-operative Bank Ltd., Patna.

[14][xxx]

[15][xxx]

[16][xxx]

[17][xxx]

---

1 "Bastar Kshetriya Gramin Bank, Jagdalpur, Chhatisgarh" excluded by RBI Noti. No. RPCD.CO. RRB. No. 7431/03.05.100/2008-09, dt. 27-1-2009.

2 "Basti Gramin Bank, Basti, Uttar Pradesh" excluded by RBI Noti. No. RPCD.CO. RRB. No. 7431/03.05.100/2008-09, dt. 27-1-2009.

3 "Begusarai Kshetriya Gramin Bank, Begusarai (Bihar)" excluded by RBI Noti. No. RPCD.CO. RRB. No. 7812-B/03.05.100/2009-10, dt. 21-1-2010.

4 "Benaras State Bank Ltd." excluded by Noti. No. DBOD. No. PSBD. 1326/16.01.070/003-2004, dt. 1-72003.

5 "Bhagalpur-Banka Kshetriya Gramin Bank, Bhagalpur (Bihar)" excluded by RBI Noti. No. RPCD.CO. RRB. No. 7812-B/03.05.100/2009-10, dt. 21-1-2010.

6 "Bhagirath Gramin Bank, Sitapur (Uttar Pradesh)" excluded by RBI Noti. No. RPCD.CO. RRB. No. 3230/03.05.100/2008-09, dt. 22-9-2008.

7 "Bhandara Gramin Bank, Bhandara (Mahrashtra)" excluded by RBI Noti. No. RPCD.CO. RRB. No. 7812-B/03.05.100/2009-10, dt. 21-1-2010.

8 Substituted for "Bharat Co-operative Bank Ltd., Mumbai, Maharashtra" vide Noti. No. UBD. No. BR. 150/16.05.00/97-98, dt. 3-4-1998.

9 "Bharatiya Mahila Bank" excluded vide Noti. DBR. No. Ret. B.C. 57/12.06.004/2017-18, dt. 30-3-2017.

10 "Bhilwara Ajmer Kshetriya Gamin Bank (Rajasthan)" excluded by RBI Noti. No. RPCD.CO. RRB. No. 1782-B/03.05.100/2009-10, dt. 21-1-2010.

11 "Bhojpur Rohtas Gramin Bank, Arrah (Bihar)" excluded by RBI Noti. No. RPCD.CO. RRB. No. 3230/03.05.100/2008-09, dt. 22-9-2008.

12 Included by RBI Notification No. RPCD.CO. RRB. No. 55/03.05.100/2013-14, dt. 14-11-2013.

13 "Bihar Kshetriya Gramin Bank, Munger, Bihar" excluded by RBI Noti. No. RPCD.CO. RRB. No. 56/03.05.100/2013-14, dt. 14-11-2013.

14 "Bijapur Grameena Bank, Bijapur (Karnataka)" excluded by RBI Noti. No. RPCD.CO.RRB. No. 3230/03.05.100/2008-09, dt. 22-9-2008.

15 "Bikaner Kshetriya Gramin Bank, Bikaner, Rajasthan" excluded by RBI Noti. No. RPCD.CO. RRB. No. 7431/03.05.100/2008-09, dt. 27-1-2009.

16 "Bilaspur Raipur Kshetriya Gramin Bank, Bilaspur, Chhatisgarh" excluded by RBI Noti. No. RPCD.CO.RRB.N. 131/03.05.100/2008-09, dt. 27-1-2009.

17 "Bolangir Anclalik Gramya Bank, Bolangir (Orissa)" excluded by RBI Noti. No. RPCD.CO.RRB. No. 11379/3.5.100/2010-11, dt. 31-3-2011.

Bombay Mercantile Co-operative Bank Ltd., Bombay.

[1][xxx]

[2][xxx]

[3][xxx]

[4][xxx]

[5][xxx]

Canara Bank.

Canara Industrial and Banking Syndicate, Udipi.

[6][CSB Bank Limited], Trichur.

[7][xxx]

[8][xxx]

Central Bank of India.

[9][Central Madhya Pradesh Gramin Bank, Chhindwara, Madhya Pradesh.]

[10][Centurion Bank of Punjab Limited]*.

[11][xxx]

Chaitanya Godavari Grameena Bank, Guntur, (Andhra Pradesh).

[12][xxx]

[13][xxx]

[14][xxx]

[15][xxx]

[16][xxx]

---

1 "British Bank of the Middle East", omitted by Noti. No. DBOD.IBS.817/23, 13.022/99, dt. 25-9-1999.

2 "Buldhana Gramin Bank, Buldhana, Maharashtra" excluded by RBI Noti. No. RPCD.CC.PRB. No. 7431/03.05.100/2008-09, dt. 27-1-2009.

3 "Bundelkhand Kshetriya Gramin Bank, Tikamgarh (Madhya Pradesh)" excluded by RBI Noti. No. RPCD.CO. RRB. No. 3230/03.05.100/2008-09, dt. 22-9-2008.

4 "Bundi-Chhittorgarh Kshetriya Gramin Bank, Bundi (Rajasthan)" excluded by RBI Noti. No. RPCD.CO.RRB. No. 7812-B/03-05.100/2009-10, dt. 21-1-2010.

5 "Cachar Gramin Bank, Silchar Assam" excluded by RBI Noti. No. RPCD.CO.RRB. No. 7431/03.05.100/2008-09, dt. 27-1-2009.

6 Substituted for "The Catholic Syrian Bank Ltd." vide Noti. DBR.PSBD. No. 503/16.01.160/2019-20, dt. 17-7-2019, w.e.f. 10-6-2019.

7 "Cauvery Grameena Bank, Mysore (Karnataka)" excluded by RBI Noti. No. RPCD.CO.RRB. No. 3230/03.05.100/2008-09, dt. 22-9-2008.

8 "Cauvery Kalpatharu Grameena Bank, Mysore, Karnataka" excluded by RBI Noti. No. RPCD.CO. RRB. No. 47/03.05.100/2013-14, dt. 22-10-2013.

9 Included by RBI Noti. No. RPCD.CO. RRB. No. 55/03.05.100/2013-14, dt. 14-11-2013.

10 Substituted for "Centurion Bank Limited" by Noti. No. DBOD. No. PSBD. 390/16-01/130/2005-06, dt. 21-10-2005.

* "**Centurion** Bank of Punjab" has been merged with HDFC Bank with effect from 23-5-2008.

11 "Chaitanya Grameena Bank, Tenali, Guntur (Andhra Pradesh)" excluded by RBI Noti. No. RPCD.CO.RRB. No. 3230/03.05.100/2008-09, dt. 22-9-2008.

12 "Chambal Kshetriya Gramin Bank, Morena (Madhya Pradesh)" excluded by RBI Noti. No. RPCD.CO.RRB. No. 7812-B/03-05.100/2009-10, dt. 21-1-2010.

13 "Champaran Kshetriya Gramin Bank, Motihari (Bihar)" excluded by RBI Noti. No. RPCD.CO.RRB. No. 7812-B/03-05.100/2009-10, dt. 21-1-2010.

14 "Chandrapur Gadchiroli Gramin Bank, Chandrapur (Maharastra)" excluded by RBI Noti. No. RPCD.CO.RRB. No. 7812-B/03-05.100/2009-10, dt. 21-1-2010.

15 "Charminar Co-operative Urban Bank Ltd., Hyderabad (Andhra Pradesh)" omitted by Noti. No. F. No. UBD/CO/BSD III/12.24.013/2011-12, dt. 24-11-2011.

16 "Charotar Nagrik Sahakari Bank Ltd., Anand (Gujarat)" excluded by Noti. No. UBD.CO.BSD (SCB) 12.03.208/2003-04, dt. 11-8-2003.

Chase Manhattan Bank (17-8-1996).

[1][xxx]

[2][xxx]

[3][Chhattisgarh Rajya Sahakari Bank Maryadit, Raipur].

[4][Chhattisgarh Rajya Gramin Bank, Raipur, Chhattisgarh.]

[5][xxx]

[6][xxx]

Chinatrust Commercial Bank (22-6-1996).

[7][xxx]

Citi Bank N.A.

City Union Bank Ltd.

Commerce Bank AG (1996).

Commercial Bank of Korea Ltd. (10-5-1997).

[8][xxx]

Comptoir National D Escompte de Paris.

[9][xxx]

[10][xxx].

[11][Credit Agricale Corporate Investment Bank.]

[12][xxx]

[13][xxx]

[14][xxx]

[15][xxx]

[16][DBS Bank India Limited]

[17][xxx]

---

1 "Chattrasal Gramin Bank, Orai (Uttar Pradesh)" excluded by RBI Noti. No. RPCD.CO.RRB. No. 3230/03.05.100/2008-09, dt. 22-9-2008.
2 "Chhattisgarh Gramin Bank, Raipur, Chhattisgarh" excluded by RBI Noti. No. RPCD.CO.RRB.BC. No. 99/03.05.100/2013-14, dt. 8-5-2014.
3 Included by RBI Noti. No. RPCD.RCB.BC No. 34/07.04.007/2013-14, dt. 16-9-2013.
4 Included by RBI Noti. No. RPCD.CO.RRB.BC No. 98/03.05.100/2013-14, dt. 8-5-2014.
5 "Chhindawara - Seoni Kshetriya Gramin Bank, Chhindawara (Madhya Pradesh)" excluded by RBI Noti. No. RPCD.CO.RRB. No. 7812-B/03-05.100/2009-10, dt. 21-1-2010.
6 "Chikmagalur-Kodagu Grameena Bank, Chikmagalur, Karnataka" excluded by RBI Noti. No. RPCD.CO.RRB. No. 47/03.05.100/2013-14, dt. 22-10-2013.
7 "Chitradurga Gramin Bank, Chitradurga (Karnataka)" excluded by RBI Noti. No. RPCD.CO.RRB. No. 3230/03.05.100/2008-09, dt. 22-9-2008.
8 "Commonwealth Bank of Australia" excluded vide Noti. DBR. IBD. No. 2223/23.13. 127/2017-18, dt. 5-9-2017.
9 "The Co-operative Bank of Ahmedabad Ltd., Ahmedabad", excluded by Noti. No. UBD/CO/BCD/01/12.22.040/2005-2006, dt. 20-6-2006.
10 "Corporation Bank" excluded vide Noti. DOR. No. Ret. BC. 55/12.01.001/2019-20, dt. 27-3-2020, w.e.f. 1-4-2020.
11 Substituted for "Calyon Bank" by RBI Noti. No. 16813/23.13.025/2009-10, dated 31-3-2010.
12 "Credit Lyonnais Bank" excluded by Noti. No. Ret. BC. No. 1/12.06.115/2004-05, dt. 6-7-2004.
13 "Credit Suisse A.G." excluded by RBI Noti. No. DoR/LIC.No. S1373/23.03.025/2024-25, dt. 4-6-2024.
14 "Cuttack Gramya Bank, Cuttack (Orissa)" excluded by RBI Noti. No. RPCD.CO. RRB.BC. No. 95/03.05.100/2013-14, dt. 9-4-2014.
15 "DBS Bank Limited" excluded vide Noti. DBR. IBD. No. 7336/23.13. 046/2018-19, dt. 6-3-2019.
16 Included vide Noti. DBR.IBD No. 6408/23.13.046/2018-19, dt. 4-2-2019.
17 "Damoh-Panna-Sagar Kshetriya Gramin Bank, Damoh (Madhya Pradesh)" excluded by RIM Noti. No. RPCD.CO.RRB. No. 3230/03.05.100/2008-09, dt. 22-9-2008.

[1][Deccan Grameena Bank, Rangareddy (Andhra Pradesh).]
[2][xxx]
[1][Dena Gujarat Gramin Bank, Gandhi Nagar (Gujarat).]
Deutsche Bank A.G. (1988).
Development Co-operative Bank Ltd., Bombay (1995).
Development Credit Bank Limited (1995).
[3][xxx]
[4][xxx]
[5][Dhanalakshmi Bank Ltd.]; Trichur.
[6][xxx]
[7][xxx]
[8][xxx]
[9][xxx]
Eastern Bank.
Ellaquai Dehati Bank, Srinagar (Jammu & Kashmir).
Emirates Commercial Bank Ltd.
[10][Emirates NBD Bank (P.J.S.C.)]
[11][ESAF Small Finance Bank Limited]
[12][xxx]
[13][xxx]
European Asian Bank.
[14][xxx]
Faridkot Bhatinda Kshetriya Gramin Bank, Bhatinda (Punjab).
[15][xxx]
[16][xxx]

---

1 Included by RBI Noti. No. RPCD.CO.RRB. No. 3231/03.05.100/2008-09, dt. 22-9-2008.
2 "Dena Bank" excluded vide Noti. DBR. No. Ret. BC.35/12.01.001/2018-19, dt. 10-4-2019, w.e.f. 1-4-2019.
3 "Devi Patan Kshetriya Gramin Bank, Gonda, Uttar Pradesh" excluded by RBI Noti. No. RPCD.CO.RRB. No. 7431/03.05.100/2008-09, dt. 27-1-2009.
4 "Dewas Shajapur Kshetriya Gramin Bank, Dewas (Madhya Pradesh)" excluded by RBI Noti. No. RPCD.CO.RRB. No. 3230/03.05.100/2008-09, dt. 22-9-2008.
5 Substituted for "The Dhanalakshmi Bank Limited" by Noti. No. DBOD.PSBD. 7516/16.01.061/2010-11, dt. 3-11-2010.
6 "Dhenkanal Gramya Bank, Dhenkanal (Orissa)" excluded by RBI Noti. No. RPCD.CO.RRB. No. 7812-B/03-05.100/2009-10, dt. 21-1-2010.
7 "Dresdner Bank AG" excluded by Noti. No. IBS 612/23-13-063/2002-2003, dt. 21-9-2002.
8 "Dungarpur-Banswara Kshetriya Gramin Bank Dungarpur (Rajasthan)" excluded by RBI Noti. No. RPCD.CO.RRB. No. 7812-B/03-05.100/2009-10, dt. 21-1-2010.
9 "Durg-Rajanandgaon Gramin Bank, Rajanandgaon, Chhattisgarh" excluded by RBI Noti. No. RPCD.CO.RRB.BC. No. 99/03.05.100/2013-14, dt. 8-5-2014.
10 Included vide Noti. DBR.IBD. No. 855/23.13.014/2017-18, dt. 26-4-2017.
11 Included vide Noti. DBR.NBD. (SFB-ESAF) No. 4083/16.13.216/2018-19, dt. 12-11-2018.
12 "Etah Gramin Bank, Etah (Uttar Pradesh)" excluded by RBI Noti. No. RPCD.CO.RRB. No. 3230/03.05.100/2008-09, dt. 22-9-2008.
13 "Etawah Kshetriya Gramin Bank, Etawah (Uttar Pradesh)" excluded by RBI Noti. No. RPCD.CO.RRB. No. 11379/3.5.100/2010-11, dt. 31-3-2011.
14 "Faizabad Kshetriya Gramin Bank, Faizabad, Uttar Pradesh" excluded by RBI Noti. No. RPCD.CO. RRB. No. 7431/03.05.100/2008-09, dt. 27-1-2009.
15 "Farook College Employees' Co-operative Society Ltd.," ceased to be a Co-operative Bank, vide Noti. No. 4BD. BR. 128/16.43.300/95-96, dt. 1-9-1995.
16 "Farrukhabad Gramin Bank, Farrukhabad (Uttar Pradesh)" excluded by RBI Noti No. RPCD.CO.RRB. No. 3230/03.05.100/2008-09, dt. 22-9-2008.

[1][xxx]

Federal Bank Ltd., Alwaye.

[2][xxx]

[3][Fino Payments Bank Limited]

Fuji Bank Limited (20-7-1996).

Gadodia Bank, Bombay.

[4][xxx]

[5][xxx]

[6][xxx]

General Bank of Netherlands.

[7][xxx]

[8][xxx]

Goa State Co-operative Bank Ltd. (1994).

[9][GP Parsik Sahakari Bank Ltd., Kalwa, Thane]

[10][xxx]

[11][xxx]

[12][xxx]

[13][xxx]

[14][xxx]

[15][Gramin Bank of Aryavart, Lucknow, Uttar Pradesh.]

Grindlays Bank P.L.C.

Gujarat State Co-operative Bank Ltd., Ahmedabad.

[16][xxx]

Gurgaon Gramin Bank, Gurgaon (Haryana).

---

1 "Fatehpur Kshetriya Gramin Bank, Fatehpur, Uttar Pradesh" excluded by RBI Noti. No. RPCD.CO.RRB. No. 7431/03.05.100/2008-09, dt. 27-1-2009.

2 "Fincare Small Finance Bank Limited" excluded by RBI Noti. No. DoR.HOL.No.S173/16.02.003/2024-25, dt. 8-4-2024, w.e.f. 1-4-2024.

3 Included vide Noti. No. DOR.NBD. No. 2138/16.03.005/2020-21, dt. 1-1-2021.

4 "The Ganesh Bank of Kurundwad Ltd." excluded by Noti. DBOD. No. PSBD.2915/16.01.103/2006-07, dt. 26-9-2006, w.e.f. 21-10-2006.

5 "Ganga Yamuna Gramin Bank, Dehradun (Uttar Pradesh)" excluded by RBI Noti. No. RPCD.CO.RRB. No. 3230/03.05.100/2008-09, dt. 22-9-2008.

6 "Gaur Gramin Bank, Malda (West Bengal)" excluded by RBI Noti. No. RPCD.CO.RRB. No. 7812-B/03-05.100/2009-10, dt. 21-1-2010.

7 "Giridih Kshetriya Gramin Bank, Giridih (Bihar)" excluded by RBI Noti. No. RPCD.CO.RRB. No. 7812-B/03-05.100/2009-10, dt. 21-1-2010.

8 "The Global Trust Bank Ltd." excluded by Noti. DBOD. No. PSBS.BC.42116. 01.129/2004-05, dt. 15-9-2004, w.e.f. 20-11-2004.

9 Substituted for "Gopinath Patil Parsik Janata Sahakari Bank Ltd., Thane" vide Noti. DCBR.RAD.(PCB). Noti. No. 1/08.02.205/2016-17, dt. 15-3-2017.

10 "Godavari Grameena Bank, Rajahmundry (Andhra Pradesh)" excluded by RBI Noti. No. RPCD.CO.RRB. No. 3230/03.05.100/2008-09, dt. 22-9-2008.

11 "Golconda Gramin Bank, Hyderabad (Andhra Pradesh)" excluded by RBI Noti. No. RPCD.CO.RRB. No. 3230/03.05.100/2008-09, dt. 22-9-2008.

12 "Gomati Gramin Bank, Jaunpur (Uttar Pradesh)" excluded by RBI Noti. No. RPCD.CO.RRB. No. 3230/03.05.100/2008-09, dt. 22-9-2008.

13 "Gopalganj Kshetriya Gramin Bank, Gopalganj (Bihar)" excluded by RBI Noti. No. RPCD.CO. RRB. No. 7812-B/03-05.100/2009-10, dt. 21-1-2010.

14 "Gorakhpur Kshetriya Gramin Bank, Gorakhpur, Uttar Pradesh" excluded by RBI Noti. No. RPCD.CO.RRB. No. 7431/03.05.100/2008-09, dt. 27-1-2009.

15 Included by RBI Noti. No. RPCD.CO.RRB. No. 55/03.05.100/2013-14, dt. 14-11-2013.

16 "Gurdaspur Amritsar Kshetriya Gramin Vikas Bank, Gurdaspur (Punjab)" excluded by RBI Noti. No. RPCD.CO.RRB. No. 3230/03.05.100/2008-09, dt. 22-9-2008.

[1][xxx]

HDFC Bank Ltd. (1995).

Habib Bank Ltd.

[2][xxx]

[3][xxx]

Hardoi-Unnao Gramin Bank, Hardoi (Uttar Pradesh).

[4][Haryana Gramin Bank, Rohtak (Haryana).]

[5][xxx]

Haryana State Co-operative Bank Ltd., Ambala City, with Headquarters at Chandigarh.

[6][xxx]

[7][Himachal Pradesh Gramin Bank Mandi, Himachal Pradesh.]

[8][xxx]

[9][xxx]

Hindustan Commercial Bank Ltd., Cawnpore.

[10][xxx]

Hongkong and Shanghai Banking Corporation.

[11][xxx]

[12][HSBC Bank Oman S.A.O.G.]

ICICI Bank Ltd.

[13][IDBI Bank Limited.]

Indian Bank, Madras.

[14][Indian Mercantile Co-operative Bank Ltd., 26-A, Cantonment Road, Lucknow-226001 (Uttar Pradesh) (w.e.f. 3-11-2001).]

Indian Overseas Bank, Madras.

[15][xxx]

---

1 "Gwalior Datia Kshetriya Gramin Bank, Datia (Madhya Pradesh)" excluded by RBI Noti. No. RPCD.CO.RRB. No. 7812-B/03-05.100/2009-10, dt. 21-1-2010.

2 "Hadoti Kshetriya Gramin Bank, Kota, Rajasthan" excluded by RBI Noti. No. RPCD.CO.RRB. No. 56/03.05.100/2013-14, dt. 14-112013.

3 "Hamil Bank" excluded by Notification IBS. 571/23.13.086/99-2000, dt. 28-81999.

4 Included by RBI Noti. No. RPCD.CO.RRB. No. 3231/03.05.100/2008-09, dt. 22-9-2008.

5 "Haryana Kshetriya Gramin Bank, Bhiwani (Haryana)" excluded by RBI Noti. No. RPCD.CO.RRB. No. 3230/03.05.100/2008-09, dt. 22-9-2008.

6 "Hazaribagh Kshetriya Gramin Bank, Hazaribagh (Bihar)" excluded by RBI Noti. No. RPCD.CO.RRB. No. 7812-B/03-05.100/2009-10, dt. 21-1-2010.

7 Included by RBI Noti. No. RPCD.CO.RRB. No. 55/03.05.100/2013-14, dt. 14-11-2013.

8 "Himachal Gramin Bank, Mandi, Himachal Pradesh" excluded by RBI Noti. No. RPCD.CO.RRB. No. 56/03.05.100/2013-14, dt. 14-11-2013.

9 "Hindon Gramin Bank, Ghaziabad (Uttar Pradesh)" excluded by RBI Noti. No. RPCD.CO.RRB.BC. No. 95/03.05.100/2013-14, dt. 9-4-2014.

10 "Hissar-Sirsa Kshetriya Gramin Bank, Hissar (Haryana)" excluded by RBI Noti. No. RPCD.CO.RRB. No. 3230/03.05.100/2008-09, dt. 22-9-2008.

11 "Howrah Gramin Bank, Howrah (West Bengal)" excluded by RBI Noti. No. RPCD.CO.RRB.BC. No. 95/03.05.100/2013-14, dt. 9-4-2014.

12 Substituted for "Oman International Bank S.A.O.G." by RBI Noti. No. DBOD.IBD. No. 4591/23.13.030/2012-13, dt. 26-9-2012.

13 Substituted for "Industrial Development Bank of India Limited" by Noti. DBOD.BP.BC.No. 21.01.002/2007-08, dt. 16-5-2008, w.r.e.f. 7-5-2008.

14 Included by Noti. No. UBD.10.BR./16-05.00/2001-2003, dt. 26-9-2001.

15 "Indore-Ujjain Kshitriya Gramin Bank, Ujjain (Madhya Pradesh)" excluded by RBI Noti. No. RPCD.CO.RRB. No. 3230/03.05.100/2008-09, dt. 22-9-2008.

[1][xxx]

[2][ING Vyasa Bank Ltd., Bangalore City.]

IndusInd Bank Limited (1994).

[3][IDFC FIRST Bank Limited]

International Nederlanden Bank N.V. (1994).

[4][xxx]

[5][xxx]

Jalgaon Janta Sahakari Bank Ltd., Jalgaon (Maharashtra) (w.e.f. 29-1-2000).

Jammu and Kashmir Bank Ltd., Srinagar.

[6][xxx]

[7][J & K Grameen Bank, Jammu & Kashmir.]

[8][xxx]

[9][xxx]

[10][Jana Small Finance Bank Limited]

Janakalyan Sahakari Bank Ltd., Chembur, Mumbai (1998).

Janalaxmi Co-operative Bank Ltd., Nashik (Maharashtra) (w.e.f. 29-1-2000)

Janata Sahakari Bank Ltd., Pune.

[11][xxx]

[12][Jharkhand Gramin Bank, Ranchi (Jharkhand)].

[13][JP Morgan Chase Bank National Association].

[14][JSC VTB Bank.]

[15][xxx]

Ka Bank Nongkyndong Ri Khasi Jaintia (Meghalaya) (1981).

[16][xxx]

1 "ING Bank NV" excluded by Noti. No. IBD.616/23.13.017/2005-06, dt. 28-10-2005.

2 Substituted for "ING Vyasa Bank" by Noti. No. PSBS.596/16.01.077/2002-03, dt. 21-11-2002.

3 Substituted for "IDFC Bank Limited" vide Noti. DBR.PSBD No. 7234/16.01.146/2018-19, dt. 1-3-2019, w.e.f. 12-1-2019.

4 "Jaipur Nagaur Anchalik Gramin Bank, Jaipur (Rajasthan)" excluded by RBI Noti. No. RPCD.CO.RRB. No. 3230/03.05.100/2008-09, dt. 22-9-2008.

5 "Jaipur Thar Gramin Bank, Jaipur (Rajasthan)" excluded by RBI Noti. No. RPCD.CO.RRB.BC. No. 77/03.05.100/2013-14, dt. 27-1-2014.

6 "Jammu Rural Bank, Jammu (Jammu & Kashmir)" excluded by RBI Noti. No. RPCD.CO.RRB. No. 11379/3.5.100/2010-11, dt. 31-3-2011.

7 Included by RBI Noti. No. RPCD.CO.RRB. No. 11377/3.5.100/2010-11, dt. 31-3-2011.

8 "Jamnagar Gramin Bank, Jamnagar (Gujarat) (1978)" excluded by RBI Noti. No. RPCD.CO.RRB. No. 3230/03.05.100/2008-09, dt. 22-9-2008.

9 "Jamuna Gramin Bank, Agra (Uttar Pradesh)" excluded by RBI Noti. No. RPCD.CO.RRB. No. 3230/03.05.100/2008-09, dt. 22-9-2008.

10 Included vide Noti. DBR.NBD. No. 499/16.02.011/2019-20, dt. 16-7-2019.

11 "Jhabua-Dhar Kshetriya Gramin Bank, Jhabua, Madhya Pradesh" excluded by RBI Noti. No. RPCD.CO.RRB. No. 56/03.05.100/2013-14, dt. 14-11-2013.

12 Included by RBI Noti. No. RPCD.CO.RRB. No. 7812-A/03-05.100/2009-10, dt. 21-1-2010.

13 Substituted for "JP Morgan Chase Bank". by Noti. No. Ret. BC. 70/12.06.090/2004-05, dt. 4-2-2005.

14 Included by RBI Noti. No. DBOD.IBD. No. 2091/23.13.126/2008-09, dt. 30-7-2008.

15 "Junagadh-Amreli Gramin Bank, Junagadh (Gujarat)" excluded by RBI Noti. No. RPCD.CO.RRB. No. 3230/03.05.100/2008-09, dt. 22-9-2008.

16 "Kakathiya Grameena Bank, Warangal (Andhra Pradesh)" excluded by RBI Noti. No. RPCD.CO.RRB. No. 3230/03.05.100/2008-09, dt. 22-9-2008.

[1][xxx]

[2][Kallappanna Awade Ichalkaranji Janata Sahakari Bank Ltd., Ichalkaranji].

[3][xxx]

Kalupur Commercial Co-operative Bank Ltd., Ahmedabad.

Kalyan Janta Sahakari Bank Ltd., Kalyan (Maharashtra) (w.e.f. 29-1-2000).

Kamani Industrial Bank.

[4][xxx]

[5][xxx]

[6][xxx]

[7][xxx]

Karad Urban Co-operative Bank Ltd., Karad (Maharashtra) (w.e.f. 29-1-2000).

Karbi N.C. Rural Bank, Diphu (Assam) (1982).

Karnataka Bank Ltd., Mangalore.

Karnataka State Co-operative Bank Ltd., Bangalore.

[8][Karnataka Vikas Grameena Bank, Dharwad (Karnataka).]

Karur Vysya Bank Ltd.

[9][Baroda UP Bank, Gorakhpur, Uttar Pradesh]

[10][xxx]

[11][Kaveri Grameen Bank, Mysore, Karnataka.]

[12][Kerala Gramin Bank, Malappuram, Kerala.]

Kerala State Co-operative Bank Ltd., Trivandrum.

Khamgaon Urban Co-operative Bank Ltd., Khamgaon (Maharashtra) (w.e.f.22-5-1999).

Khasi Jaintia Rural Bank, Shillong (Meghalaya).

[13][xxx]

[14][xxx]

---

1 "Kalahandi Anchalika Gramya Bank, Bhawanipatna (Orissa)" excluded by RBI Noti. No. RPCD.CO.RRB. No. 11379/3.5.100/2010-11, dt. 31-3-2011.

2 Substituted for "Ichalkaranji Janata Sahakari Bank Ltd., Ichalkaranji" by Noti. No. UBD.CO.BPD.8/16.05.000/2006-07, dt. 21-5-2007.

3 "Kalpatharu Grameena Bank, Tumkur (Andhra Pradesh)" excluded by RBI Noti. No. RPCD.CO.RRB. No. 3230/03.05.100/2008-09, dt. 22-9-2008.

4 "Kamraz Rural Bank, Sopore (Jammu & Kashmir)" excluded by RBI Noti. No. RPCD.CO.RRB. No. 11379/3.5.100/2010-11, dt. 31-3-2011.

5 "Kanakadurga Gramin Bank, Gudivada (Andhra Pradesh)" excluded by RBI Noti. No. RPCD.CO.RRB. No. 3230/03.05.100/2008-09, dt. 22-9-2008.

6 "Kapol Co-operative Bank Ltd., Mumbai (1998)" excluded by RBI Noti. No. DoR-REG/LIC. No. S6720/07.12.000/2023-24, dt. 22-02-2024.

7 "Kapurthala Firozpur Kshetriya Gramin Bank, Kapurthala (Punjab)" excluded by RBI Noti. No. RPCD.CO.RRB. No. 3230/03.05.100/2008-09, dt. 22-9-2008.

8 Included by RBI Noti. No. RPCD.CO.RRB. No. 3231/03.05.100/2008-09, dt. 22-9-2008.

9 Included in place of "Kashi Gomti Samyut Gramin Bank" vide Noti. DOR.Rur.S1765/31.04.002/2021-22, dt. 12-10-2021.

10 "Kashi Gramin Bank, Varanasi (Uttar Pradesh)" excluded by RBI Noti. No. RPCD.CO.RRB. No. 3230/03.05.100/2008-09, dt. 22-9-2008.

11 Included by RBI Noti. No. RPCD.CO.RRB. No. 46/03.05.100/2013-14, dt. 22-10-2013.

12 Included by RBI Noti. No. RPCD.CO.RRB. BC No. 98/03.05.100/2013-14, dt. 8-5-2014.

13 "Kissan Gramin Bank, Budaun, Uttar Pradesh" excluded by RBI Noti. No. RPCD.CO.RRB. No. 7431/03.05.100/2008-09, dt. 27-1-2009.

14 "Kolar Gramin Bank, Kolar (Karnataka)" excluded by RBI Noti. No. RPCD.CO.RRB. No. 3230/03.05.100/2008-09, dt. 22-9-2008.

[1][xxx]

[2][xxx]

[3][xxx]

Krishnaram Baldeo Bank (Private) Ltd., Gwalior.

[4][xxx]

[5][xxx]

[6][xxx]

Kumbakonam City Union Bank Ltd.

[7][xxx]

[8][xxx]

Lakshmi Commercial Bank Ltd.

Lakshmi Vilas Bank Ltd., Karur.

Langpi Dehangi Rural Bank, Diphu (Assam).

[9][xxx]

[10][xxx]

[11][xxx]

[12][xxx]

[13][Madhya Bihar Gramin Bank, Patna (Bihar).]

Madhya Pradesh Rajya Sahakari Bank Maryadit, Jabalpur.

[14][Madhyanchal Gramin Bank, Sagar, Madhya Pradesh.]

[15][xxx]

---

1 "Koraput Panchabati Gramya Bank, Jeypore (Orissa)" excluded by RBI Noti. No. RPCD.CO.RRB. No. 11379/3.5.100/2010-11, dt. 31-3-2011.

2 "Kosi Kshetriya Gramin Bank, Purnea (Bihar)" excluded by RBI Noti. No. RPCD.CO.RRB. No. 7812-B/03-05.100/2009-10, dt. 21-1-2010.

3 "Krishna Grameena Bank, Gulbarga (Karnataka)" excluded by RBI Noti. No. RPCD.CO.RRB.BC. No. 99/03.05.100/2013-14, dt. 8-5-2014.

4 "Krung Thai Bank Public Company Limited (25-1-1997)" excluded by RBI Noti. No. DoR.LIC.No. S1998/23.13.066/2024-25, dt. 3-7-2024.

5 "Kshetriya Gramin Bank, Hoshangabad (Madhya Pradesh)" excluded by RBI Noti. No. RPCD.CO.RRB. No. 7812-B/03-05.100/2009-10, dt. 21-1-2010.

6 "Kshetriya KisanGramin Bank, Mainpuri, Uttar Pradesh" excluded by RBI Noti. No. RPCD.CO.RRB. No. 56/03.05.100/2013-14, dt. 14-11-2013.

7 "Kutch Gramin Bank, Bhuj (Gujarat)" excluded by RBI Noti. No. RPCD.CO.RRB. No. 3230/03.05.100/2008-09, dt. 22-9-2008.

8 "Lakhimi Gaonlia Bank, Golaghat, Assam" excluded by RBI Noti. No. RPCD.CO.RRB. No. 7431/03.05.100/2008-09, dt. 27-1-2009.

9 "Lord Krishna Bank" excluded by Noti. DBOD. No. PSBD.2536/16.01.130/2007-08, dt. 6-9-2007.

10 "Lucknow Kshetriya Gramin Bank, Sitapur (Uttar Pradesh)" excluded by RBI Noti. No. RPCD.CO.RRB. No. 11379/3.5.100/2010-11, dated 31-3-2011.

11 "Madhubani Kshetriya Gramin Bank, Madhubani (Bihar)" excluded by RBI Noti. No. RPCD.CO.RRB. No. 7812-B/03-05.100/2009-10, dt. 21-1-2010.

12 "Madhya Bharat Gramin Bank, Sagar, Madhya Pradesh" excluded by RBI Noti. No. RPCD.CO.RRB. No. 56/03.05.100/2013-14, dt. 14-11-2013.

13 Included by RBI Noti. No. RPCD.CO.RRB. No. 3231/03.05.100/2008-09, dt. 22-9-2008.

14 Included by RBI Noti. No. RPCD.CO.RRB. No. 55/03.05.100/2013-14, dt. 14-11-2013.

15 "Magadh Gramin Bank, Gaya (Bihar)" excluded by RBI Noti. No. RPCD.CO.RRB. No. 3230/03.05.100/2008-09, dt. 22-9-2008.

[1][xxx]

[2][xxx]

[3][Maharashtra Gramin Bank, Maharashtra.]

Maharashtra State Co-operative Bank Ltd., Bombay.

[4][xxx]

[5][xxx]

Malwa Gramin Bank, Sangrur (Punjab).

[6][xxx]

[7][xxx]

Manipur Rural Bank, Imphal (Manipur).

[8][xxx]

[9][xxx]

[10][xxx]

[11][xxx]

[12][Marudhara Gramin Bank, Jodhpur, Rajasthan.]

[13][xxx]

[14][xxx]

[15][xxx]

Mehasana Urban Co-operative Bank Ltd., Mahsana (Gujarat) (w.e.f. 29-1-2000).

Mellabhum Gramin Bank, Bankura (1976).

Mewar Anchalik Gramin Bank, Udaipur (Rajasthan)

---

1 "Mahakaushal Kshetriya Gramin Bank, Narsinghpur, Madhya Pradesh" excluded by RBI Noti. No. RPCD.CO.RRB. No. 56/03.05.100/2013-14, dt. 14-11-2013.

2 "Maharashtra Godavari Gramin Bank, Aurangabad, Maharashtra" excluded by RBI Noti. No. RPCD.CO.RRB. No. 11379/3.5.100/2010-11, dt. 31-3-2011.

3 Included by RBI Noti. No. RPCD.CO. RRB. No. 11377/3.5.100/2010-11, dt. 31-3-2011.

4 "Malaprabha Grameena Bank, Dharwar (Karnataka)" excluded by RBI Noti. No. RPCD.CO.RRB. No. 3230/03.05.100/2008-09, dt. 22-9-2008.

5 "MallabhumGramin Bank, Bankura (West Bengal)" excluded by RBI Noti. No. RPCD.CO.RRB. No. 7812-B/03-05.100/2009-10, dt. 21-1-2010.

6 "Mandla Balaghat Kshetriya Gramin Bank, Mandla (Madhya Pradesh)" excluded by RBI Noti. No. RPCD.CO.RRB. No. 7812-B/03-05.100/2009-10, dt. 21-1-2010.

7 "Mandvi Co-operative Bank Ltd., Mumbai" excluded by Noti. No. UBD/CO/BSD(SCB) No. 01/12.22.136/2007-08, dt. 1-11-2007.

8 "Manjira Grameena Bank, Sangareddy, Medak (Andhra Pradesh)" excluded by RBI Noti. No. RPCD.CO.RRB. No. 3230/03.05.100/2008-09, dt. 22-9-2008.

9 "Mapusa Urban Co-operative Bank of Goa Ltd., Mapusa (Goa)" excluded by Noti. DOR.MON/4347/12.22.156/2021-22, dt. 10-3-2022.

10 "Marathwada Gramin Bank, Nanded (Maharashtra)" excluded by RBI Noti. No. RPCD.CO.RRB. No. 11379/3.5.100/2010-11, dt. 31-3-2011.

11 "Marudhar Kshetriya Gramin Bank, Churu (Rajasthan)" excluded by RBI Noti. No. RPCD.CO.RRB. No. 7812-B/03-05.100/2009-10, dt. 21-1-2010.

12 Included by RBI Noti. No. RPCD.CO.RRB.BC. No. 76/03.05.100/2013-14, dt. 27-1-2014.

13 "Marwar Ganganagar Bikaner Gramin Bank, Pali, Rajasthan" excluded by RBI Noti. No. RPCD.CO.RRB.BC. No. 77/03.05.100/2013-14, dt. 27-1-2014.

14 "Marwar Gramin Bank, Pali, Rajasthan" excluded by RBI Noti. No. RPCD.CO.RRB. No. 7431/03.05.100/2008-09, dt. 27-1-2009.

15 "Mayurakshi Gramin Bank, Suri (West Bengal)" excluded by RBI Noti. No. RPCD.CO.RRB.BC. No. 95/03.05.100/2013-14, dt. 9-4-2014.

Miraj State Bank Ltd.

[1][xxx]

Mitsui Bank Ltd.

Mizoram Rural Bank (Mizoram).

[2][xxx]

[3][xxx]

[4][xxx]

Nadar Bank, Tuticorin.

[5][xxx]

Nagaland Rural Bank, Kohima (Nagaland).

[6][xxx]

[7][xxx]

Nagpur Nagrik Sahakari Bank Ltd., Nagpur (Maharashtra) (w.e.f. 22-5-1999).

[8][xxx]

Nainital Bank Ltd.

[9][xxx]

[10][Narmada Jhabua Gramin Bank, Indore, Madhya Pradesh].

[11][xxx]

[12][National Bank of Abu Dhabi PJSC]

National Bank of Pakistan.

[13][xxx]

[14][xxx]

[15][xxx]

[16][xxx]

---

1 "Mithila Kshetriya Gramin Bank, Darbhanga (Bihar)" excluded by RBI Noti. No. RPCD.CO.RRB. No. 7812-B/03-05.100/2009-10, dt. 21-1-2010.

2 "Monghyr Kshetriya Gramin Bank, Monghyr (Bihar)" excluded by RBI Noti. No. RPCD.CO.RRB. No. 7812-B/03-05.100/2009-10, dt. 21-1-2010.

3 "Murshidabad Gramin Bank, Berhampore (West Bengal)" excluded by RBI Noti. No. RPCD.CO.RRB. No. 7812-B/03-05100/2009-10, dt. 21-1-2010.

4 "Muzaffarnagar Kshetriya Gramin Bank, Muzaffarnagar (Uttar Pradesh)" excluded by RBI Noti. No. RPCD.CO.RRB.BC. No. 95/03.05.100/2013-14, dt. 9-4-2014.

5 "Nadia Gramin Bank, Krishnagar (West Bengal)" excluded by RBI Noti. No. RPCD.CO.RRB. No. 7812-B/03-05.100/2009-10, dt. 21-1-2010.

6 "Nagar Urban Co-operative Bank Ltd." excluded by RBI Noti. No. DoR.REG/LIC.No. S8/08.27.159/2024-25, dt. 1-4-2024.

7 "Nagarjuna Grameena Bank, Khammam (Andhra Pradesh)" excluded by RBI Noti. No. RPCD.CO.RRB. No. 3230/03.05.100/2008-09, dt. 22-9-2008.

8 "Nainital Almora Kshetriya Gramin Bank, Nainital, Uttarakhand" excluded by RBI Noti. No. RPCD.CO.RRB. No. 56/03.05.100/2013-14, dt. 14-11-2013.

9 "Nalanda Gramin Bank, Biharshariff (Bihar)" excluded by RBI Noti. No. RPCD.CO.RRB. No. 3230/03.05.100/2008-09, dt. 22-9-2008.

10 Included by RBI Noti. No. RPCD.CO.RRB. No. 55/03.05.100/2013-14, dt. 14-11-2013.

11 "Narmada MalwaGramin Bank, Indore, Madhya Pradesh" excluded by RBI Noti. No. RPCD.CO.RRB. No. 56/03.05.100/2013-14, dt. 14-11-2013.

12 Included by RBI Noti. No. DBR.IDB. No. 5196/23.03.030/2015-16, dt. 26-10-2015.

13 "Nedungadi Bank Ltd." excluded by Noti. No. DBOD. No. PSB. 1326/16.01.070/200320004, dt. 1-7-2003.

14 "Netravati Grameena Bank, Mangalore (Karnataka)" excluded by RBI Noti. No. RPCD.CO.RRB. No. 3230/03.05.100/2008-09, dt. 22-9-2008.

15 "New Bank of India, New Delhi" omitted by Noti. No. DBOD. No. 344/Escl/ 16:19:001/93, dt. 8-10-1993.

16 "Neelachal Gramya Bank, Bhubneshwar, Orissa" excluded by RBI Noti. No. RPCD.CO.RRB. No. 47/03.05.100/2013-14, dt. 22-10-2013.

[1][xxx]

[2][North East Small Finance Bank Limited]

[3][NKGSB Co-operative Bank Ltd., Mumbai].

[4][xxx]

Nutan Nagarik Shakari Bank Ltd., Ahmedabad (Gujrat) (w.e.f. 29-1-2000).

[5][Odisha Gramya Bank, Bhubaneswar, Odisha.]

[6][xxx]

[7][The Odisha State Co-operative Bank Ltd.], Cuttack.

[8][xxx]

[9][xxx]

Palamau Kshetriya Gramin Bank, Daltonganj (Bihar).

Pallavan Grama Bank, Salem (Tamil Nadu).

[10][xxx]

Pandyan Bank

Pandyan Grama Bank, Sattur (Tamil Nadu).

Parsik Janata Sahakari Bank Ltd., Thane (1998).

Parur Central Bank Ltd.

[11][xxx]

[12][Paschim Banga Gramin Bank, Howrah, West Bengal.]

[13][xxx]

[14][xxx]

[15][xxx]

[16][Paytm Payments Bank Ltd.]

---

1 "Nimar Kshetriya Gramin Bank, Khargone (Madhya Pradesh)" excluded by RBI Noti. No. RPCD.CO.RRB. No. 3230/03.05.100/2008-09, dt. 22-9-2008.
2 Included vide Noti. DBR.NBD. No. 31/16.02.010/2019-20, dt. 1-7-2019.
3 Substituted for "North Kanara GSB Co-operative Bank Ltd., Mumbai, Maharashtra" by Noti. No. UBD.CO.1/16.05.000/2005-2006, dt. 24-12006.
4 "North Malabar Gramin Bank, Kanpur, Kerala" excluded by RBI Noti. No. RPCD.CO.RRB.BC. No. 99/03.05.100/2013-14, dt. 8-5-2014.
5 Included by RBI Noti. No. RPCD.CO.RRB. No. 46/03.05.100/2013-14, dt. 22-10-2013.
6 "Oriental Bank of Commerce" excluded vide Noti. DOR. No. Ret.BC. 56/12.01.001/2019-20, dt. 27-3-2020, w.e.f. 1-4-2020.
7 Substituted for "The Orissa State Co-operative Bank Ltd." vide Noti. DCBR.CO.RCBD. No.01/19.51.025/2016-17, dt. 9-12-2016.
8 "The Overseas-Chinese Banking Corporation Limited" excluded by Noti. No. Ret. BC. No. 65/12.06.110/2003-04, dt. 5-2-2004.
9 "Palamau Kshetriya Gramin Bank, Daltonganj (Jharkhand)" excluded by RBI Noti. No. RPCD.CO.RRB. No. 7812-B/03-05.100/2009-10, dt. 21-1-2010.
10 "Panchamahal Gramin Bank, Godhra (Gujarat)" excluded by RBI Noti. No. RPCD.CO.RRB. No. 3230/03.05.100/2008-09, dt. 22-9-2008.
11 "Parvatiya Gramin Bank, Chamba, Himachal Pradesh" excluded by RBI Noti. No. RPCD.CO.RRB. No. 56/03.05.100/2013-14, dt. 14-11-2013.
12 Inserted by RBI Noti. No. RPCD.CO.RRB.BC. No. 94/03.05.100/2013-14, dt. 9-4-2014.
13 "Patliputra Gramin Bank, Patna (Bihar)" excluded by RBI Noti. No. RPCD.CO.RRB. No. 3230/03.05.100/2008-09, dt. 22-9-2008.
14 "Pinakini Grameena Bank, Nellore (Andhra Pradesh)" excluded by RBI Noti. No. RPCD.CO.RRB. No. 3230/03.05.100/2008-09, dt. 22-9-2008.
15 "Pithoragarh Kshetriya Gramin Bank, Pithoragrah (Uttaranchal)" excluded by RBI Noti. No. RPCD.CO.RRB. No. 3230/03.05.100/2008-09, dt. 22-9-2008.
16 Included vide Noti. DOR.LIC. No. S 926/16.03.006/2021-22, dt. 6-9-2021.

Pondicherry State Cooperative Bank Ltd. (w.e.f. 20-7-1995).

[1][xxx]

[2][xxx]

[3][Pragthi Krishna Gramin Bank, Bellary, Karnataka.]

[4][Prahara Sahakari Bank Ltd., Loni Dist., Ahmednagar (Maharashtra).]

[5][xxx]

Prathama Bank, Moradabad (Uttar Pradesh).

[6][xxx]

Punjab and Sind Bank, Amritsar.

Punjab Co-operative Bank Ltd., Amritsar.

[7][Punjab Gramin Bank, Kapurthala (Punjab).]

Punjab National Bank.

Punjab State Co-operative Bank Ltd., Chandigarh.

Purbanchal Bank Ltd., Gauhati.

[8][xxx]

[9][Baroda UP Bank, Gorakhpur, Uttar Pradesh]

[10][xxx]

[11][xxx]

[12][xxx]

[13][xxx]

Rajasthan State Co-operative Bank Ltd., Jaipur.

[14][xxx]

Rajkot Nagrik Sahakari Bank Ltd., Bombay.

[15][xxx]

---

1 "Pragathi Gramin Bank, Belary (Karnatak)" excluded by RBI Noti. No. RPCD.CO.RRB.BC. No. 99/03.05.100/2013-14, dt. 8-5-2014.

2 "Pragyotish Gaonlia Bank, Nalbari, Assam" excluded by RBI Noti. No. RPCD.CO.RRB. No. 7431/03.05.100/2008-09, dt. 27-1-2009.

3 Included by RBI Noti. No. RPCD.CO.RRB.BC No. 98/03.05.100/2013-14, dt. 8-5-2014.

4 Included by Noti. No. UBD.CO/BP/22/16.05.00/2002-2003, dt. 3-3-2003.

5 "Pratapgarh Kshetriya Gramin Bank, Pratapgarh, Uttar Pradesh" excluded by RBI Noti. No. RPCD.CO.RRB. No. 7431/03.05.100/2008-09, dt. 27-1-2008.

6 "Punjab and Maharashtra Co-operative Bank Ltd., Mumbai (Maharashtra) (w.e.f.29-1-2000)" excluded vide Noti. DOR.MON. No. 3764/12.01.000/2021-22, dt. 10-3-2022.

7 Included by RBI Noti. No. RPCD.CO.RRB. No. 3231/03.05.100/2008-09, dt. 22-9-2008.

8 "Puri Gramya Bank, Pipli (Orissa)" excluded by RBI Noti. No. RPCD.CO.RRB. No. 7812-B/03-05.100/2009-10, dt. 21-1-2010.

9 Included in place of "Purvanchal Bank" vide Noti. DOR.Rur.S1765/31.04.002/2021-22, dt. 12-10-2021.

10 "Purvanchal Gramin Bank, Gorakhpur, Uttar Pradesh" excluded by RBI Noti. No. RPCD.CO.RRB. No. 47/03.05.100/2013-14, dt. 22-10-2013.

11 "Raebareli Kshetriya Gramin Bank, Raebareli, Uttar Pradesh" excluded by RBI Noti. No. RPCD.CO.RRB. No. 7431/03.05.100/2008-09, dt. 27-1-2009.

12 "Raigarh Kshetriya Gramin Bank, Raigarh, Madhya Pradesh" excluded by RBI Noti. No. RPCD.CO.RRB. No. 7431/03.05.100/2008-09, dt. 27-1-2009.

13 "Rajasthan Gramin Bank, Alwar, Rajasthan" excluded by RBI Noti. No. RPCD.CO.RRB. No. 56/03.05.100/2013-14, dt. 14-11-2013.

14 "Rajgarh Sehore Kshetriya Gramin Bank, Rajgarh (Madhya Pradesh)" excluded by RBI Noti. No. RPCD.CO.RRB. No. 3230/03.05.100/2008-09, dt. 22-9-2008.

15 "Ranchi Kshetriya Gramin Bank, Ranchi (Bihar)" excluded by RBI Noti. No. RPCD.CO.RRB. No. 7812-B/03-05.100/2009-10, dt. 21-1-2010.

[1][xxx]
[2][xxx]
[3][xxx]
Ratnakar Bank Ltd., Kolhapur.
[4][xxx]
[5][xxx]
[6][NatWest Markets Plc]
[7][xxx]
[8][xxx]
[9][xxx]
Sakma Bank Limited (1992).
[10][xxx]
[11][xxx]
[12][xxx]
[13][xxx]
[14][xxx]
[15][xxx]
Sangli Urban Co-operative Bank Ltd., Sangli.
[16][xxx]
[17][Saptagiri Grameena Bank, Chitoor (Andhra Pradesh).]

---

1 "Rani Laxmi Bai Kshetriya Gramin Bank, Jhansi, Uttar Pradesh" excluded by RBI Noti. No. RPCD.CO.RRB. No. 7431/03.05.100/2008-09, dt. 27-1-2009.
2 "Ratlam Mandsaur Kshetriya Gramin Bank, Mandsaur (Madhya Pradesh)" excluded by RBI Noti. No. RPCD.CO.RRB. No. 7812-B/03-05.100/2009-10, dt. 21-1-2010.
3 "Ratnagiri Sindhudurg Gramin Bank, Ratnagiri (Maharashtra)" excluded by RBI Noti. No. RPCD.CO.RRB. No. 7812-B/03-05.100/2009-10, dt. 21-1-2010.
4 "Rayalaseema Grameena Bank, Cuddapah (Andhra Pradesh)" excluded by RBI Noti. No. RPCD.CO.RRB. No. 3230/03.05.100/2008-09, dt. 22-9-2008.
5 "Rewa Sidhi Gramin Bank, Rewa Madhya Pradesh" excluded by RBI Noti. No. RPCD.CO.RRB. No. 56/03.05.100/2013-14, dt. 14-11-2013.
6 Substituted for "The Royal Bank of Scotland P/C" by Noti. No. DBR.IBD. No. 10678/23.03.031/2018-19, dt. 24-6-2019.
7 "Rupee Co-operative Bank Ltd., Pune" excluded by RBI Noti. No. DoR/REG/LIC No. S4847/07.12.000/2023-24, dt. 29-11-2023.
8 "Rushikulya Gramya Bank, Berhampur, Orissa" excluded by RBI Noti. No. RPCD.CO.RRB. No. 47/03.05.100/2013-14, dt. 22-10-2013.
9 "Sabarkantha-Gandhinagar Gramin Bank, Himatnagar (Gujarat)" excluded by RBI Noti. No. RPCD.CO.RRB. No. 3230/03.05.100/2008-09, dt. 22-9-2008.
10 "Sagar Gramin Bank, Amtala (West Bengal)" excluded by RBI Noti. No. RPCD.CO.RRB. No. 7812-B/03-05.100/2009-10, dt. 21-1-2010.
11 "Sahyadri Gramin Bank, Shimoga (Karnataka)" excluded by RBI Noti. No. RPCD.CO.RRB. No. 3230/03.05.100/2008-09, dt. 22-9-2008.
12 "Samastipur Kshetriya Gramin Bank, Samastipur, Bihar" excluded by RBI Noti. No. RPCD.CO.RRB. No. 56/03.05.100/2013-14, dt. 14-11-2013.
13 "Samyut Kshetriya Gramin Bank, Belisa Azamgarh (Uttar Pradesh)" excluded by RBI Noti. No. RPCD.CO.RRB. No. 3230/03.05.100/2008-09, dt. 22-9-2008.
14 "Sangameswaran Grameena Bank, Mehboob Nagar (Andhra Pradesh)" excluded by RBI Noti. No. RPCD.CO.RRB. No. 3230/03.05.100/2008-09, dt. 22-9-2008.
15 "The Sangli Bank Ltd" excluded by Noti. DBOD. No. PSBD. 11188/16.01.073/2006-07, dt. 14-5-2007.
16 "Santhal Parganas Gramin Bank, Dumka (Jharkhand)" excluded by RBI Noti. No. RPCD.CO.RRB. No. 7812-B/03-05.100/2009-10, dt. 21-1-2010.
17 Included by RBI Noti. No. RPCD.CO.RRB. No. 3231/03.05.100/2008-09, dt. 22-9-2008.

[1][xxx]

Saraswat Co-operative Bank Ltd., Bombay.

[2][xxx]

[3][SBPP Co-operative Bank Ltd. Kill Pardi, Dist. Valsad (Gujarat)]].

[4][Sarva Uttar Pradesh Gramin Bank, Meerut, Uttar Pradesh.]

[5][xxx]

[2][Saurashtra Gramin Bank, Rajkot (Gujarat).]

[6][Sber Bank]]

[7][xxx]

[8][xxx]

Shamrao Vithal Co-operative Bank Ltd., Bombay.

[9][xxx]

[10][xxx]

Shikshak Sahakari Bank Ltd., Nagpur (Maharashtra) (w.e.f. 22-5-1999).

[11][Shinhan Bank]

[12][xxx]

[13][xxx]

[14][xxx]

[15][Shivalik Small Finance Bank Limited]

[16][xxx]

[17][xxx]

---

1 "Saran Kshetriya Gramin Bank, Chapra (Bihar)" excluded by RBI Noti. No. RPCD.CO.RRB. No. 7812-B/03-05.100/2009-10, dt. 21-1-2010.

2 "Sarayu Gramin Bank, (Lakhimpur) (Uttar Pradesh)" excluded by RBI Noti. No. RPCD.CO.RRB. No. 3230/03.05.100/2008-09, dt. 22-9-2008.

3 Substituted for "Sardar Bhiladwala Pardi Peoples Co-operative Bank Ltd., Killa Pardi, District Valsad (Gujarat)" vide Noti. DCBR.RAD. (PCB). Noti. No. 5/08.26.213/2017-18, dt. 7-9-2017.

4 Included by RBI Noti. No. RPCD.CO.RRB. No. 7430/03.05.100/2008-09, dt. 27-1-2009.

5 "Satpura Narmada KeshtriyaGramin Bank, Chhindwara, Madhya Pradesh" excluded by RBI Noti. No. RPCD.CO.RRB. No. 56/03.05.100/2013-14, dt. 14-11-2013.

6 Included by RBI Noti. No. DBOD.IBD. No. 13982/23.03.022/2010-11, dt. 8-3-2011.

7 "Shahadol Kshetriya Gramin Bank, Shahadol (Madhya Pradesh)" excluded by RBI Noti. No. RPCD.CO.RRB. No. 7812-B/03-05.100/2009-10, dt. 21-1-2010.

8 "Shahjahanpur Kshetriya Gramin Bank, Shahjahanpur, Uttar Pradesh" excluded by RBI Noti. No. RPCD.CO.RRB. No. 7431/03.05.100/2008-09, dt. 27-1-2009.

9 "Sharda Gramin Bank, Satna, Madhya Pradesh" excluded by RBI Noti. No. RPCD.CO.RRB. No. 56/03.05.100/2013-14, dt. 14-11-2013.

10 "Shekhawati Gramin Bank, Sikar (Rajasthan)" excluded by RBI Noti. No. RPCD.CO.RRB. No. 3230/03.05.100/2008-09, dt. 22-9-2008.

11 Name of "Chohung Bank" changed to "Shinhan Bank" by Noti. DBOD. No. IBD.114/23.13.072/2006-07, dt. 25-7-2006, w.e.f. 12-8-2006.

12 "Shivalik Kshetriya Gramin Bank, Hoshiarpur (Punjab)" excluded by RBI Noti. No. RPCD.CO.RRB. No. 3230/03.05.100/2008-09, dt. 22-9-2008.

13 "Shivpuri Guna Kshetriya Gramin Bank, Shivpuri (Madhya Pradesh)" excluded by RBI Noti. No. RPCD.CO.RRB. No. 3230/03.05.100/2008-09, dt. 22-9-2008.

14 "Shreyas Gramin Bank, Aligarh, Uttar Pradesh" excluded by RBI Noti. No. RPCD.CO.RRB. No. 56/03.05.100/2013-14, dt. 14-11-2013.

15 Included vide Noti. DoR.LIC (Shivalik SFB) No. S 159/16.13.223/2021-22, dt. 15-6-2021.

16 "Shri Sathavahana Grameena Bank, Karimnagar (Andhra Pradesh)" excluded by RBI Noti. No. RPCD.CO.RRB. No. 3230/03.05.100/2008-09, dt. 22-9-2008.

17 "Shri Venkateswara Grameena Bank, Chittoor (Andhra Pradesh)" excluded by RBI Noti. No. RPCD.CO.RRB. No. 3230/03.05.100/2008-09, dt. 22-9-2008.

Siam Commercial Bank Public Company Limited (1996).

[1][Sikkim State Co-operative Bank Ltd.]

[2][xxx]

[3][xxx]

[4][xxx]

Solapur Janta Sahakari Bank Ltd., Solapur-413007 (Maharashtra) (w.e.f. 1-6-2002).

[5][Sonali Bank PLC]

South Indian Bank Ltd.

[6][xxx]

South Malabar Gramin Bank, Cannonore (1976).

[7][xxx]

[8][xxx]

[9][xxx]

[10][xxx]

[11][xxx]

[12][xxx]

[13][SBM Bank (India) Limited]

Standard Chartered Bank.

[14][xxx]

[15][xxx]

State Bank of India.

[16][xxx]

State Bank of Jaipur

---

1 Included vide Noti. F. No. Dor. RUR No. S1627/19.51.025/2021-22, dt. 12-10-2021.

2 "Singhbum Kshetriya Gramin Bank, Chaibasa (Bihar)" excluded by RBI Noti. No. RPCD.CO.RRB. No. 7812-B/03-05.100/2009-10, dt. 21-1-2010.

3 "Siwan Kshetriya Gramin Bank, Siwan (Bihar)" excluded by RBI Noti. No. RPCD.CO.RRB. No. 7812-B/03-05.100/2009-10, dt. 21-1-2010.

4 "Solapur Gramin Bank, Solapur (Maharashtra)" excluded by RBI Noti. No. RPCD.CO.RRB. No. 7812-B/03-05.100/2009-10, dt. 21-1-2010.

5 Substituted for "Sonali Bank Limited" by Noti. No. DoR.LIC No. S6044/23.13.032/2023-24, d.t 17-1-2024.

6 "South Malabar Gramin Bank, Malappuram (Kerala)" excluded by RBI Noti. No. RPCD.CO.RRB.BC. No. 99/03.05.100/2013-14, dt. 8-5-2014.

7 "Sravasthi Gramin Bank, Bahraich (Uttar Pradesh)" excluded by RBI Noti. No. RPCD.CO.RRB. No. 3230/03.05.100/2008-09, dt. 22-9-2008.

8 "Sree Anantha Grameena Bank, Anantpur (Andhra Pradesh)" excluded by RBI Noti. No. RPCD.CO.RRB. No. 3230/03.05.100/2008-09, dt. 22-9-2008.

9 "Sri SaraswatiGrameena Bank, Adilabad (Andhra Pradesh)" excluded by RBI Noti. No. RPCD.CO.RRB. No. 3230/03.05.100/2008-09, dt. 22-9-2008.

10 "Sri Visakha Grameena Bank, Srikakulam (Andhra Pradesh)" excluded by RBI Noti. No. RPCD.CO.RRB. No. 3230/03.05.100/2008-09, dt. 22-9-2008.

11 "Sriganganagar Kshetriya Gramin Bank, Sriganganagar, Rajasthan" excluded by RBI Noti. No. RPCD.CO.RRB. No. 7431/03.05.100/2008-09, dt. 27-1-2008.

12 "Srirama Gramin Bank, Nizamabad (Andhra Pradesh)" excluded by RBI Noti. No. RPCD.CO.RRB. No. 3230/03.05.100/2008-09, dt. 22-9-2008.

13 Included vide Noti. DBR.IBD.No. 3645/23.13.043/2018-19, dt. 30-10-2018.

14 "State Bank of Bikaner & Jaipur" excluded vide Noti. DBR. No. Ret. B.C. 57/12.06.004/2017-18, dt. 30-3-2017.

15 "State Bank of Hyderabad" excluded, ibid.

16 "State Bank of Indore" excluded by RBI Noti. No. DBOD No. Ret. BC. 37/12.06.004/2010-11, dt. 27-8-2010, w.e.f. 26-8-2010.

[1][xxx]

[2][xxx]

[3][xxx]

[4][xxx]

[5][xxx]

[6][xxx]

[7][Sumitomo Mitsui Banking Corporation.]

[8][xxx]

Surat Peoples Co-operative Bank Ltd., Surat.

[9][xxx]

[10][xxx]

[11][xxx]

[12][Sber bank]

[13][Suryoday Small Finance Bank Limited]

Tamil Nadu State Co-operative Bank Ltd., Madras.

Tamilnad Mercantile Bank Ltd.

Tanjore Permanent Bank Ltd., Tanjore.

[14][Telangana State Co-operative Apex Bank Ltd., Hyderabad]

[15][Thane Bharat Sahakari Bank Ltd. Thane Maharashtra.]

[16][xxx]

[17][xxx]

Times Bank Limited (1995).

[18][TJSB Sahakari Bank Ltd.]

---

1 "State Bank of Mysore" excluded vide Noti. DBR. No. Ret.B.C. 57/12.06.004/2017-18, dt. 30-3-2017.
2 "State Bank of Patiala" excluded, ibid.
3 "State Bank of Saurashtra" excluded by RBI Noti. No. DBDD. No. Ref. BC 49/ 12.06.007/2008-09, dt. 16-10-2008, w.e.f. 13-8-2008.
4 "State Bank of Travancore" excluded vide Noti. DBR. No. Ret.B.C. 57/12.06.004/2017-18, dt. 30-3-2017.
5 "Subansiri Gaonlia Bank, North Lakhimpur, Assam" excluded by RBI Noti. No. RPCD.CO.RRB. No. 7431/03.05.100/2008-09, dt. 27-1-2009.
6 "Sultanpur Kshetriya Gramin Bank, Sultanpur, Uttar Pradesh" excluded by RBI Noti. No. RPCD.CO.RRB. No. 7431/03.05.100/2008-09, dt. 27-1-2009.
7 Included by RBI Noti. No. DBOD.IBD. No. 49808/23.13.155/2012-13, dt. 9-1-2013.
8 "Surat-Bharuch Gramin Bank, Baruch (Gujarat)" excluded by RBI Noti. No. RPCD.CO.RRB. No. 3230/03.05.100/2008-09, dt. 22-9-2008.
9 "Surendranagar Bhavnagar Gramin Bank, Surendranagar (Gujarat)" excluded by RBI Noti. No. RPCD.CO.RRB. No. 3230/03.05.100/2008-09, dt. 22-9-2008.
10 "Surguja Kshetriya Gramin Bank, Ambikapur, Chhattishgarh" excluded by RBI Noti. No. RPCD.CO.RRB.BC. No. 99/03.05.100/2013-14, dt. 8-5-2014.
11 "Syndicate Bank" excluded vide Noti. DOR. No. Ret. BC.57/12.01.001/2019-20, dt. 27-3-2020, w.e.f. 1-4-2020.
12 Included by Noti. No. DBOD.IBD. No. 13982/23.03.022/2010-11, dt. 8-3-2011.
13 Included vide Noti. No. DBR.NBD. (SFB-Suryoday) No. 766/16.13.216/2017-18, dt. 24-7-2017.
14 Included vide Noti. DCBR.CO.RCBD No. 02/19.51.025/2016-17, dt. 29-3-2017.
15 Included by Noti. No. UBD.CO/BP/20/16.05.00/2002-2003, dt. 23-1-2003.
16 "Thane Gramin Bank, Thane, Maharashtra" excluded by RBI Noti. No. RPCD.CO.RRB. No. 7431/03.05.100/2008-09, dt. 27-1-2009.
17 "Thar-Anchalik Gramin Bank, Jodhpur (Rajasthan)" excluded by RBI Noti. No. RPCD.CO.RRB. No. 3230/03.05.100/2008-09, dt. 22-9-2008.
18 Substituted for "Thane Janata Sahakari Bank Ltd., Thane" by RBI Noti. No. UBD.CO.BPD. 2/16.05.000/2011-12, dt. 3-11-2011.

Traders Bank Ltd.

Travancore Bank Ltd., Trivandrum Taluk.

Tripura Gramin Bank, Agartala (Tripura).

[1][xxx]

[2][xxx]

[3][xxx]

[4][xxx]

[5][UBS AG]

[6][xxx]

[7][Ujjivan Small Finance Bank Limited,] New Delhi

Union Bank of India.

[8][xxx]

United Commercial Bank.

United Industrial Bank Ltd., Calcutta.

[9][United Overseas Bank Ltd.]

[10][xxx]

[11][Utkal Grameen Bank, Bolangir.]

[12][Utkarsh Small Finance Bank Limited,] Varanasi, Uttar Pradesh

[13][xxx]

Uttar Banga Kshetriya Gramin Bank, Cooch Behar (West Bengal).

[14][Uttar Pradesh Gramin Bank, Muzaffarpur (Bihar)].

Uttar Pradesh State Co-operative Bank Ltd., Lucknow.

[15][Uttarakhand Gramin Bank, Dehradun, Uttarakhand.]

[16][xxx]

[17][xxx]

---

1 "Triveni Kshetriya Gramin Bank, Orai (Uttar Pradesh)" excluded by RBI Noti. No. RPCD.CO.RRB. No. 11379/3.5.100/2010-11, dt. 31-3-2011.

2 "Tuisi Gramin Bank, Banda (Uttar Pradesh)" excluded by RBI Noti. No. RPCD.CO.RRB. No. 3230/03.05.100/2008-09, dt. 22-9-2008.

3 "The Toronto Dominion Bank" excluded by Noti. No. IBS.BC. 32/23.13.004/2003-4, dt. 10-10-2003.

4 "Tungabhadra Gramin Bank, Bellary (Karnataka)" excluded by RBI Noti. No. RPCD.CO.RRB. No. 3230/03.05.100/2008-09, dt. 22-9-2008.

5 Included vide Noti. No. DoR.LIC No. S1371/23.03.025/2024-25, dt. 4-6-2024.

6 "UFJ Bank Ltd." excluded by Noti. No. DBOD. No. IBD 947/23.03.007/2005-2006, dt. 26-12-2005.

7 Included vide Noti. DBR.PSBD. No. 467/16.02.006/2017-18, dt. 3-7-2017.

8 "United Bank of India" excluded vide Noti. DOR. No. Ret.BC.56/12.01.001/2019-20, dt. 27-3-2020, w.e.f. 1-4-2020.

9 Included by RBI Noti. No. DBOD.IBD. No. 16919/23.03.020/2009-10, dt. 26-3-2010.

10 "United Western Bank Ltd." excluded by Noti. No. DBOD. No. PSBD.4146/16.01.076/2006-2007, dt. 3-11-2006, w.e.f. 25-11-2006.

11 Included by RBI Noti. No. RPCD.CO.RRB. No. 46/03.05.100/2013-14, dt. 22-10-2013.

12 Included vide Noti. DBR.NBD. (SFB.UMFL). No. 2689/16.13.216 2017-18, dt. 4-10-2017.

13 "Utkal Gramya Bank, Odisha" excluded by RBI Noti. No. RPCD.CO.RRB. No. 47/03.05.100/2013-14, dt. 22-10-2013.

14 Included by RBI Noti. No. RPCD.CO.RRB. No. 7812-A/03-05.100/2009-10, dt. 21-1-2010.

15 Included by RBI Noti. No. RPCD.CO.RRB. No. 55/03.05.100/2013-14, dt. 14-11-2013.

16 "Uttaranchal Gramin Bank, Dehradun, Uttaranchal" excluded by RBI Noti. No. RPCD.CO.RRB. No. 56/03.05.100/2013-14, dt. 14-11-2013.

17 "Vaishali Kshetriya Gramin Bank, Muzaffarpur (Bihar)" excluded by RBI Noti. No. RPCD.CO.RRB. No. 7812-B/03-05.100/2009-10, dt. 21-1-2010.

[1][xxx]

[2][xxx]

[3][Vananchal Gramin Bank, Dumka (Jharkhand)].

[4][xxx]

Vasavi Co-operative Urban Bank Ltd., Hyderabad (Andhra Pradesh) (w.e.f. 22-5-1999).

[5][Vasai Vikas Sahakari Bank Ltd., Vasai, Thane]

[6][Vidharbha Konkan Gramin Bank, Nagpur, Maharashtra.]

[7][xxx]

[8][xxx]

[9][xxx]

[10][xxx]

[11][xxx]

Visakha Grameena Bank, Srikakulam (1976).

Visa Nagar Nagrik Sahakari Bank Ltd., Visanagar, District Mehsana (Guajarat) (w.e.f. 29-1-2000).

[12][xxx]

[13][Vysya Bank Ltd.], Bangalore City.

[14][The West Bengal State Co-operative Bank Ltd.,] Calcutta.

[15][xxx]

[16][Westpac Banking Corporation.]

[17][xxx]

[18][Yes Bank Limited.]

[19][Zoroastrain Co-operative Bank Ltd. Mumbai-400023, Maharashtra.]

---

1 "Vallalor Gramin Bank, Cuddalore (Tamil Nadu)" excluded by RBI Noti. No. RPCD.CO.RRB. No. 3230/03.05.100/2008-09, dt. 22-9-2008.

2 "Valsad-Dangs Gramin Bank, Bulsar (Gujarat)" excluded by RBI Noti. No. RPCD.CO.RRB. No. 3230/03.05.100/2008-09, dt. 22-9-2008.

3 Included by RBI Noti. No. RPCD.CO.RRB. No. 7812-A/03-05.100/2009-10, dt. 21-1-2010.

4 "Varada Grameena Bank, Kumta (Karnataka)" excluded by RBI Noti. No. RPCD.CO.RRB. No. 3230/03.05.100/2008-09, dt. 22-9-2008.

5 Included by RBI Noti. No. DCBR.CO.BPD. No. 02/16.05.000/2015-16, dt. 17-12-2015.

6 Included by RBI Noti. No. RPCD.CO.RRB. No. 46/03.05.100/2013-14, dt. 22-10-2013.

7 "Vidharbha Kshetriya Gramin Bank, Akola, Maharashtra" excluded by RIM Noti. No. RPCD.CO.RRB. No. 47/03.05.100/2013-14, dt. 22-10-2013.

8 "Vidisha Bhopal Kshetriya Gramin Bank, Vidisha, Madhya Pradesh" excluded by RBI Noti. No. RPCD.CO.RRB. No. 56/03.05.100/2013-14, dt. 14-11-2013.

9 "Vidur Gramin Bank, Bijnor (Uttar Pradesh)" excluded by RBI Noti. No. RPCD.CO.RRB.BC. No. 95/03.05.100/2013-14, dt. 9-4-2014.

10 "Vijaya Bank" excluded vide Noti. DBR. No. Ret. BC.35/12.01.001/2018-19, dt. 10-4-2019, w.e.f. 1-4-2019.

11 "Vindhyavasini Gramin Bank, Mirzapur (Uttar Pradesh)" excluded by RBI Noti. No. RPCD.CO.RRB. No. 3230/03.05.100/2008-09, dt. 22-9-2008.

12 "Vishveshwaraya Grameena Bank, Mandya (Karnataka)" excluded by RBI Noti. No. RPCD.CO.RRB. No. 47/03.05.100/2013-14, dt. 22-10-2013.

13 Substituted by Noti. No. PSBS.596/16.01.677/2002-2003, dt. 21-11-2002.

14 Substituted for "West Bengal State Co-operative Bank Ltd." vide Noti. DCBR.CO.RCBD. No. 01/19.51.025/2019-20, dt. 31-7-2019, Gazette dated 31-8 -- 6-9-2019.

15 "Wainganga Krishna Gramin Bank, Solapur (Maharashtra)" excluded by RBI Noti. No. RPCD.CO.RRB. No. 47/03.05.100/2013-14, dt. 22-10-2013.

16 Included by RBI Noti. No. DBOD.IBD. No. 8297/23.13.138/2012-13, dt. 10-12-2012.

17 "Yavatmal Gramin Bank, Yavatmal, Maharashtra" excluded by RBI Noti. No. RPCD.CO. RRB. No. 7431/03.05.100/2008-09, dt. 27-1-2009.

18 Included vide Noti. No. Ref. UBD No. BP/20/16.05.00/2002-2003, dt. 23-1-2003.

19 Included vide Noti. No. PSBS.BC. 30/16.01.13/2004-05, dt. 16-8-2004.

THE THIRD SCHEDULE

[Omitted by the State Bank of India Act, 1955 (23 of 1955), w.e.f. 1-7-1955]

THE FOURTH SCHEDULE

[Omitted by the Reserve Bank (Transfer to Public Ownership) Act, 1948 (62 of 1948, w.e.f 1-1-1949]

THE FIFTH SCHEDULE

[Repealed by the India and Burma (Burma Monetary Arrangements) Order, 1937]

THE RESERVE BANK OF INDIA (NOTE REFUND) RULES, 2009

(Notification F. No. Nil, ADVT-III/4/Exty. 93/09, dt. 13-7-2009)
[*As amended vide Noti. RBI/DCM (NE) No. 631/08.01.01/2018-19, dt. 5-9-2018*]

In exercise of the powers conferred by the proviso to section 28, read with clause (q) of sub-sections (1) and (2) of section 58, of the Reserve Bank of India Act, 1934 (2 of 1934) and in supersession of the Reserve Bank of India (Notes Refund) Rules, 1975, except as respect things done or omitted to be done before such supersession, the Central Board with the previous sanction of the Central Government, hereby makes the following rules for specifying the circumstances in, and the conditions and limitations subject to which, the value of lost, stolen, mutilated or imperfect note may be refunded as a matter of grace, namely:—

1. Short title, application and commencement

(1) These rules may be called the Reserve Bank of India (Note Refund) Rules, 2009.

(2) They shall apply to a note, which is a legal tender on the date of its presentation before the Bank.

(3) They shall come into force on the date[1] of their publication in the Official Gazette.

2. Definitions

In these rules, unless the context otherwise requires,—

(a) "Act" means the Reserve Bank of India Act, 1934 (2 of 1934);

(b) "Bank" means the Reserve Bank of India constituted by section 2 of the Act;

(c) "Bank note" means any note issued by the Bank, but does not include a Government note other than one rupee note, which has been deemed to be bank note as per the Notification No. GSR 426, dated the 28th March, 1980 issued by the Government of India, Ministry of Finance, Department of Economic Affairs;

(d) "essential features" means the features, including security features, which are necessary for the identification of a note, namely—

(i) the name of the issuing authority in Hindi and/or English, that is; Bank or Government of India, as the case may be;

(ii) the guarantee clause in Hindi and/or in English;

(iii) the promise clause in Hindi and/or in English;

(iv) the signature in Hindi and/or in English;

(v) the Ashoka Pillar emblem or Mahatma Gandhi portrait, as the case may be; and

1 Enforced w.e.f. 17-7-2009.

(vi) the water-mark of the Ashoka Pillar emblem or Mahatma Gandhi portrait, as the case may be.

Explanation : For the purposes of this clause,—

(A) the security features of a note, for deciding the genuineness or otherwise, include,—

(i) paper quality;

(ii) size and shape of numbers;

(iii) security thread;

(iv) intaglio printing;

(v) latent image in vertical band;

(vi) electrotype watermark (in watermark window);

(vii) micro lettering;

(viii) fluorescence (number panels and central band);

(ix) optically Variable Ink (in rupee five hundred and rupee one thousand denominations);

(x) see-through Register; and

(xi) any other security feature that may be introduced by the Bank,

(B) the essential features of a note have been enumerated with a view to help the prescribed officer to establish the genuineness or otherwise of a mutilated note;

(e) "Government note" means any note issued by the Central Government or supplied by the Central Government to the Bank and issued by the Bank, provided the liability for the payment of the value in respect of such note has devolved on and been taken over by the Bank;

(f) "imperfect note" means any note, which is wholly or partially, obliterated, shrunk, washed, altered or indecipherable but does not include a mutilated note;

(g) "mutilated note" means a note of which a portion is missing or which is composed of more than two pieces;

(h) "mismatched note" means a mutilated note which has been formed by joining a half note of any one note to a half note of another note.

Explanation : For the removal of doubts, it is hereby declared that a mismatched note can be identified on the basis of number, signature etc. and/or after examining other security features;

(i) "note" means a Bank note or a Government note;

(j) "Prescribed Officer" means any officer of the Issue Department of the Bank or any officer of an agent of the Bank/designated by the Bank by arrangement through agreement in this behalf as authorised to receive mutilated notes for adjudication under these rules;

(k) "soiled note" means a note which, has become dirty due to usage and also includes a two piece note pasted together wherein both the pieces presented belong to the same note, and form the entire note.

(2) Words and expressions used herein not defined but defined in the Act have the same meaning as assigned to them in the Act.

3. Decision on adjudication of mutilated note

If any dispute arises in relation to adjudication of mutilated note the same shall be referred to the Bank for its decision and its decision shall be binding on the claimant, his nominees and legal heirs or representatives as the case may be.

4. Presentation and disposal of claim

A claim in respect of any note may be presented before the prescribed officer for adjudication and payment of value under these rules.

5. Right to call for information or to hold enquiries

The prescribed officer may, if it is considered necessary so to do, call for any information or hold any inquiry relating to any claim presented before him under these rules, and where the genuineness of the note is doubtful, he shall send such doubtful note for expert opinion to the General Manager, Currency Note Press, Nashik Road or to any other authority as designated under any law in force for this purpose.

6. General provisions in relation to all claims

(1) No claim in respect of a note, which is alleged to have been stolen, lost or wholly destroyed, shall be entertained.

(2) If the prescribed officer is satisfied that a mutilated note presented before him is one which appears to have been cancelled at any office of the Bank or the claim is one which appears to have already been paid under these rules, he may, after making enquiries under rule 5 above reject the claim on such note.

(3) A claim in respect of a note, which,—

(i) cannot be identified with certainty as a genuine note for which the Bank is liable under the Act;

(ii) has been made imperfect or mutilated, thereby causing the note to appear to be of a higher denomination, or has been deliberately cut, torn, defaced, altered or dealt with in any other manner, not necessarily by the claimants, enabling the use of the same for making of a false claim under these rules or otherwise to defraud the Bank or the public;

(iii) carries any extrinsic words or visible representations intended to convey or capable of conveying any message of a political or religious character or furthering the interest of any person or entity;

(iv) has been imported into India by the claimant from any place outside India in contravention of the provision of any law;

(v) any information called for by the prescribed officer or the Bank, as the case may be, is not furnished by a claimant within a period of three months from the date of receipt of the notice or letter asking for the information; or

(vi) in the opinion of the prescribed officer, a deliberate fraudulent intention appears in respect of such a claim shall be rejected and shall not be eligible for consideration under any other law for the time being in force.

7. Imperfect note

The value of an imperfect note may be paid for full value/half value as specified in the tables given in rule 8, if—

(a) the matter, which is printed on the note has not become totally illegible, and

(b) the prescribed officer is satisfied, having regard to the printed matter which is legible on the note, that it is a genuine note.

8. Mutilated notes

(1) The adjudication of claims in respect of notes of [1][less than fifty rupees] denomination shall be made in the following manner, namely:—

(i) If the area of the single largest undivided piece of the note presented is more than 50 percent of the area of the respective denomination, rounded off to the next complete square centimetre, full value on mutilated notes of the above denominations shall be payable.

(ii) If the area of the largest undivided piece of the note presented is less than or equal to 50 percent of the area of the note, the claim shall be rejected.

[2][*Explanation*: For the purposes of this sub-rule, it is hereby clarified that the value of a mutilated note of less than rupees fifty denomination may be refunded in full if the undivided area of the single largest piece of the note is as specified in column (5) of the Table 1 below.

TABLE-1

Denomination	*Length (cm)*	*Width (cm)*	*Area (in cm^2)*	*Minimum area (in cm^2) required for payment of full value**
(1)	(2)	(3)	(4)	(5)
1	9.7	6.3	61.11	31
2	10.7	6.3	67.41	34
5	11.7	6.3	73.71	37
10	13.7	6.3	86.31	44
10 (New MG Series)	12.3	6.3	77.49	39
20	14.7	6.3	92.61	47
20 (New MG Series)	12.9	6.3	81.27	41

* Indicated as the next complete higher square centimetre after half of the area of the notes in a particular denomination.]

(2) The payment of claim in respect of note of rupees fifty and above denominations shall be made in the following manner, namely:—

(i) Full value of the mutilated notes of the above denominations shall be payable if the area of the single largest undivided piece of the note presented is more than [3][80] percent of the area of the respective denomination rounded off to the next complete square centimetre;

(ii) If the undivided area of the single largest undivided piece of the note presented is equal to or more than 40 percent and less than or equal to [3][80] percent of the area of the respective denomination rounded off to the next complete square centimetre, half the value of the note is payable.

---

1 Substituted for "one rupee, two rupee, five rupee, ten rupee and twenty rupees" vide Noti. RBI/DCM (NE) No. 631/08.01.01/2018-19, dt. 5-9-2018, w.e.f. 6-9-2018.
2 Substituted, ibid.
3 Substituted for "65", ibid.

(iii) If the area of the single largest undivided piece of the note is less than 40 percent, no value shall be payable, and the claim shall be rejected.

[1][(iv) if the claim of mutilated notes of rupees fifty and above denominations consist of a note composed of two pieces of the same note and the two pieces, individually have an area equal to or more than 40 percent of the total area of the note in that denomination, then the claim may be refunded for full value of the note.]

[2][*Explanation*: For the purposes of this sub-rule, it is hereby clarified that the value of a mutilated note of equal to or more than rupees fifty denomination may be refunded in full or half, as the case may be, if the minimum undivided area of the single largest piece of the note is as specified in column (5) or (6) of the Table 2 below.

TABLE-2

Denomination	*Length (cm)*	*Width (cm)*	*Area (in cm^2)*	*Minimum area (in cm^2) required for payment of full value*@	*Minimum area (in cm^2) required for payment of half value***
(1)	(2)	(3)	(4)	(5)	(6)
50	14.7	7.3	107.31	86	43
50 (New MG Series)	13.5	6.6	89.10	72	36
100	15.7	7.3	114.61	92	46
100 (New MG Series)	14.2	6.6	93.72	75	38
200	14.6	6.6	96.36	78	39
500	15.0	6.6	99.00	80	40
2000	16.6	6.6	109.56	88	44

@ Rounded off to the next complete higher square centimetre of 80% of the area of the notes in a particular denomination.

** Rounded off to the next complete higher square centimetre of 40% of the area of the notes in a particular denomination.]

9. Payment of claim in respect of mismatched note

The payment of claim in respect of a mismatched note may be dealt with as follows, namely:—

(a) In case of notes upto rupees twenty denomination notes, the area of the larger of the two pieces presented may be measured and adjudicated as per the provisions of sub-rule (1) of Rule 8, ignoring the smaller half.

---

1 Substituted vide Noti. RBI/DCM (NE) No. 631/08.01.01/2018-19, dt. 5-9-2018, w.e.f. 6-9-2018. Prior to substitution, clause (iv) read as under:
"(iv) If the claim of mutilated notes of rupees fifty to rupees one thousand denomination notes consists of a note composed of two pieces of the same note and the two pieces, individually, have an area equal to or more than 40 percent of the total area of the note in that denomination, then the claim may be refunded for full value and need not be treated as consisting of two tenders for half value."

2 Substituted, ibid.

(b) If none of the two pieces presented meets the minimum area stipulated as per the provisions of clause (i) of sub-rule (1) of rule 8 above, the claim shall be rejected.

(c) In case of rupees fifty and above denominations, the two pieces may be treated as two separate claims and dealt with accordingly.

10. Claimants to be bound by rules

(1) Any payment which is provided under these rules shall be made only as matter of grace and the Bank may, as it deems fit, from time to time issue such supplementary or detailed instructions for carrying out the provisions of these rules, for the guidance of the prescribed officer.

(2) Any person who makes any claim on account of an imperfect note or mutilated note shall be deemed to have made the said claim under the proviso to section 28 of the Act and subject to the provisions of these rules, which shall be deemed to be binding on all claimants and their heirs or assigns.

11. Retention and destruction of note

Notwithstanding the denomination of a note or the decision of the prescribed officer on the claim, a note presented before the prescribed officer for the purpose of making a claim shall be retained and destroyed or otherwise disposed of by the Bank in the following manner, namely:—

(a) In the case of a note in respect of which full payment is made, at any time after the payment; and

(b) In the case of a note in respect of which no payment is made, or on which half value payment has been made, on the expiry of a period of three months from the date of the decision rejecting the claim or to pay half-value, as the case may be, unless within this period, an order from a competent court is submitted to any office of the Bank or branch of the designated Bank restraining the Bank from destroying or otherwise disposing of the said note.

12. Payment to legal heirs or nominees

(1) If a claimant who has submitted a claim under these rules, is dead, his legal representatives shall be eligible to receive the payment due to the claimant subject to the determination of the claim by the prescribed officer.

(2) The legal representatives shall be entitled to receive the payment due to the claimant, if any, upon furnishing to the prescribed officer an indemnity bond executed by the legal representative in favour of the branch or office of the Bank or any other institution or entity as designated by the Bank for this purpose:

PROVIDED payment upto an amount of rupees five hundred may be made to the legal heir of the claimant on a declaration for this purpose.

(3) In case of mutilated note presented at the Bank through Triple Lock Receptacle (TLR) cover, the tenderer shall indicate his name and address alongwith other details, such as, bank account number, etc. as specified on the cover, and the individual tenderers, may, at their option, in addition, also indicate on the cover, the name and address of the nominee who may receive the amount that is determined to be due on the claim without production of indemnity, subject to proper identification.

13. Printed Forms

Where any indemnity bond as referred to in rule 12 is to be executed in favour of the Bank a printed copy of the bond shall be supplied free of cost to the claimant or the person eligible to receive the payment under these rules.

14. Stamp Duty

The value of the stamp duty on the indemnity bond shall be paid by the person executing the bond.

15. Procedure when payee is untraced

(1) In case of the note having been adjudicated at the office of the Bank, the value or part of the value of a note is payable to the claimant and if such claimant, is not found or is dead, his legal representatives or the nominee specified by him cannot be found or fails within a period of three months from the date of communication to him the decision to take steps to receive payment, the amount payable shall be paid to the Banking Department of the Bank.

(2) In case of the mutilated note having been adjudicated at the branch of designated Bank or other entities, such payment may be credited with the Issue Office of the Bank after a period of three months from the date of communication to the tenderer of the decision to take steps to receive the exchange value.

Reserve Bank of India (Note Refund) Rules, 2009

PART I

INTRODUCTION

The Reserve Bank has been extending facilities to the public for exchanging cut and mutilated notes at all its Issue Offices and currency chest branches of commercial banks. In order to make the Note Refund Rules easy to understand and to apply, these have been comprehensively revised and simplified. It has also been decided that any officer of the designated branch can adjudicate mutilated notes presented thereat. It is hoped that simplification and liberalisation of the rules would help both, the prescribed officers as well as the tenderers of mutilated notes to easily comprehend the revised rules and enable the former to apply the Note Refund Rules without leaving any scope for subjectivity.

While the facility for exchange of soiled notes is to be provided by all banks at all of their branches, the facility of exchange of mutilated notes would be available at designated bank branches (including cooperative banks and RRBs) to all tenderers whether they are account holders or not. This is a duty that the banking system as a whole owes to the public. It needs no emphasis that the object of simplification of RBI Note Refund Rules and its extension is to help members of the public exchange the cut/mutilated notes in their possession without difficulty. The designated bank branches should play an active role and ensure that the facility is operated for the benefit of the members of public at large and is not pre-empted by a group of persons.

This booklet contains Rules and Procedures to be followed under the Scheme. The procedure required to be followed by the branches for acceptance, adjudication, and maintenance of records of mutilated notes is also laid down in this booklet. All further instructions to be issued on the subject will be with reference to this booklet and branches of the banks shall update the booklet by making necessary amendments to it. If any clarification is needed on the scheme, a reference should be made either to the Issue Department of the Reserve Bank of India at its offices or the Chief General Manager,

Reserve Bank of India, Central Office, Department of Currency Management, Mumbai-400 001 (e-mail address : cgmincdcm@rbi.org.in or helpdcm@rbi.ora.in).

PART II

[1]**[Reserve Bank of India (Note Refund) Rules 2009 with explanations:]**

A. *Provisions in the Reserve Bank of India Act, 1934:*

Section 28 : Notwithstanding anything contained in any enactment or rule of law to the contrary, no person shall of right be entitled to recover from the Central Government or the Bank, the value of any lost, stolen, mutilated or imperfect currency note, provided that the Bank may, with the previous sanction of the Central Government, prescribe the circumstances in and the conditions and limitations subject to which the value of such currency notes or bank notes may be refunded as of grace and the rules made under this proviso shall be laid on the table of Parliament.

Section 58(1) : The Central Board may, with the previous sanction of the Central Government, by notification in the Official Gazette, make regulations consistent with this Act to provide for all matters for which provision is necessary or convenient for the purpose of giving effect to the provisions of this Act.

Section 58(2) : In particular and without prejudice to the generality of the foregoing provisions, such regulations may provide for all or any of the following matters, viz.:—

(a)..

(b)..

(c)..

(d)..

....

(q) the circumstances in which, and the conditions and limitations subject to which the value of any lost, stolen, mutilated or imperfect currency note of the Government of India or bank note may be refunded.

1 Corrected by Corrigendum No. Nil (ADVT III/4/Exty./93/09, dt. 30-7-2009, Gazette dt. 4-8-2009.

THE RESERVE BANK OF INDIA (BOARD FOR FINANCIAL SUPERVISION) REGULATIONS, 1994

[Noti. DBOD No. BP-213/21.04.050-94, dt. 21-7-1994]

In exercise of the powers conferred by section 58 of the Reserve Bank of India Act, 1934 (2 of 1934), the Central Board of the Reserve Bank of India, with the previous sanction of the Central Government, is pleased to make the following Regulations, namely:—

CHAPTER I
INTRODUCTORY

1. Short title and commencement

(1) These regulations may be called the Reserve Bank of India (Board for Financial Supervision) Regulations, 1994.

(2) These regulations shall come into force on the date[1] of their publication in the Official Gazette.

2. Regulations not in derogation of General Regulations, 1949

The provisions of these regulations shall be in addition to and not in derogation of the Reserve Bank of India General Regulations, 1949 save as hereinafter expressly provided in these regulations.

In case of inconsistency the provisions of these regulations shall have overriding effect.

3. Definitions

In these regulations, unless there is anything repugnant in the subject or context,—

(a) "Act" means the Reserve Bank of India Act, 1934 (2 of 1934);

(b) "the Bank" means the Reserve Bank of India constituted by the Act;

(c) "banking company" means a banking company as defined in section 5(c) of the Banking Regulation Act, 1949 (10 of 1949) and shall include a corresponding new bank constituted under section 3 of the Banking Companies (Acquisition and Transfer of Undertakings) Act, 1970 (5 of 1970) or under section 3 of the Banking Companies (Acquisition and Transfer of Undertakings) Act, 1980 (40 of 1980) State Bank of India constituted under State Bank of India Act, 1955 (33 of 1955) and a subsidiary bank as defined in the State Bank of India (Subsidiary Banks) Act, 1959 (38 of 1959);

1 Enforceable w.e.f. 28-7-1994.

(d) "Board" means the Committee known as the Board for Financial Supervision constituted under regulation 4;

(e) "Central Board" means the Central Board of Directors of the Bank constituted under section 8 of the Act;

(f) "Director" means Director of the Central Board nominated under section 8(1)(b) or section 8(1)(c) of the Act;

(g) "Executive Committee" means a sub-committee known as the Executive Committee constituted under sub-regulation (1) of regulation 12;

(h) "General Regulations" means Reserve Bank of India General Regulations, 1949;

(i) "Member" means a member of the Board;

(j) "Notified" means notified in the Official Gazette;

(k) "Vice-Chairman" means the Deputy Governor designated as Vice-Chairman of the Board;

(l) Other expressions used but not defined in these regulations and defined in the Act shall have the meanings respectively assigned to them in the Act.

4. Composition of the Board

(1) There shall be a Committee to be known as the "Board for Financial Supervision" (hereinafter referred to as the Board).

(2) The Board shall consist of the following members, namely:—

(a) Governor, Reserve Bank of India, who shall be the Chairman of the Board.

(b) Deputy Governors, Reserve Bank of India - of whom one Deputy Governor shall be nominated by the Governor as full time Vice-Chairman.

(c) Four Directors from the Central Board of Reserve Bank of India to be nominated by the Governor as members.

5. Functions and powers of the Board

(1) The Board shall perform the functions and exercise the powers of supervision and inspection under the Act and under the Banking Regulation Act, 1949 (10 of 1949) in relation to different sectors of the financial system such as banking companies, financial institutions and non-banking institutions.

(2) It shall also perform such other functions and exercise such other powers, as may be notified by the Central Board, from time to time.

6. Assistance to the Board

The Board shall be assisted by the Department of Supervision constituted from the staff of the Bank which shall report directly to the Board and wherever necessary personnel from outside either on deputation or through direct recruitment or on contract or tenure basis, may be taken by the Board.

7. Nominations

All nominations to the Board shall be made by the Governor in consultation with Central Board for such term as may be specified.

8. Vacation of offices

A Member shall cease to hold office if he absents himself without the leave of the Chairman from three consecutive meetings of the Board convened under regulation 11.

9. Powers on behalf of the Board by whom to be exercised

Notwithstanding anything contained in sub-regulation (1) of regulation 17 of the General Regulations, but subject to the provisions of the Act, any regulation made by

Central Board in regard to expenditure to be incurred by or on behalf of the Bank and any direction which may be given by the Central Board generally or in particular with regard to the conduct of the business of the Bank—

(1) the Board is authorised to exercise the powers of supervision and inspection under the Act and under the Banking Regulation Act, 1949 (10 of 1949) in relation to the banking companies, financial institutions and the non-banking institutions and such other powers and functions as may be notified by the Central Board from time to time;

(2) the Chairman, the Vice-Chairman and the Members shall jointly and severally exercise such powers as may be specified from time to time by the Central Board;

(3) any other officer of the Department of Supervision of the Bank not below the rank of an officer in Grade 'D' may, if authorised and to the extent that he is so authorised by the Board with prior approval of the Central Board, exercise all the powers in relation to matters pertaining to the Department of Supervision and in relation to such matters do all acts and things which may be exercised or done by the Bank provided, that power exercised or action taken under this sub-regulation shall be exercised to taken subject to such directions, if any, as may be given by any higher officer or authority in this behalf.

10. Applicability of the General Regulations

The following provisions of the General Regulations shall apply *mutatis mutandis* as specified below:—

(a) Regulations 3, 4, 7, 13 and 24 of the General Regulations shall apply to the Members of the Board.

(b) Regulations 3 and 24 shall apply to the Members of the Advisory Council and the sub-committees.

(c) Regulations 16, 18 and 19 shall apply to the officers of the Department of Supervision.

11. Meetings of the Board and Quorum

(1) The Board shall ordinarily meet at least once a month at the office of the Bank or any other place in the area in which the Governor or in his absence the Vice-Chairman has his headquarters for the time being, to attend to the current business of the Board.

Sufficient notice shall be given to the Members to enable them to attend.

(2) Three Members of whom one shall be the Chairman or the Vice-Chairman shall form a quorum for the transaction of business of the Board.

(3) Save as otherwise provided in these regulations, the provisions of the Act and the General Regulations shall apply to meetings of the Board, as if they were meetings of the Central Board.

12. Constitution of Sub-Committees

(1) The Board shall have the power to constitute Sub-Committees as may be deemed necessary to assist it in its work from time to time. From such Committees, one Sub-Committee shall be known as the Executive Committee.

(2) The Executive Committee shall comprise of the Vice-Chairman who shall be the *ex-officio* Chairman and not less than two Members of the Board.

13. Functions and meetings of Executive Committee

(1) The Executive Committee constituted under regulation 12(1) shall carry on such functions as may be specified by the Board from time to time.

(2) The Executive Committee shall meet as frequently as may be necessary.

14. Functions and meetings of Advisory Council

(1) Subject to the provisions of the Act or Regulations made thereunder, the Governor may constitute an Advisory Council from time to time, which shall consist of not less than five persons having special knowledge of accountancy, law, economics, banking, finance and management.

(2) The Advisory Council shall tender advice to the Board on such matters relating to supervision and inspection of financial system, as may be deemed fit by the Board.

(3) The Governor shall whenever present preside over the meetings of the Advisory Council and the Vice-Chairman and the Members of the Board shall be permanent invitees to the meetings. In the absence of the Governor, the Members of the Advisory Council who are present may elect one amongst themselves to preside over the meeting of the Advisory Council.

15. Report to the Central Board

The Board shall submit a report to the Central Board half-yearly.

APPLICATION FOR A CERTIFICATE OF REGISTRATION TO COMMENCE/CARRY ON* THE BUSINESS OF A NON-BANKING FINANCIAL INSTITUTION

Name and Address of Registered office of the company (in block letters)	

By Registered Post A.D./Hand Delivery

To

The General/Dy. General Manager,
Department of Supervision,
(Financial Companies Wing),
Reserve Bank of India,
Regional Office
....
(Place)

Dear Sir,

We make this application in terms of sub-section (2) of section 45IA of the Reserve Bank of India Act, 1934 for issue of a Certificate of Registration. The required documents/information as per the instructions are furnished.

We are desirous of commencing/carrying on* the business of a non-banking financial institution. Hence, we hereby request you to kindly issue the necessary Certificate of Registration under sub-section (1) of section 45IA of the Reserve Bank of India Act, 1934 to enable our company to commence/carry on* the business of a non-banking financial institution.

We declare that to the best of our knowledge and belief the information furnished in the statements/annexures enclosed hereto is true/correct and complete.

Yours Faithfully,

Signature :........................

Date Name :.............................

Place Designation:....................

Company seal :

Encls:......Sheets

* *Strike out whichever is not applicable.*

DOCUMENTS REQUIRED TO BE ENCLOSED TO THE APPLICATION FORM

1. Identification particulars (Annexure-I)
2. Statement on prudential norms (Annexure-II)
3. Information about the management (Annexure-III)

4. Certified copies of up-to-date Memorandum and Articles of Association of the company.
5. Certified copies of Certificate of Incorporation and Certificate of Commencement of Business.
6. A board resolution specifically approving the submission of the application and its contents.
7. A copy each of the Profit and Loss account and audited Balance Sheet for last 3 years or for such shorter period as are available (for companies already in existence).
8. Business plan of the company for the next three years giving details of its (a) thrust of business; (b) market segment; and (c) projection of investments and income.
9. A company which is incorporated before January 9, 1997 and has net owned fund of less than Rs. 25 lakhs as on the date of application, may also furnish a time bound programme as to how it proposes to attain the minimum net owned found of Rs. 25 lakhs.

INSTRUCTIONS

(Fill up the application form strictly in accordance with these instructions)

General

(1) Application should be made in the prescribed form only. Wherever space is insufficient, information may be furnished in separate sheet/s.

(2) Application along with enclosures duly completed should be submitted in duplicate, before July 8, 1997 to the Department of Supervision (Financial Companies Wing), Reserve Bank of India, Regional Office under whose jurisdiction the registered office of the company is situated.

(3) A photo copy of the application as submitted may be kept with the company for its record.

(4) Application should be signed by any of the following officials authorised by the Board of Directors in this behalf (viz., Chairman, Managing Director, Chief Executive Officer, Company Secretary, a Whole Time Director or any other official).

(5) Application should bear common seal of the company.

(6) An acknowledgment for having submitted the application may be obtained from the Regional Office concerned.

(7) The particulars/information to be furnished in Annexure-II of the application should be based on figures as disclosed in the latest annual audited balance-sheet. However, in the case of a company incorporated after 9.1.1997, such particulars/information should be based on the balance-sheet as on a date falling within thirty days preceding the date of application.

Annexure-I

(8) In case the company has changed its name earlier, a list of all the earlier names of the company and date/s of change together with the names of Chief Executive Officer and Chairman at the time of change of name should be furnished.

(9) If the company was registered with Reserve Bank of India in terms of Circular DFC (COC) No. 828/174-92/93, dated April 12, 1993, *the letter in original advising registration should be enclosed.*

(10) If the company has ever defaulted in timely repayment of deposit and payment of interest, a list of all such pending cases and the action taken in respect of each case should be furnished. The company should also submit a list containing the details of all the court cases pending against it, including those pending in consumer fora, pertaining to its deposit acceptance activities.

Annexure-II

(11) This statement is to be filled only by a non-banking financial company which was in existence as on January 9, 1997 and carrying on business of a non-banking financial institution.

(12) For filling up Annexure II, please refer to the guidelines to non-banking financial companies (copy enclosed) on prudential norms for income recognition, accounting standards, asset classification, provisioning for bad and doubtful debts, capital adequacy, concentration of credit/investment, etc.

(13) The contents of Annexure-II should be certified by a Chartered Accountant.

Annexure-III

(14) 'Substantial interest' means holding of beneficial interest by an individual or his/her spouse or minor child, whether singly or taken together, in shares of a company/capital of a firm, the amount paid-up on which exceeds 10 per cent of the paid-up capital of the company or total capital subscribed by all the partners of a partnership firm.

Annexure-I

IDENTIFICATION PARTICULARS

COMPANY CODE
(to be filed by RBI
....

1.1 Name of the company ....

1.2 Whether the company had changed its name earlier [please see item (8) of instructions] Yes/No

2. Date of incorporation ....

3. Date of commencement of business ....

4. State in which the company is registered ....

5. Full address of the company ....
(i) Registered office

Phone..
Fax..

	(ii) Corporate/Administrative* office	.... Phone.................................... Fax..
	(iii) No. of branches	....
6.	Status	(a) Public (b) Private (c) Deemed public (d) Government company (e) Other (to be specified)
7.	Whether the company was transacting the business of non-banking financial institution as on January 9, 1997?	Yes/No
	If yes,	
	(i) the date of commencement of such business	....
	(ii) Classification as made by RBI (EL/HP/LC/IC/Nidhi/RNBC/MNBC)	....
	(iii) Reference No. and date of RBI Classification advice	....
	(iv) Whether the company was already registered with RBI [Please see item (9) of Instructions]	Yes/No
	If yes	
	(a) Registration No.	....
	(b) Reference No. and date of RBI advice	....
	(v) Whether the company has been issued a certificate in terms of Circular DFC (COC) No. 2/02.04/96-97, dated July 24, 1996	Yes/No
	If yes,	
	(a) Certificate No.	....
	(b) Reference No. and date of RBI advice	....
	(vi) Whether the company has ever defaulted in the repayment of principal and/or payment of interest on deposits [Please see item (10) of instructions]	Yes/No
8.	Name/s of statutory auditor/s with address/es	....

* *Strike out whichever is not applicable*

9.1 Name/s & address/es of bankers ....
....
....

9.2 Whether the company has committed any default in repayment of any loan, advance or any other credit facility availed from any bank ? Yes/No

9.3 If yes, furnish full details, such as name of Bank/Branch, type of facility, period and quantum of default, etc.
....
....
....

10. Name and designation of CEO/authorised official ....
....

Signature : ....

Date: Name : ....

Place: Designation : ....

Company seal :

* *Strike out whichever is not applicable.*

Annexure II

Statement of capital funds and risk assets as on*..

(Rs. in thousand)

PART–A

Capital funds — Tier I

Item name	*Item code*	*Amount*
(i) Paid-up Equity Capital	111	
(ii) Free reserves (please see note below)		
(a) General Reserves	112	
(b) Share Premium	113	
(c) Capital Reserves (representing) surplus on sale of assets held in separate account)	114	
(d) Debenture Redemption Reserve	115	
(e) Capital Redemption Reserve	116	
(f) Credit Balance in P & L Account	117	
(g) Other free reserves (to be specified)	118	

(iii) Total	...(111 to 118)	110
(iv) Accumulated balance of loss		121
(v) Deferred Revenue Expenditure		122
(vi) Other intangible Assets		123
(vii) Total	...(121 to 123)	120
(viii) Owned Funds	...(110 to 120)	130
(ix) Investment in shares of : [Please see Note (2) below] (a) Subsidiaries		141
(b) Companies in the same Group		142
(c) Other non-banking financial companies		143
(x) The book value of debentures, bonds, outstanding loans and advances (including hire-purchase and lease finance) made to, and deposits with [Please see note (3) below] (a) Subsidiaries		144
(b) Companies in the same Group		145
(xi) Total	... (141 to 145) :	140
(xii) Amount of item 140 in excess of 10 per cent of item 130 above		150
(xiii) Tier I Capital : Net owned funds (130 to 150)		151

Notes :

1. 'Free reserves' shall include balance in share premium account, capital and debenture redemption reserves and any other reserves shown in the balance sheet and created through an allocation out of profits but not being (a) a reserve created for repayment of any future liability or for depreciation on assets or for bad debts, or (b) a reserve created by revaluation of assets of the company.
2. Investment in shares includes investment in fully convertible debentures and/or convertible portion of partially convertible debentures. Investment held either in investment account or stock in-trade should be included under this item.
3. Debentures whether held in investment account or way of stock-in-trade should be included under this item. Non-convertible debentures, non-convertible portion of partially convertible debentures and optionally convertible debentures should also be included under this item.

* *Date of the latest audited balance sheet*

PART B
Capital funds — Tier II

Item name	Item code	Amount
(i) Preference Share Capital	161	
(ii) Revaluation reserves (see Para 5.2.2 of guidelines)	162	
(iii) General provisions and loss reserves (see Para 5.2.3 of guidelines)	163	
(iv) Hybrid debt capital instruments (see Para 5.2.4 of guidelines)	164	
(v) Subordinated debt (see Para 5.2.5 of guidelines)	165	
(vi) Aggregate Tier II Capital 161 to 165 (see Para 6 of the guidelines)	160	
Total Capital Funds (151 + 160)	170	

PART C
Risk assets and off-balance sheet items

Item name	Item code	Amount
(i) Adjusted value of funded risk assets, i.e., on-balance sheet item (to tally with Part D)	181	
(ii) Adjusted value of non-funded and off-balance sheet items (to tally with Part E)	182	
(iii) Total risk weighted assets/exposure (181 + 182)	180	
(iv) Percentage of capital funds to risk weighted assets/exposures		
(a) Tier I capital (Percentage of Item 151 to Item 180)	191	
(b) Tier II capital (Percentage of Item 160 to Item 180)	192	
(c) Total (Percentage of Item 170 to Item 180)	193	

PART D
Weighted assets, i.e., On-Balance Sheet items

Item name	Item code	Book value	Risk weight	Adjusted value
I. Cash and bank balances including fixed deposits & Certificates of Deposits	210		0	0

II. Investments (see Para 2.6.1 to 2.6.7 of the guidelines)			
(a) Government and approved securities as defined under section 45 IB of RBI Act, 1934	221	0	0
(b) Shares/debentures/bonds/units of mutual funds			
(i) Amounts deducted in Part 'A' Item (ix)	222	0	0
(ii) Amounts not deducted in Part A	223	100	
III. Current assets			
(a) Stock on hire (Please see Note 3 below)			
(i) Amounts deducted in Part A [Item (x)]	231	0	0
(ii) Amounts not deducted in Part A	232	100	
(b) Intercorporate loans/deposits			
(i) Amounts deducted in Part A [Item (x)]	233	0	0
(ii) Amounts not deducted in Part A	234	100	
(c) Loans and advances fully secured by company's own deposits	235	0	0
(d) Loans to staff	236	0	0
(e) Other secured loans and advances considered good			
(i) Amounts deducted in Part A [Item (x)]	241	0	0
(ii) Amounts not deducted in Part A	242	100	
(f) Bills purchased/discounted	243	0	0
(i) Amounts deducted in Part A [Item (x)]			
(ii) Amounts not deducted in Part A	244	100	
(g) Others (to be specified)	245	100	
IV. Fixed Assets (net of depreciation)			
(a) Assets leased out			
(i) Amounts deducted in Part A [Item (x)]	251	0	0
(ii) Amounts not deducted in Part A	252	100	
(b) Premises	253	100	
(c) Furniture & Fixtures	254	100	
V. Other assets			
(a) Income-tax deducted at source (net of provisions)	255	0	0
(b) Advance tax paid (net of provisions)	256	0	0
(c) Interest due on government securities	257	0	0
(d) Others (to be specified)	258	100	
Total weighted assets (Items 210 to 258)	200	—	

Notes : 1. Netting may be done in respect of assets where provisions for depreciation or for bad and doubtful debts have been made.

2. Unquoted shares are to be valued at cost or break-up value of the shares (as per last audited balance sheet of the company concerned) whichever is less.

3. Stock on hire should be shown net of finance charges, i.e., interest and other charges, recoverable.

4. Assets which have been deducted from owned fund to arrive at net owned fund pursuant to Paragraph 5.1 of the guidelines will have a weightage of (0).

PART E

Weighted non-funded exposures/off-balance sheet items

Items	*Item code*	*Book value*	*Conversion factor*	*Equivalent value*	*Risk weight*	*Adjusted value*
1. Financial & other guarantees	310		100		100	
2. Share/debenture underwriting obligations	320		50		100	
3. Partly paid shares/debentures	330		100		100	
4. Bills discounted/ rediscounted	340		100		100	
5. Lease contracts entered into but yet to be executed	350		100		100	
6. Other contingent liabilities (to be specified)	360		50		100	
Total non-funded exposures (Items 310 to 360)	300	—			—	

PART F

Other data

I. Aggregate of credit exposures categorised into :

Item name	*Item code*	*Amount*
(i) Standard assets	411	
(ii) Sub-standard assets	412	
(iii) Doubtful assets	413	
(iv) Loss assets	414	

II. Aggregate provisioning in respect of I above as per the guidelines prescribed

Item name	*Item code*	*Provision required*	*Actual provision made*
(i) Sub-standard assets (10% of total outstanding)	421		

Item name	*Item code*	*Provision required*	*Actual provision made*
(ii) Doubtful assets (100% to the extent not covered by realisable value of security + 20 to 50% of the secured portion for the period the asset has remained doubtful (see Para 4 of the guidelines)	422		
(iii) Loss assets (100% of the outstanding balance)	423		
III. Other provisions in respect of :			
(i) Depreciation in fixed assets	431		
(ii) Depreciation in investments	432		
(iii) Loss/intangible assets	433		
(iv) Taxation	434		
(v) Gratuity/provident fund	435		
(vi) Others (to be specified)	436		

PART G

Particulars regarding investments in and advances to companies/firms in the same group and other NBFCs

Item name	*Item code*	*Amount*
(i) Outstanding loans and advances to and deposits with subsidiaries and companies in the same group (Details enclosed in Appendix No..........)	510	
(ii) Investments in shares of subsidiaries, companies in the same group and non-banking financial companies (Details enclosed in Appendix No.........)	520	
(iii) Investments by way of shares, debentures, loans and advances, leasing, hire purchase finance, deposits, etc., in other companies, firms and proprietary concerns where directors of the company hold substantial interest (Details enclosed in Appendix No.........)	530	

PART H

Particulars regarding concentration of advances (including off-balance sheet exposure and investments) to parties other than those in Part G above

Item name	*Item Code*	*Amount*
(i) Loans and advances, including off-balance sheet exposures, to any single party in excess of 15 per cent of owned fund of the NBFC. (Details enclosed in Appendix No.....)	610	

(ii) Loans and advances, including off-balance sheet exposures, to a single group of parties in excess of 25 per cent of owned fund of the NBFC. (Details enclosed in Appendix No........)	620
(iii) Investments in other companies in excess of 25 per cent of the owned fund of the NBFC. (Details enclosed in Appendix No.....)	630

Certified that the data/information furnished in this statement are in accordance with the guidelines issued by the Reserve Bank of India relating to income recognition, accounting standards, asset classification, provisioning for bad and doubtful debts, capital adequacy and concentration of credit and investments. They have been compiled from the books of accounts and other records of the company and to the best of my knowledge and belief they are correct.

For and on behalf of

Name of the company :..

Signature :..

Date : Name :..

Place : Designation :..

Company Seal :

Auditor's Report

We have examined the books of accounts and other records maintained by..................................Limited in respect of the capital funds, risk assets/exposure and risk assets ratio, etc., as on..............................and report that to the best of our knowledge and according to the information and explanations given to us and as shown by the record examined by us, the figures shown in Parts A, B, C, D, E, F, G and H of the statement are correct.

Place : Chartered Accountants

Date :

Annexure III

Information about the Promoters, Chairman, Managing Director, Directors and the Chief Executive Officer of the company

Note : Separate form should be submitted in respect of each of such functionaries.

1.	Name	....
2.	Designation	Chairman/ Managing Director/ Director/ Chief Executive Officer*
3.	Nationality	....
4.	Age	....
5.	Business address	....
6.	Residential address	....
7.	Educational/professional qualifications	....
8.	Line of business or vocation	....
9.	Name/s of other companies in which the person has held the post of Chairman/ Managing Director/Director/Chief Executive Officer	....
10.	(i) Whether associated as Promoter, Managing Director, Chairman or Director with any NBFC including a Residuary Non-Banking Financial Company which has been prohibited from accepting deposits/prosecuted by RBI	Yes/No
	(ii) If yes, the name/s of the company/ies	....
11.	(i) Whether prosecuted/convicted for any economic offence either in the individual capacity or as a partner/director of any firm/company	Yes/No
	(ii) If yes, the name/s of the company/ies	....
12.	Experience in the business of NBFC (Number of years)	....

* *Strike out whichever is not applicable.*

13. Equity share holding in the company

No. of shares	....
Face value	Rs..
Percentage of total equity share capital of the company	....

14. Name/s of the companies, firms and proprietary concerns in which the person holds substantial interest. (Please see item 14 of instructions at page 2) ....

15. Names of the principal bankers to the concerns at 14 above ....

Signature :..

Date Name :..

Place : Designation :..

(Chief Executive Officer) :..

Company seal :

[These guidelines may be detached and retained for future reference]

Reserve Bank of India's Guidelines to non-banking financial companies on prudential norms for income recognition, accounting standards, asset classification, provisioning for bad and doubtful debts, capital adequacy and concentration of credit/investments

1. Income recognition and accounting standards—General :

The policy on income recognition to be objective should be based on recognised accounting principles. An asset becomes non-performing when it ceases to yield income. Since it is not reasonably certain that the income from non-performing assets (NPAs) will be realised, such income should be considered to have accrued and be recognised only when it is actually received. NPA is an asset in respect of which interest has remained unpaid and has become 'past due'. An amount is to be treated as 'past due' when it remains unpaid for 30 days beyond the due date. Interest on NPAs should not be booked as income if such interest has remained outstanding for more than six months on and from March 31, 1995. The basis of treating a credit facility as NPA should be as under :

2.1 *Term loan beyond one year*

If interest amount remains 'past due' for six months, a term loan is to be treated as NPA. Where the instalment is overdue for more than six months, the entire outstanding loan, inclusive of unpaid interest, if any, should also be treated as NPA.

2.2 *Lease rentals/hire purchase instalments*

Where lease rentals/hire purchase instalments are 'past due' for six months, the entire dues from the leasee/hirer should be treated as NPA.

2.3 *Bills purchased/discounted*

A bill is to be treated as NPA if it remains overdue and unpaid for six months. Overdue interest is not to be taken to income account.

2.4 *Other credit facilities*

All other credit facilities in the nature of short term loans/advances should be treated as NPA if any amount to be received in respect of such a facility remains past due for a period of six months.

2.5 All Accounting Standards and Guidance Notes issued by the Institute of Chartered Accountants of India (ICAI) dealing with lease accounting/depreciation/income recognition, etc., may be followed.

2.6.1 *Accounting for investments*

All investments in securities should be bifurcated into current investments and long-term investments.

2.6.2 A current investment is an investment that is by its nature readily realisable and is intended to be held for not more than one year from the date on which such investment is made. Current investment should be valued at the lower of cost and market value (net of expenses necessarily to be incurred on or before disposal) for each investment individually.

2.6.3 A long-term investment is an investment other than a current investment. Long-term investments should be valued at cost. However, provision for diminution should be made to recognise a decline, other than temporary, in the value of long-term investments, such reduction being determined and made for each investment individually.

2.6.4 Unquoted shares are to be valued at cost or break-up value of the shares as per the last audited balance sheet of the company concerned, whichever is less.

2.6.5 Investments in units of mutual funds which are not quoted in the market should be valued at lower of cost or latest NAV declared by the mutual fund in respect of each particular scheme.

2.6.6 Commercial Papers and Treasury/Bills should be valued at carrying cost.

2.6.7 Unquoted debentures, depending on the tenor, are to be treated as long-term loans or other credit facilities for the purpose of income recognition and asset classification.

3.1 *Asset classification*

NBFCs should classify their loans and advances and any other form of credit into four broad groups, viz. (i) standard assets, (ii) sub-standard assets, (iii) doubtful assets and (iv) loss assets. Broadly speaking, classification of credit into the above categories should be done taking into account the degree of well defined credit weaknesses and extent of dependence on collateral security for realisation of dues. NBFCs should keep the following definitions in mind while classifying the assets.

3.2 *Standard assets*

A standard asset is one in respect of which no default in repayment of principal or payment of interest is perceived and which does not disclose any problems nor carry more than normal risk attached to the business. Such an asset is not an NPA.

3.3 *Sub-standard assets*

A sub-standard asset is one which has been classified as an NPA for a period not exceeding two years. Such an asset will have well defined credit weaknesses that jeopardise liquidation of the debt and are characterised by a distinct possibility that the NBFC will sustain some loss, if deficiencies are not corrected. Term loans, where interest and/or instalments of principal are overdue for six months should be treated as sub-standard. An asset where the terms of the loan agreement regarding interest and principal have been renegotiated or rescheduled after commencement of operations, should be classified as sub-standard and should remain in such category for at least two years of satisfactory performance under the renegotiated or rescheduled terms. The classification of an asset should not be upgraded merely as a result of rescheduling, unless there is satisfactory compliance of the above condition.

3.4 *Doubtful assets*

A doubtful asset is one which has remained an NPA for a period exceeding two years. Term loans, where instalments of principal have remained overdue for a period exceeding two years, should be treated as doubtful. Here too, as in the case of sub-standard assets, rescheduling does not entitle an NBFC to upgrade the quality of an advance automatically. A loan classified as doubtful has all the weaknesses inherent in that classified as sub-standard with the added characteristic that the weaknesses make collection or liquidation in full, on the basis of currently known facts, conditions and values, highly questionable and improbable.

3.5 *Loss assets*

A loss asset is one where loss has been identified by the NBFC or internal or external auditors or the RBI inspection but the amount has not been written off, wholly or partly. In other words, such an asset is considered uncollectable although there may be some salvage or recovery value.

4. Provisioning for loans and advances

Taking into account the time-lag between an account becoming doubtful of recovery, its recognition as such, the realisation of the security and the erosion over time in the value of security charged, it has been decided that NBFCs should make provision against sub-standard assets, doubtful assets and loss assets as under :

(i) Loss assets — The entire asset should be written off. If the assets are permitted to remain in the books for any reasons, 100 per cent of the outstanding should be provided for.

(ii) Doubtful assets — (a) 100 per cent provision to the extent to which the advance is not covered by the realisable value of the security to which the NBFC has a valid recourse should be made. The realisable value is to be estimated on a realistic basis.

(b) Over and above item (a) above, depending upon the period for which the asset has remained doubtful, provision to the extent of 20 per cent to 50 per cent of the secured portion (i.e., estimated realisable value of the outstandings) should be made on the following basis.

Period for which the asset has been considered as doubtful	*% of provision*
Up to one year	20
One to three years	30
More than three years	50

(iii) Sub-standard assets — A general provision of 10 per cent of total outstanding should be made.

5.1 *Capital adequacy norms—Risk weighted capital ratio*

Capital will be divided into two tiers—Tier I and Tier II. While Tier I capital is the core capital which provides the most permanent and readily available support against unexpected losses, Tier II capital will consist of elements that are not permanent in nature or are not readily available. Tier I capital will consist of paid-up equity capital, free reserves, balance in share premium account and capital reserves representing surplus arising out of sale proceeds of assets but not reserves created by revaluation of assets. From the aggregate of these items will be deducted accumulated loss balance and book value of intangible assets, deferred revenue expenditure, if any, to arrive at owned fund investments in shares of other NBFCs and in shares, debentures of subsidiaries and group companies and loans and advances to and deposits with subsidiaries and companies in the same group in excess of 10 per cent of the owned fund mentioned above will be deducted to arrive at the net owned funds, i.e., Tier I capital.

5.2 *Tier II capital will consist of—*

5.2.1 *Preference shares*

Preference shares have the characteristics similar to equity capital inasmuch as the shareholders' funds are subordinated to the claims of creditors. These are also redeemed out of accumulated profits.

5.2.2 *Revaluation reserves*

These reserves often serve as a cushion against unexpected losses but they are less permanent in nature and cannot be considered as 'core capital'. Revaluation reserves arise from revaluation of assets that are under-valued in the books, typically premises and marketable securities. The extent to which the revaluation reserves can be relied upon as a cushion for unexpected losses depends mainly upon the level of certainty that can be placed on estimates of the market values of the relevant assets, the subsequent deterioration in values under difficult market conditions, or in a forced sales, potential for actual liquidation at those values, tax consequences of revaluation, etc. Therefore, it would be prudent to consider revaluation reserves at a discount of 55 per cent when determining their value of inclusion in Tier II capital. Such reserves will have to be reflected on the face of the Balance Sheet as revaluation reserves.

5.2.3 *General provisions and loss reserves*

If these are not attributable to the actual diminution in value or identifiable potential loss in any specific asset and are available to meet unexpected losses, they can be included in Tier II capital. Adequate care must be taken to see that sufficient provisions have been made to meet all known losses and foreseeable potential losses before considering general provisions and loss reserves to be part of Tier II capital. General provisions/loss reserves will be admitted up to a maximum of 1.25 per cent of weighted risk assets.

5.2.4 *Hybrid debt capital instruments*

In this category fall a number of capital instruments which combine certain characteristics of equity and certain characteristics of debt. Each has a particular feature which can be considered to affect its quality as capital. Where these instruments have close similarities to equity, in particular when they are able to support losses on an on-going basis without triggering liquidation, they may be included in Tier II capital.

5.2.5 *Subordinated debt*

To be eligible for inclusion in Tier II capital, the instrument should be fully paid-up, unsecured, subordinated to the claims of other creditors, free of restrictive clauses and should not be redeemable at the initiative of the holder or without the consent of the NBFC's supervisory authorities. These instruments often carry a fixed maturity and, as they approach maturity, they should be subjected to progressive discount for inclusion in Tier II capital. The rate of discounting will be as under :

(i)	Where the date of maturity is beyond 5 years	50 per cent
(ii)	Where the date of maturity is beyond 4 years but does not exceed 5 years	60 per cent
(iii)	Where the date of maturity is beyond 3 years but does not exceed 4 years	70 per cent
(iv)	Where the date of maturity is beyond 2 years but does not exceed 3 years	80 per cent
(v)	Where the date of maturity is beyond one year but does not exceed 2 years	90 per cent
(vi)	Where the date of maturity does not exceed one year	100 per cent

Subordinated debt instruments will be limited to 50 per cent of Tier I capital.

5.2.6 Although instruments of the types mentioned in items 5.2.4 and 5.2.5 above are not in vogue, it is expected that such instruments may develop in due course.

6. Minimum requirement of capital funds

The registered NBFCs should achieve a minimum capital adequacy norm of 6 per cent of the risk weighted assets and off-balance sheet items by March 31, 1995 and 8 per cent by March 31, 1996. The total of Tier II elements will be limited to a maximum of 100 per cent of total of Tier I elements for the purpose of compliance with the norms.

7. Risk weighted assets and off-Balance Sheet items

Risk weighted assets would mean the weighted aggregate of funded and non-funded items as detailed below. Degrees of credit risks expressed as percentage weightings have been assigned to balance sheet assets and conversion factors to off-balance sheet items. The value of each assets/item shall be multiplied by the relevant weights to produce risk adjusted value of assets and off-balance sheet items.

The aggregate will be taken into account for reckoning the minimum capital ratio. The weights allotted to each of the items of assets and off-balance sheet items are furnished below :

7.1 *Weighted assets, i.e., On-Balance Sheet items*

		Percentage weight
(i)	Cash and bank balances including fixed deposits and certificates of deposits with banks	0
(ii)	Investments	
	(a) Government and approved securities as defined under section 45IB of RBI Act	0
	(b) Shares/debentures/bonds/units of mutual funds/CPs	100
(iii)	Current assets	
	(a) Stock on hire (Please see note No. 2 below)	100
	(b) Intercorporate loans/deposits	100

	(c) Loans and advances fully secured by company's own deposits	0
	(d) Loans to staff	0
	(e) Other secured loans and advances considered good	100
	(f) Bills purchased/discounted	100
	(g) Others (to be specified)	100
(iv)	Fixed assets (net of depreciation)	
	(a) Assets leased out	100
	(b) Premises	100
	(c) Furniture & fixtures	100
(v)	Other assets	
	(a) Income-tax deducted at source (net of provision)	0
	(b) Advance tax paid (net of provision)	0
	(c) Interest due on government securities	0
	(d) Others (to be specified)	100

7.2 ***Off-Balance Sheet items***

The credit risk exposure attached to off-balance sheet items has to be first calculated by multiplying the face amount of each of the off-balance sheet items by the "credit conversion factor" as indicated in the table below. This will then have to be again multiplied by the risk weight of 100.

	Nature of items	*Credit conversion factor (%)*
(i)	Financial & other guarantees	100
(ii)	Share/debenture underwriting obligations	50
(iii)	Partly-paid shares/debentures	100
(iv)	Bills discounted/rediscounted	100
(v)	Lease contracts entered into but yet to be executed	100
(vi)	Other contingent liabilities (to be specified)	50

8.1 *Concentration of credit/investments*

It is prudent that an NBFC should not lend more than 15 per cent of its owned fund to any single party or 25 per cent of its owned fund to a single group of parties. For determining the limits, off-balance sheet exposures will be converted into credit risks by applying the conversion factors indicated in paragraph 7.2 of these guidelines. The companies in the same group in these guidelines would mean the companies as defined in section 372(ii) of the Companies Act, 1956. So far as partnership firms and proprietary concerns are concerned, they would mean concerns where directors of the NBFC hold substantial interest. 'Substantial interest' means holding of a beneficial interest by an individual or his spouse or minor child, whether singly or taken together, in the shares of a company, the amount paid-up on which exceeds 10 per cent of the paid-up capital of the company or total capital subscribed by all the partners of a partnership firm. Excess lendings/exposures, if any, on the date of issue of these guidelines, should be brought down in the course of repayment of the dues as scheduled. However, the NBFC should not grant any fresh loans or have fresh exposures to any single customer or group of customers where the limit of 15 per cent or 25 per cent of owned fund has already been reached.

8.2 As regards investment, the NBFC should not invest more than 25 per cent of its owned funds in shares and debentures/bonds of another company. In regard to investments in companies belonging to a group or in a particular industry, the NBFC should keep in mind the attendant risks and endeavour to diversify the portfolio.

Notes : 1. Netting may be done only in respect of assets where provisions for depreciation or for bad and doubtful debts have been made.

2. Stock on hire should be shown net of finance charges, i.e., interest and other charges recoverable.

3. Assets which have been deducted from owned fund to arrive at net owned fund pursuant to item 5.1 will have a weightage of "0".

4. Cash margins/deposits shall be deducted before applying the conversion factor.

THE
RESERVE BANK COMMERCIAL PAPER DIRECTIONS, 2012

[Notification No. IDMD. PCD. 1284/14.01.02/2012-13, dt. 16-10-2012]

Whereas the Reserve Bank of India, in exercise of the powers conferred by sections 45-J, 45-K, 45-L of the Reserve Bank of India Act, 1934, and of all the powers enabling it in this behalf, notified the Non-Banking Companies (Acceptance of Deposits through Commercial Paper) Directions, 1989 vide Noti. No. IECD. 1/87(CP)-89/90, dated December, 11, 1989.

And whereas the said directions having been amended from time to time vide Notification No. IECD.14/08.15.01/96-97, dated September 6, 1996; Notification No. IECD.21/08.15.01/97-98, dated June 17, 1998, and Notification No. IECD 3/08.15.01/2000-2001, dated October 10, 2000 respectively.

And whereas Section 45W of the Reserve Bank of India Act provides that the Bank may, in public interest, or to regulate the financial system of the country to its advantage, determine the policy relating to interest rates or interest rate products and give directions in that behalf to all agencies or any of them, dealing in securities, money market instruments, foreign exchange, derivatives, or other instruments of like nature as the Bank may specify from time to time;

And whereas Commercial Paper is a 'money market instrument' for the purposes of Section 45W of the Reserve Bank of India Act;

Now therefore, in exercise of the powers conferred under sections 45J, 45K, 45L and 45W, and in supercession of the Notifications referred hereinabove, and all other instructions issued in this behalf, on the subject, the Reserve Bank of India, having considered it necessary in the public interest and being satisfied that for the purpose of enabling the Bank to regulate the credit and financial system to the advantage of the country, hereby issues the following directions, namely:—

1. Short title and commencement

These directions shall be called the Reserve Bank Commercial Paper Directions, 2012 and shall come into force on the date[1] of their publication in the Official gazette.

2. Definitions

For the purpose of these directions, unless the context otherwise requires,—

(a) "RBI" means the Reserve Bank of India;

(b) "Banks" means a banking company as defined in clause (c) of section 5 of the Banking Regulation Act, 1949 (10 of 1949) or a "corresponding new bank", "State Bank of India" or a "subsidiary bank" as defined in clause (da), clause (nc) and clause (nd) respectively thereof and includes a "cooperative bank" as defined in clause (cci) of section 5 read with section 56 of the said Act;

1 Enforceable w.e.f. 30-10-2012.

(c) "Scheduled bank" means a bank included in the Second Schedule of the RBI Act, 1934;

(d) "All India Financial Institution" (FI) means an all India Financial Institution specified in the list indicated at Annex 3 to the RBI Master Circular DBOD. No. Dir.BC.3/13.03.00/2012-13, dated July 02, 2012 on Exposure Norms as amended from time to time;

(e) "Primary Dealer (PD)" means a Non-Banking Financial Company (NBFC) that holds a valid letter of authorisation as a PD issued by the Reserve Bank, in terms of the "*Guidelines for Primary Dealer in Government Securities Market*" dated March 29, 1995, as amended from time to time;

(f) "Company" means a company as defined in section 3 of the Companies Act, 1956;

(g) "Issuing and Paying Agent (IPA)" means a Scheduled Bank acting as an IPA;

(h) "CRA" means a Credit Rating Agency registered with Securities Exchange Board of India;

(i) "CP" means Commercial Paper issued in accordance with these directions;

(j) Words and expressions used but not defined herein and defined in the Reserve Bank of India Act, 1934 shall have the same meaning as assigned to them in the said Act.

3. Eligibility for issue of CP

(a) Companies, PDs and FIs are permitted to raise short-term resources through CP within the umbrella limits specified under paragraph 4.

(b) A company would be eligible to issue CP provided—

(i) the tangible net worth of the company, as per the latest audited balance sheet, is not less than Rs. 4 crore;

(ii) the company has been sanctioned working capital limit by bank/s or FIs; and

(iii) the borrowal account of the company is classified as a Standard Asset by the financing bank/institution.

4. Issue of CP - Credit enhancement, limits, etc.

(a) CP shall be issued as a 'stand alone' product. Further, it would not be obligatory in any manner on the part of the banks and FIs to provide stand-by facility to the issuers of CP.

(b) Banks and FIs may, based on their commercial judgement, subject to the prudential norms as applicable to them, with the specific approval of their respective Boards, choose to provide stand-by assistance/credit, back-stop facility etc. by way of credit enhancement for a CP issue.

(c) Non-bank entities (including corporates) may provide unconditional and irrevocable guarantee for credit enhancement for CP issue provided—

(i) the issuer fulfils the eligibility criteria prescribed for issuance of CP;

(ii) the guarantor has a credit rating at least one notch higher than the issuer given by an approved CRA; and

(iii) the offer document for CP properly discloses the net worth of the guarantor company, the names of the companies to which the guarantor has issued similar guarantees, the extent of the guarantees offered by the guarantor company, and the conditions under which the guarantee will be invoked.

(d) The aggregate amount of CP that can be issued by an issuer shall at all times be within the limit as approved by its Board of Directors or the quantum indicated by the CRA for the specified rating, whichever is lower.

(e) Banks and FIs shall have the flexibility to fix working capital limits, duly taking into account the resource pattern of company's financing, including CP.

(f) An issue of CP by an FI shall be within the overall umbrella limit prescribed in the Master Circular on Resource Raising Norms for FIs, issued by the Reserve Bank of India, Department of Banking Operations and Development, as prescribed/updated from time-to-time.

(g) The total amount of CP proposed to be issued should be raised within a period of two weeks from the date on which the issuer opens the issue for subscription. CP may be issued on a single date or in parts on different dates provided that in the latter case, each CP shall have the same maturity date.

(h) Every issue of CP, and every renewal of a CP, shall be treated as a fresh issue.

5. Eligibility for investment in CP

(a) Individuals, banks, other corporate bodies (registered or incorporated in India) and unincorporated bodies, Non-Resident Indians and Foreign Institutional Investors (FIIs) shall be eligible to invest in CP.

(b) FIIs shall be eligible to invest in CPs subject to (i) such conditions as may be set for them by Securities Exchange Board of India (SEBI) and (ii) compliance with the provisions of the Foreign Exchange Management Act, 1999, the Foreign Exchange (Deposit) Regulations, 2000 and the Foreign Exchange Management (Transfer or Issue of Security by a Person Resident Outside India) Regulations, 2000, as amended from time to time.

6. Form of the instrument, mode of issuance and redemption

6.1 *Form*

(a) CP shall be issued in the form of a promissory note (as specified in Schedule I to these Directions) and held in physical form or in a dematerialized form through any of the depositories approved by and registered with SEBI, provided that all RBI regulated entities can deal in and hold CP only in dematerialised form through such depositories.

(b) Fresh investments by all RBI-regulated entities shall be only in dematerialised form.

(c) CP shall be issued in denominations of Rs. 5 lakh and multiples thereof. The amount invested by a single investor should not be less than Rs. 5 lakh (face value).

(d) CP shall be issued at a discount to face value as may be determined by the issuer.

(e) No issuer shall have the issue of CP underwritten or co-accepted.

(f) Options (call/put) are not permitted on CP.

6.2 *Tenor*

(a) CP shall be issued for maturities between a minimum of 7 days and a maximum of up to one year from the date of issue.

(b) The maturity date of the CP shall not go beyond the date up to which the credit rating of the issuer is valid.

6.3 *Procedure for issuance*

(a) Every issuer must appoint an IPA for issuance of CP.

(b) The issuer should disclose to the potential investors, its latest financial position as per the standard market practice.

(c) After the exchange of confirmation of the deal between the investor and the issuer, the issuer shall arrange for crediting the CP to the Demat account of the investor with the depository through the IPA.

(d) The issuer shall give to the investor a copy of IPA certificate to the effect that the issuer has a valid agreement with the IPA and documents are in order (Schedule II).

6.4 *Rating requirement*

Eligible participants/issuers shall obtain credit rating for issuance of CP from any one of the SEBI registered CRAs. The minimum credit rating shall be 'A3' as per rating symbol and definition prescribed by SEBI. The issuers shall ensure at the time of issuance of the CP that the rating so obtained is current and has not fallen due for review.

6.5 *Investment/Redemption*

(a) The investor in CP (primary subscriber) shall pay the discounted value of the CP to the account of the issuer through the IPA.

(b) The investor holding the CP in physical form shall, on maturity, present the instrument for payment to the issuer through the IPA.

(c) Payment through the IPA.

6.6 *Documentation Procedures*

(a) Standardised procedures and documentation for CPs are prescribed in consultation with Fixed Income Money Market and Derivatives Association of India (FIMMDA) in consonance with international best practices.

(b) Time, with the approval of RBI.

7. Trading and Settlement of CP

(a) All OTC trades in CP shall be reported within 15 minutes of the trade to FIMMDA reporting platform.

(b) OTC trades in CP shall be settled through the clearing house of the National Stock Exchange (NSE), i.e., the National Securities Clearing Corporation Limited (NSCCL) and the clearing house of the Bombay Stock Exchange (BSE), i.e., Indian Clearing Corporation Limited (ICCL), as per the norms specified by NSCCL and ICCL from time to time.

(c) The settlement cycle for OTC trades in CP shall either be T+0 or T+1.

8. Buyback of CP

(a) Issuers may buyback the CP, issued by them to the investors, before maturity.

(b) Buyback of CP shall be through the secondary market and at prevailing market price.

(c) The CP shall not be bought back before a minimum period of 7 days from the date of issue.

(d) Issuer shall intimate the IPA of the buyback undertaken.

(e) Buyback of CPs should be undertaken after taking approval from the Board of Directors.

9. Duties and Obligations

The duties and obligations of the Issuer, IPA and CRA are set out below:—

I. *Issuer*

The issuer shall ensure that the guidelines and procedures laid down for the issuance of CP are strictly adhered to.

II. *IPA*

(a) The IPA shall ensure that the issuer has the minimum credit rating as stipulated by RBI and the amount mobilised through issuance of CP is within the quantum indicated by CRA for the specified rating or as approved by its Board of Directors, whichever is lower.

(b) The IPA shall certify that it has a valid agreement with the issuer (Schedule II).

(c) The IPA shall verify that all the documents submitted by the issuer, viz., copy of board resolution, signatures of authorised executants (when CP is issued in physical form) are in order and shall issue a certificate to this effect.

(d) Certified copies of original documents, verified by the IPA, shall be held in the custody of IPA.

(e) All scheduled banks, acting as IPAs, shall report the details of issuance of CP on the Online Returns Filing System (ORFS) module of the RBI within two days from the date of issuance of the CP.

(f) IPAs, shall immediately report, on occurrence, full particulars of defaults in repayment of CP to the Chief General Manager, Financial Markets Department, Reserve Bank of India, Central Office, Fort, Mumbai-400001 (reportfmd@rbi.org.in) in the format as given in Schedule III of these directions.

(g) IPAs shall also report all instances of buyback of CPs undertaken by the issuer to the Chief General Manager, Financial Markets Department, Reserve Bank of India, Central Office, Fort, Mumbai-400001 (reportfmd@rbi.org.in) in the format as given in Schedule IV of these directions.

III. *CRA*

(a) CRAs shall abide by the Code of Conduct prescribed by the SEBI for CRAs for undertaking rating of capital market instruments, which shall be applicable for rating CPs.

(b) The CRAs shall have the discretion to determine the validity period of the rating depending upon their perception about the strength of the issuer; and they shall, at the time of rating, clearly indicate the date when the rating is due for review.

(c) The CRAs shall closely monitor the rating assigned to issuers vis-a-vis their track record at regular intervals and shall make their revision in the ratings public through their publications and website.

10. Non-applicability of Certain Other Directions

Nothing contained in the Non-Banking Financial Companies Acceptance of Public Deposits (Reserve Bank) Directions, 1998 shall apply to the acceptance of deposit by issuance of CP, by any NBFC in accordance with these directions.

11. All existing directions and guidelines stand superceded with immediate effect but shall continue to apply to CPs already issued from the corresponding dates of effect.

SCHEDULE I

[Refer para 6.1(a)]

PROFORMA OF COMMERCIAL PAPER (CP)

To be stamped as per the applicable rate in force in the State in which it is to be issued

(NAME OF THE ISSUING COMPANY/INSTITUTION)

SERIAL NO.

Issued at : .... Date of issue : ....

(PLACE)

Date of Maturity .... (If such date happens to fall on a holiday, payment shall be made on the immediate preceding working day) without days of grace.

For value received .... hereby (NAME OF THE ISSUING COMPANY/INSTITUTION) promise to pay .... or order on the (NAME OF THE INVESTOR) maturity date as specified above the sum of Rs. .... (in words) upon presentation and surrender of this Commercial Paper to .... (NAME OF THE ISSUING AND PAYING AGENT)

For and on behalf of .... (NAME OF THE ISSUING COMPANY/INSTITUTION)

(AUTHORISED SIGNATORY/SIGNATORIES)

ALL ENDORSEMENTS UPON THIS COMMERCIAL PAPER MUST BE CLEAN AND DISTINCT. EACH ENDORSEMENT SHOULD BE WRITTEN WITHIN THE SPACE ALLOTTED.

Pay to .... (NAME OF TRANSFEREE) or order the amount within named.

For and on behalf of

....

(NAME OF THE TRANSFEROR)

---

1. "
2. "
3. "
4. "

SCHEDULE II

[Refer para 6.3(d)/9.II(b)]

IPA CERTIFICATE

We have a valid IPA agreement with the .... (Name of Issuing Company/Institution).

2. We have verified the documents viz., board resolution and certificate issued by Credit Rating Agency submitted by [Name of the Issuing Company/Institution] and

certify that the documents are in order. Certified copies of original documents are held in our custody.

3. *We also hereby certify that the signatures of the executants of the attached Commercial Paper bearing Sr. No. .... dated .... for Rs. .... (Rupees ....) (in words) tally with the specimen signatures filed by [Name of the issuing Company/Institution].

(Authorised Signatory/Signatories)
(Name and address of Issuing and Paying Agent)

Place:
Date:
*(Applicable to Commercial Paper in physical form/Strike out if not applicable)

SCHEDULE III

[Refer para 9.II(f)]

DETAILS OF DEFAULTS ON REPAYMENT OF CP

Name of the issuer	*Date of issue of CP*	*Amount (Rs. in cr.)*	*Due date of repayment*	*Initial Rating*	*Latest Rating*	*Whether the CP issue enjoyed a standby assistance/credit back stop facility/guarantee*	*If so, the name of the entity providing the facility indicated at Col. (7)*	*Whether the facility at Col. (7) has been honoured and payment made*
(1)	(2)	(3)	(4)	(5)	(6)	(7)	(8)	(9)

[Authorized Signatory/Signatories]

SCHEDULE IV

[Refer para 9.II(g)]

REPORTING OF BUYBACK OF CPs

Date of trade	*Issuer*	*ISIN*	*Date of Issue*	*Date of Maturity*	*Amount (Rs. in crore)*	*#Nature of Buyback*

Indicate whether the CPs have been extinguished by the Issuer.

[Authorized Signatory/Signatories]

****

THE RESERVE BANK OF INDIA MONETARY POLICY COMMITTEE AND MONETARY POLICY PROCESS REGULATIONS, 2016

[Noti. No. M.P.D.P.M.D. No. 17/02.02.015/17-18, dt. 14-7-2017]

In exercise of the powers conferred by clause (qa), (qb), (qc), (qd) and (qe) of Section 58 of the Reserve Bank of India Act, 1934 (2 of 1934) amended in 2016, the Central Board of the Reserve Bank of India, with the previous sanction of the Central Government, hereby makes the following regulations:—

1. Monetary Policy Process

(i) These regulations shall be called as the Reserve Bank of India Monetary Policy Committee and Monetary Policy Process Regulations, 2016.

(ii) They shall come into force effective from 1st August, 2016.

2. Interpretations

In these regulations:

(a) "the Act" means the Reserve Bank of India Act, 1934 (2 of 1934);

(b) "the Bank" means the Reserve Bank of India;

(c) "the Board" means the Central Board of the Reserve Bank of India;

(d) "Committee" means the Monetary Policy Committee (MPC) constituted under sub-section 1 of Section 45ZB of the Reserve Bank of India Act, 1934 (2 of 1934);

(e) "Members" means members of the Monetary Policy Committee appointed by the Central Government under sub-section (2) of Section 45ZB of the Reserve Bank of India Act, 1934 (2 of 1934);

(f) "Secretary" means the secretary to the Monetary Policy Committee;

(g) "Monetary Policy Report" means the Monetary Policy Report as mentioned in Section 45ZM of the Act;

(h) Other expressions used but not defined in these Regulations and used in the Act have the meanings respectively assigned to them in the Act.

3. Remuneration and other allowances payable to the members

(i) Members appointed under clause (d) of sub-section (2) of section 45ZB of the Act shall receive a remuneration of Rs 1,50,000 (rupees one lakh fifty thousand) for devoting time and work for each meeting of the Committee to be conducted under sub-section (1) of section 45ZI of the Act which they attend and other expenses relating to air travel, local transportation and accommodation as may be decided by the Central Board from time to time.

(ii) The Secretary to the MPC shall make arrangements to provide logistical support to members appointed under clause (d) of sub-section (2) of section

45ZB of the Act during each MPC meeting to be conducted under sub-section (1) of section 45ZI of the Act.

4. Functions and manner in which the Secretary shall perform the functions

(i) The head of the Monetary Policy Department (MPD) shall be the Secretary to the committee. In his/her absence, the representative nominated by him/her not below the rank of senior officer in MPD shall function as the Secretary.

(ii) ***Role and Functions of the Secretary and Secretariat***

(a) Assist the MPC in smooth conduct of all its meetings, and ensure that the processes set out at regulation 5(i) below are followed in letter and spirit;

(b) Assist in preparing the agenda for every MPC meeting;

(c) Ensure that analytical and data requirements for MPC meetings and of members are met through an effective coordination mechanism involving staff across various departments of the Bank;

(d) Prepare (i) draft policy proposal (resolution and statement) for voting by the MPC; (ii) minutes/proceedings of MPC meetings; and (iii) ensure release of policy resolution and statement as well as minutes after the MPCs approval in accordance with the schedule;

(e) Record and preserve minutes of all meetings; and

(f) Assume responsibility for publication of documents.

5. Procedure, conduct, code of confidentiality and other matters

(i) ***The Monetary Policy Process***

(a) The schedule of monetary policy voting/decision meetings for the entire fiscal year shall be announced in advance.

(b) Ordinarily not less than fifteen days notice shall be given to members for meetings of the Committee. Should it be found necessary to convene an emergency meeting, 24 hours notice shall be given to every member to enable him/her to attend, with technology-enabled arrangements for even shorter notice period for meetings.

(c) The duration of monetary policy meetings shall be such as decided by the Committee. The policy resolution will be publicly released after the conclusion of the MPC meeting keeping in view the functioning and timing of financial markets.

(d) The resolution shall include the policy repo rate, and at the discretion of the Chairperson, any other monetary policy measures including those relating to the operating framework of monetary policy.

(e) Minutes of the decision making meeting(s) shall include: (a) the resolution adopted by the MPC; (b) the voting of each member on the resolution; and (c) short written statements of individual members justifying the vote, consistent with the provisions of Section 45ZL of the Act. Minutes shall be released at 5 pm on the 14th day from the date of the policy day (or next earliest working day, if a holiday in Mumbai).

(ii) ***Code of Conduct for MPC Members***

This code aims at providing broad guidance to members of the MPC on their ethical conduct, which shall help enhance public trust and confidence in the Bank and its policies.

- MPC members shall act in a manner consistent with the integrity, dignity and reputation of their office.
- MPC members shall be guided by the objectives of monetary policy set out in the Act and the inflation target set by the Central Government, and shall independently and candidly express their views in the MPC meetings before voting.
- Members shall take adequate precaution to ensure utmost confidentiality of the MPCs policy decision before it is made public and preserve confidentiality about the decision making process.
- While interacting with profit-making organizations or making personal financial decisions, they shall be mindful of, and weigh carefully, any scope for conflict between personal interest and public interest.

External Communication Policy

- Members shall observe a silent or blackout period, starting seven days before the voting/decision day, and ending seven days after the day policy is announced. During this period, they will avoid public comment on issues related to monetary policy, other than through the MPC's communication framework.
- Members shall ensure that personal views expressed outside the silent or blackout period are attributable only to themselves, and that no confidential information accessed during the monetary policy deliberations is revealed outside the Committee.
- Members shall not use resources made available by the Bank (including human resources) for private/ commercial gain.

Internal Communication and Information Seeking

Members seeking information from the Bank under sub-section (1) and sub-section (2) of section 45ZH of the Act shall make requests to the Secretary only. All internal communication of members with the staff of the Bank shall be through the Secretary only.

Code for Personal Financial Transactions

After their appointment, members shall disclose their assets and liabilities in a document held by the Secretary of the Committee. This information shall be updated once every year.

Code for High Ethical Standards

Members shall maintain the highest standards of probity consistent with public office.

Oath of Secrecy

Before the first formal meeting of the MPC, every new member shall sign a declaration in the form set out in the Schedule pledging not to reveal any of the nonpublic matters which may come to his/her knowledge in the discharge of his/her duties, except when required or authorised to do so by the Board or by law.

Others

The Chairperson of the Committee shall forthwith inform the Central Government, if and when it comes to the notice of the Committee, that a member has become subject to any of the disqualifications specified in section 45ZC or section 45ZE of the Act.

Every member shall be indemnified by the Bank against all losses and expenses incurred in discharging assigned duties, except such as may happen from his/her own wilful act or default.

6. Document 1 (*The Bank shall publish a Document explaining the steps to be taken by it to implement the decisions of the Committee as required in Section 45ZJ of the Act*)

(i) The operating procedure of monetary policy - or the framework to implement monetary policy decisions shall be reviewed and explained in the bi-annual Monetary Policy Reports (MPRs).

Monetary policy changes involving instruments other than the repo rate and the operating procedure as decided by the MPC shall be explained in the policy statement, followed by a press release setting out details on implementation.

Document 2 (*The forms and contents of the Monetary Policy Report to be published under sub-section (2) of section 45ZM*)

(ii) The Bank shall publish the Monetary Policy Report (MPR) once in every six months.

The Monetary Policy Report shall contain the following:

(a) Explanation of inflation dynamics in the last six months and the near term inflation outlook;

(b) Projections of inflation and growth and the balance of risks;

(c) An assessment of the state of the economy, covering the real economy, financial markets and stability, fiscal situation, and the external sector, which may entail a bearing on monetary policy decisions;

(d) An updated review of the operating procedure of monetary policy; and

(e) An assessment of projection performance.

Form of the MPR

The MPR shall be released on the Bank website within 24 hours of the release of the relevant policy statement.

7. Process to be followed in the event of a failure to meet the inflation target

The Secretary to the Committee shall schedule a separate meeting as part of the normal policy process to discuss and draft the report to be sent to the Central Government under the provisions of Section 45ZN of the Act. The Report shall be sent to the Central Government within one month from the date on which the Bank has failed to meet the inflation target. The Bank shall send the report to the Central Government in the event of a failure to achieve the target as specified by Rules of the Central Government, in this regard.

THE SCHEDULE

[vide Regulation 5(ii)]

FORM OF DECLARATION OF FIDELITY AND SECRECY

I, on becoming a member of the Monetary Policy Committee (MPC), do solemnly and sincerely declare that I shall faithfully perform the duties to the best of my ability and that I will uphold the dignity of the position and that I will observe secrecy and will not directly or indirectly communicate or divulge any of the matters or any information which may come to my knowledge in the discharge of my duties, except when required or authorised to do so by these Regulations/Central Board of the Bank or by law.

(Signature)

Date:

THE ELECTORAL BOND SCHEME, 2018

(SO 29(E), dt. 2-1-2018)
[*As amended vide SO 5163(E), dt. 7-11-2022, w.e.f. 7-11-2022*]

In exercise of the powers conferred by sub-section (3) of Section 31 of the Reserve Bank of India Act, 1934 (2 of 1934), the Central Government hereby makes the following Scheme, namely:—

1. Short title and commencement

(1) This scheme may be called the Electoral Bond Scheme, 2018.

(2) It shall come into force on the date of its publication in the Official Gazette.

2. Definition

In this Scheme, unless the context otherwise requires,—

(a) "electoral bond" means a bond issued in the nature of promissory note which shall be a bearer banking instrument and shall not carry the name of the buyer or payee;

(b) "authorised bank" means the State Bank of India authorised to issue and encash the bonds in the branches specified in Annexure I to this notification;

(c) "issuing branch" means a designated branch of the authorised bank specified in Annexure I for issuing electoral bonds;

(d) "person" includes—

(i) an individual;

(ii) a Hindu undivided family;

(iii) a company;

(iv) a firm;

(v) an association of persons or a body of individuals, whether incorporated or not;

(vi) every artificial juridical person, not falling within any of the preceding sub-clauses; and

(vii) any agency, office or branch owned or controlled by such person.

3. Eligibility for purchase and encashment of electoral bond

(1) The Bond under this Scheme may be purchased by a person, who is a citizen of India or incorporated or established in India.

(2) A person being an individual can buy bonds, either singly or jointly with other individuals.

(3) Only the political parties registered under section 29A of the Representation of the People Act, 1951 (43 of 1951) and secured not less than one per cent of the votes polled in the last general election to the House of the People or the Legislative Assembly, as the case may be, shall be eligible to receive the bond.

(4) The bond shall be encashed by an eligible political party only through a bank account with the authorised bank.

4. Applicability of Know Your Customer Norms

(1) The extant instructions issued by the Reserve Bank of India regarding Know Your Customer norms of a bank's customer shall apply for buyers of the bonds.

(2) The authorised bank may call for any additional Know Your Customer documents, if it deems necessary.

5. Denomination

The bonds shall be issued in the denomination of Rs. 1000, Rs. 10,000, Rs. 1,00,000, Rs. 10,00,000 and Rs. 1,00,00,000.

6. Validity of Bond

(1) The bond shall be valid for fifteen days from the date of issue and no payment shall be made to any payee political party if the bond is deposited after expiry of the validity period.

(2) The bond deposited by any political party to its account shall be credited on the same day.

7. Procedure for making application for purchase of bonds

(1) Every buyer desirous of purchasing bond can apply with a physical or through online application in the format specified in Annexure II to this notification.

(2) Every application shall contain particulars as per the format in Annexure-II and shall be accompanied with the specified documents.

(3) On receipt of an application, the issuing branch shall issue the requisite bond, if all the requirements are fulfilled.

(4) The information furnished by the buyer shall be treated confidential by the authorised bank and shall not be disclosed to any authority for any purposes, except when demanded by a competent court or upon registration of criminal case by any law enforcement agency.

(5) A non-Know Your Customer compliant application or an application not meeting the requirements of the scheme shall be rejected.

(6) The bond shall be issued to the buyer on non-refundable basis.

[1][**8. Periodicity of issue of bonds**

(1) The bonds under this Scheme shall be available for purchase by any person in every year for a **total** maximum period of sixty days in upto six number of issuances as may be specified by the Central Government.

(2) Three additional issuances for a total additional period of **maximum** forty-five days may be specified by the Central Government in the year of general elections to the House of People.]

[2][(3) An additional period of fifteen days shall be specified by the Central Government in the year of general elections to the Legislative Assembly of States and Union territories with Legislature.]

9. Interest

No interest shall be payable on the bond.

10. Issuing offices and commission payable

No commission, brokerage or any other charges for issue of bond shall be payable by the buyer's against purchase of the bond.

---

1 Substituted vide SO 5129, dt. 4-11-2022, w.e.f. 4-11-2022. Prior to substitution, clause 8 read as under:
"8. Periodicity of issue of bonds
(1) The bonds under this Scheme shall be available for purchase by any person for a period of ten days each in the months of January, April, July and October as may be specified by the Central Government.
(2) An additional period of thirty days shall be specified by the Central Government in the year of general elections to the House of People."

2 Inserted vide SO 5163(E), dt. 7-11-2022, w.e.f. 7-11-2022.

11. Payment options

(1) All payments for the issuance of the bond shall be accepted in Indian rupees, through demand draft or cheque or through Electronic Clearing System or direct debit to the buyer's account.

(2) Where payment is made through cheque or demand draft, the same shall be drawn in favour of the issuing bank at the place of issue such bond.

12. Encashment of the bond

(1) The bond can be encashed only by an eligible political party by depositing the same in their designated bank account.

(2) The amount of bonds not encashed within the validity period of fifteen days shall be deposited by the authorized bank to the Prime Minister Relief Fund.

13. Tax treatment

The face value of the bonds shall be counted as income by way of voluntary contributions received by an eligible political party, for the purpose of exemption from Income-tax under section 13A of the Income-tax Act, 1961.

14. Trading of bonds

The bonds shall not be eligible for trading.

ANNEXURE I

NAME OF AUTHORISED BANK : STATE BANK OF INDIA

[refer clause 2(b)]

List of Issuing Branches: [refer clause 2(c)]

S. No.	*STATE*	*BCODE*	*BRANCH NAME*
1	ANDHRA PRADESH	952	VISAKHAPATNAM
		948	VIJAYAWADA
2	ANDAMAN & NICOBAR	156	PORT BLAIR
3	ARUNACHAL PRADESH	6091	ITANAGAR
4	ASSAM	78	GUWAHATI
5	BIHAR	152	PATNA MAIN BRANCH
6	CHANDIGARH	626	CHANDIGARH MAIN BRANCH
7	CHHATISGARH	461	RAIPUR
		336	BILASPUR
8	DADAR & NAGAR HAVELI	6586	SILVASSA
9	DAMAN & DIU	514	DAMAN
10	DELHI	691	NEW DELHI MAIN BRANCH
11	GOA	509	PANAJI
12	GUJARAT	1355	GANDHI NAGAR
		301	AHMEDABAD
13	HARYANA	645	NEW COLONY GURGAON

14	HIMACHAL PRADESH	718	SHIMLA
15	JAMMU& KASHMIR	2295	BADAMI BAGH BR SRINAGAR
		657	JAMMU
16	JHARKHAND	167	RANCHI
17	KARNATAKA	813	BANGALORE MAIN BRANCH
		846	HUBLI
18	KERALA	941	THIRUVANANTHAPURAM MAIN
19	LAKSHADWEEP	5080	KAVARATTI
20	MADHYA PRADESH	1308	BHOPAL MAIN BRANCH
		377	GWALIOR MAIN BRANCH
21	MAHARASHTRA	300	MUMBAI MAIN BRANCH
		432	NAGPUR
		454	PUNE MAIN BRANCH
22	MANIPUR	92	IMPHAL
23	MEGHALAYA	188	SHILONG
24	MIZORAM	1539	AIZAWL
25	NAGALAND	214	KOHIMA
26	ODISHA	41	BHUBANESHWAR
		59	CUTTACK
27	PUDUCHERRY	900	PUDUCHERRY
28	PUNJAB	674	LUDHIANA
29	RAJASTHAN	656	JAIPUR MAIN BRANCH
		659	JODHPUR
30	SIKKIM	232	GANGTOK
31	TAMILNADU	800	CHENNAI MAIN BRANCH
		827	COIMBATORE
32	TELANGANA	916	SECUNDERABAD
		5324	NIZAMABAD
		847	HYDERABAD MAIN BRANCH
33	TRIPURA	2	AGARTALA
34	UTTAR PRADESH	125	LUCKNOW
		86	GORAKHPUR

		102	JHANSI
		602	AGRA MAIN BRANCH
35	UTTARAKHAND	630	DEHARADUN MAIN BRANCH
36	WEST BENGAL	1	KOLKATA MAIN BRANCH
		184	SILIGUDI

ANNEXURE II

FORMAT OF APPLICATION FOR ISSUE OF ELECTORAL BOND:

APPLICATION FORM FOR ELECTORAL BONDS .... (YEAR)						
NAME OF ISSUING BANK:		NAME OF BRANCH:				
DATE						
MODE OF SUBSCRIPTION		CHEQUE/DD		ELECTRONIC TRANSFER		
		DETAILS OF CHEQUE/DD				DATED
AMOUNT IN FIGURES:		AMOUNT IN WORDS:				
DENOMINATION & NUMBER OF ELECTORAL BONDS REQUIRED (in denomination of Rs.1000, Rs.10,000, Rs. 1,00,000, Rs. 10,00,000 and Rs. 1,00,00,000)						
PAN NO./TAN NO. AS APPLICABLE						
APPLICANT STATUS (As per clause 3(a) of the notification No. .... dated ....)	INDIVIDUAL	HUF	COMPANY	FIRM	CHARITABLE TRUST	Others
APPLICANT (S) DETAILS (IN BLOCK LETTERS)						
FIRST/SOLE APPLICANTS NAME IN FULL:						
DETAILS OF IDENTITY: (*Passport, Aadhaar/Voter Id*)						
SECOND APPLICANT'S NAME IN FULL: **(Name of more applicant's can be added, if situation so demands)**						
DETAILS OF IDENTITY: (*Passport, Aadhaar/Voter Id*)						
FIRST/SOLE APPLICANT'S ADDRESS IN FULL:						
CONTACT DETAILS: PHONE/FAX: EMAIL:						

DECLARATION: I/We hereby declare and undertake that:
(i) The information furnished in the application form is correct in all respects.
(ii) I have read and understood the details of information for the buyer of the Electoral Bonds as well as the rights and duties of the Electoral Bond holder.

Signature 1st APPLICANT	Signature 2nd APPLICANT

IN CASE OF THUMB IMPRESSION, ATTESTATION BY TWO WITNESSES:

1st WITNESS (DETAILS) 2nd WITNESS (DETAILS)

HUF DECALARATION:

I, ... RESIDING AT THE ADDRESS GIVEN AGAINST FIRST APPLICANT, DO SOLEMNLY AFFIRM THAT I AM THE KARTA OF THE HINDU UNDIVIDED FAMILY AND AS SUCH HAVE FULL POWERS TO PURCHASE AND OTHER WISE DEAL IN THE ELECTORAL BONDS STANDING IN THE NAME OF THE HUF.

SPECIMEN SIGNATURE FOR AND ON BEHALF OF THE HUF (Name of the HUF):

Place ....
Date .... Signature of the Karta

FOR OFFICE USE

Date of receipt of application	BLA No./CIF No.	HUF status (Y/N)	Any other information

INFORMATION FOR BUYERS OF ELECTORAL BOND:

ITEM	**ELECTORAL BOND**
WHO CAN BUY	(1) The Bond under this Scheme may be purchased by a person, who is a citizen of India or incorporated or established in India. (2) A person being an individual can buy bonds, either singly or jointly with other individuals.
LIMIT OF INVESTMENT	None
FORM OF ELECTORAL BONDS	Non-refundable banking instrument, in physical form
INTEREST OPTION	No interest shall be payable
LIFE OF ELECTORAL BOND	**To be encashed within fifteen days from date of issuance.**
TRADABILITY	Not tradable.
LOANS FROM BANKS AGAINST SECURITY OF THESE ELECTORAL BONDS	Not permitted.
APPLICATION FORMS	Available at designated branches of authorised Banks.

ENCASHMENT	Only the political parties registered under section 29A of the Representation of the People Act, 1951 (43 of 1951) and secured not less than one per cent of the votes polled in the last general election to the House of the People or the Legislative Assembly, as the case may be, shall be eligible to receive the bond.

THE RESERVE BANK - INTEGRATED OMBUDSMAN SCHEME, 2021

(Noti. Ref. CEPD.PRD. No. S873/3.01.001/2021-22, dt. 12-11-2021)

A Scheme for resolving customer grievances in relation to services provided by entities regulated by Reserve Bank of India in an expeditious and cost-effective manner under Section 35A of the Banking Regulation Act, 1949 (10 of 1949), Section 45L of the Reserve Bank of India Act, 1934 (2 of 1934) and Section 18 of the Payment and Settlement Systems Act, 2007 (51 of 2007).

CHAPTER I
PRELIMINARY

1. Short Title, Commencement, Extent and Application

(1) This Scheme may be called the Reserve Bank - Integrated Ombudsman Scheme, 2021.

(2) It shall come into force on such date as the Reserve Bank may specify.

(3) It shall extend to the whole of India.

(4) The Scheme shall apply to the services provided by a Regulated Entity in India to its customers under the provisions of the Reserve Bank of India Act, 1934, the Banking Regulation Act, 1949, and the Payment and Settlement Systems Act, 2007.

2. Suspension of the Scheme

(1) The Reserve Bank, if it is satisfied that it is expedient so to do, may by order suspend for such period as may be specified in the order, the operation of all or any of the clauses of the Scheme, either generally or in relation to any specified Regulated Entity.

(2) The Reserve Bank may, by order, extend from time to time, the period of any suspension ordered as aforesaid by such period, as it may deem fit.

3. Definitions

(1) In the Scheme, unless the context otherwise requires:

(a) "Appellate Authority" means the Executive Director in-Charge of the Department of the Reserve Bank administering the Scheme;

(b) "Appellate Authority Secretariat" means the Department in the Reserve Bank which is administering the Scheme;

(c) "Authorised Representative" means a person, other than an advocate, duly appointed and authorised in writing to represent the complainant in the proceedings before the Ombudsman;

(d) "Award" means an award passed by the Ombudsman in accordance with the Scheme;

(e) "bank" means a 'banking company', a 'corresponding new bank', a 'Regional Rural Bank', 'State Bank of India' as defined in the Banking Regulation Act, 1949, a 'co-operative bank' as defined in Section 56(c) of the Banking Regulation Act, 1949 to the extent not excluded under the Scheme, but does not include a bank in resolution or winding up or under directions or any other bank as specified by the Reserve Bank;

(f) "Complaint" means a representation in writing or through other modes alleging deficiency in service on the part of a Regulated Entity, and seeking relief under the Scheme;

(g) "Deficiency in service" means a shortcoming or an inadequacy in any financial service, which the Regulated Entity is required to provide statutorily or otherwise, which may or may not result in financial loss or damage to the customer;

(h) "Deputy Ombudsman" means any person appointed by the Reserve Bank as such under the Scheme;

(i) "Non-Banking Financial Company" (NBFC) means an NBFC as defined in Section 45-I(f) of the Reserve Bank of India Act, 1934 and registered with the Reserve Bank, to the extent not excluded under the Scheme, but does not include a Core Investment Company (CIC), an Infrastructure Debt Fund-Non-Banking Financial Company (IDF-NBFC), a Non-Banking Financial Company - Infrastructure Finance Company (NBFC-IFC), a company in resolution or winding up/liquidation, or any other NBFC specified by the Reserve Bank;

Explanation: The terms CIC and IDF-NBFC shall have the same meaning assigned to them under the RBI Directions.

(j) "Regulated Entity" means a bank or a Non-Banking Financial Company or a System Participant as defined in the Scheme, or any other entity as may be specified by the Reserve Bank from time to time; to the extent not excluded under the Scheme;

(k) "Settlement" means an agreement reached by the parties to the complaint by facilitation or conciliation or mediation, as per the provisions of this Scheme;

(l) "System Participant" means a person other than the Reserve Bank and a System Provider, participating in a payment system as defined in the Payment and Settlement Systems Act, 2007;

(m) "System Provider" means and includes a person who operates an authorised payment system as defined in Section 2 of the Payment and Settlement Systems Act, 2007;

(n) "The Reserve Bank" means Reserve Bank of India constituted under Section 3 of the Reserve Bank of India Act, 1934.

(2) Words and expressions used and not defined in the Scheme, but defined in the Reserve Bank of India Act, 1934, or in the Banking Regulation Act, 1949, or in the Payment and Settlement Systems Act, 2007 or in the Regulations or guidelines or Directions issued by the Reserve Bank in exercise of its powers conferred by the Acts referred to herein above, shall have the meanings respectively assigned to them.

CHAPTER II

OFFICES UNDER THE RESERVE BANK - INTEGRATED OMBUDSMAN SCHEME, 2021

4. Appointment and Tenure of Ombudsman and Deputy Ombudsman

(1) The Reserve Bank may appoint one or more of its officers as Ombudsman and Deputy Ombudsman, to carry out the functions entrusted to them under the Scheme.

(2) The appointment of Ombudsman or the Deputy Ombudsman, as the case may be, shall be made for a period not exceeding three years at a time.

5. Location of the Office of the Ombudsman

(1) The offices of the Ombudsman shall be at such places as may be specified by the Reserve Bank.

(2) In order to expedite disposal of the complaints, the Ombudsman may hold sittings at such places and in such manner as may be considered necessary and proper in respect of a complaint.

6. Establishment of a Centralised Receipt and Processing Centre

(1) The Reserve Bank shall establish the Centralised Receipt and Processing Centre at any place as may be decided by it to receive the complaints filed under the Scheme and process them.

(2) The complaints under the Scheme made online shall be registered on the portal (*https://cms.rbi.org.in*). Complaints in electronic mode (E-mail) and physical form, including postal and hand-delivered complaints, shall be addressed and sent to the place where the Centralised Receipt and Processing Centre of the Reserve Bank is established, for scrutiny and initial processing:

PROVIDED that the complaints that are received directly in any of the offices of the Reserve Bank shall be forwarded to the Centralised Receipt and Processing Centre for further action.

7. Staffing of the Offices of Ombudsman and Centralised Receipt and Processing Centre

The Reserve Bank shall ensure that the offices of the Ombudsman and the Centralised Receipt and Processing Centre are adequately staffed and shall bear the cost thereof.

CHAPTER III
POWERS AND FUNCTIONS OF THE OMBUDSMAN

8. Powers and Functions

(1) The Ombudsman/Deputy Ombudsman shall consider the complaints of customers of Regulated Entities relating to deficiency in service.

(2) There is no limit on the amount in a dispute that can be brought before the Ombudsman for which the Ombudsman can pass an Award. However, for any consequential loss suffered by the complainant, the Ombudsman shall have the power to provide a compensation up to Rupees 20 lakh, in addition to, up to Rupees One lakh for the loss of the complainant's time, expenses incurred and for harassment/mental anguish suffered by the complainant.

(3) While the Ombudsman shall have the power to address and close all complaints, the Deputy Ombudsman shall have the power to close those complaints falling under clause 10 of the Scheme and complaints settled through facilitation as stated under clause 14 of the Scheme.

(4) The Ombudsman shall send to the Deputy Governor, Reserve Bank of India, a report, as on March 31st every year, containing a general review of the activities of the office during the preceding financial year, and shall furnish such other information as the Reserve Bank may direct.

(5) The Reserve Bank may, if it considers necessary in the public interest to do so, publish the report and the information received from the Ombudsman in such consolidated form or otherwise, as it may deem fit.

CHAPTER IV

PROCEDURE FOR REDRESSAL OF GRIEVANCE UNDER THE SCHEME

9. Grounds of Complaint

Any customer aggrieved by an act or omission of a Regulated Entity resulting in deficiency in service may file a complaint under the Scheme personally or through an authorised representative as defined under clause 3(1)(c).

10. Grounds for non-maintainability of a Complaint

(1) No complaint for deficiency in service shall lie under the Scheme in matters involving:

(a) commercial judgment/commercial decision of a Regulated Entity;

(b) a dispute between a vendor and a Regulated Entity relating to an outsourcing contract;

(c) a grievance not addressed to the Ombudsman directly;

(d) general grievances against Management or Executives of a Regulated Entity;

(e) a dispute in which action is initiated by a Regulated Entity in compliance with the orders of a statutory or law enforcing authority;

(f) a service not within the regulatory purview of the Reserve Bank;

(g) a dispute between Regulated Entities; and

(h) a dispute involving the employee-employer relationship of a Regulated Entity.

(2) A complaint under the Scheme shall not lie unless:

(a) the complainant had, before making a complaint under the Scheme, made a written complaint to the Regulated Entity concerned and—

(i) the complaint was rejected wholly or partly by the Regulated Entity, and the complainant is not satisfied with the reply; or the complainant had not received any reply within 30 days after the Regulated Entity received the complaint; and

(ii) the complaint is made to the Ombudsman within one year after the complainant has received the reply from the Regulated Entity to the complaint or, where no reply is received, within one year and 30 days from the date of the complaint.

(b) the complaint is not in respect of the same cause of action which is already—

(i) pending before an Ombudsman or settled or dealt with on merits, by an Ombudsman, whether or not received from the same complainant or along with one or more complainants, or one or more of the parties concerned;

(ii) pending before any Court, Tribunal or Arbitrator or any other Forum or Authority; or, settled or dealt with on merits, by any Court, Tribunal or Arbitrator or any other Forum or Authority, whether or not received from the same complainant or along with one or more of the complainants/parties concerned;

(c) the complaint is not abusive or frivolous or vexatious in nature;

(d) the complaint to the Regulated Entity was made before the expiry of the period of limitation prescribed under the Limitation Act, 1963, for such claims;

(e) the complainant provides complete information as specified in clause 11 of the Scheme;

(f) the complaint is lodged by the complainant personally or through an authorised representative other than an advocate unless the advocate is the aggrieved person.

Explanation 1: For the purposes of sub-clause (2)(a), 'written complaint' shall include complaints made through other modes where proof of having made a complaint can be produced by the complainant.

Explanation 2: For the purposes of sub-clause (2)(b)(ii), a complaint in respect of the same cause of action does not include criminal proceedings pending or decided before a Court or Tribunal or any police investigation initiated in a criminal offence.

11. Procedure for Filing a Complaint

(1) The complaint may be lodged online through the portal designed for the purpose (*https://cms.rbi.org.in*).

(2) The complaint may also be submitted through electronic or physical mode to the Centralised Receipt and Processing Centre as notified by the Reserve Bank. The complaint, if submitted in physical form, shall be duly signed by the complainant or by the authorised representative. The complaint shall be submitted in electronic or physical mode in such format and containing such information as may be specified by Reserve Bank.

12. Initial Scrutiny of Complaints

(1) Complaints which are in the nature of offering suggestions or seeking guidance or explanation shall not be treated as valid complaints under the Scheme and shall be closed accordingly with a suitable communication to the complainant.

(2) Complaints which are non-maintainable under clause 10 shall be separated to issue a suitable communication to the complainant.

(3) The remaining complaints shall be assigned to the offices of the Ombudsman for further examination under intimation to the complainant. A copy of the complaint shall also be forwarded to the Regulated Entity against whom the complaint is filed with a direction to submit its written version.

13. Power to Call for Information

(1) The Ombudsman may, for the purpose of carrying out duties under this Scheme, require the Regulated Entity against whom the complaint has been made or any other Regulated Entity which is a party to the dispute to provide any information or furnish certified copies of any document relating to the complaint which are or is alleged to be in its possession:

PROVIDED that in the event of failure of a Regulated Entity to comply with the requisition without sufficient cause, the Ombudsman may draw an inference that the Regulated Entity has no information to furnish.

(2) The Ombudsman shall maintain confidentiality of the information or the documents coming to its knowledge or possession in the course of discharging duties and shall not disclose such information or documents to any person except as otherwise required by law, or with the consent of the person furnishing such information or documents:

PROVIDED that nothing in this sub-clause shall prevent the Ombudsman from disclosing information or documents furnished by the parties to the proceedings to each other, to the extent considered necessary to comply with the principles of natural justice and fair play:

PROVIDED FURTHER that provisions of this sub-clause shall not apply in relation to the disclosure made or information furnished by the Ombudsman to the Reserve Bank or filing thereof before any Court, Forum or Authority.

14. Resolution of Complaints

(1) The Ombudsman/Deputy Ombudsman shall endeavour to promote settlement of a complaint by agreement between the complainant and the Regulated Entity through facilitation or conciliation or mediation.

(2) The proceedings before the Ombudsman shall be summary in nature and shall not be bound by any rules of evidence. The Ombudsman may examine either party to the complaint and record their statement.

(3) The Regulated Entity shall, on receipt of the complaint, file its written version in reply to the averments in the complaint enclosing therewith copies of the documents relied upon, within 15 days before the Ombudsman for resolution:

PROVIDED that the Ombudsman may, at the request of the Regulated Entity in writing to the satisfaction of the Ombudsman, grant such further time as may be deemed fit to file its written version and documents.

(4) In case the Regulated Entity omits or fails to file its written version and documents within the time as provided in terms of sub-clause (3), the Ombudsman may proceed *ex-parte* based on the evidence available on record and pass appropriate Order or issue an Award. There shall be no right of appeal to the Regulated Entity in respect of the Award issued on account of non-response or non-furnishing of information sought within the stipulated time.

(5) The Ombudsman/Deputy Ombudsman shall ensure that the written version or reply or documents filed by one party, to the extent relevant and pertaining to the complaint, are furnished to other party and follow such procedure and provide additional time as may be considered appropriate.

(6) In case the complaint is not resolved through facilitation, such action as may be considered appropriate, including a meeting of the complainant with the officials of Regulated Entity, for resolution of the complaint by conciliation or mediation may be initiated.

(7) The parties to the complaint shall cooperate in good faith with the Ombudsman/Deputy Ombudsman, as the case may be, in resolution of the dispute and comply with the direction for production of any evidence and other related documents within the stipulated time.

(8) If any amicable settlement of the complaint is arrived at between the parties, the same shall be recorded and signed by both the parties and thereafter, the fact of settlement may be recorded, annexing thereto the terms of settlement, directing the parties to comply with the terms within the stipulated time.

(9) The complaint would be deemed to be resolved when:

(a) it has been settled by the Regulated Entity with the complainant upon the intervention of the Ombudsman; or

(b) the complainant has agreed in writing or otherwise (which may be recorded) that the manner and the extent of resolution of the grievance is satisfactory; or

(c) the complainant has withdrawn the complaint voluntarily.

15. Award by the Ombudsman

(1) Unless the complaint is rejected under clause 16, the Ombudsman shall pass an Award in the event of:

(a) non-furnishing of documents/information as enumerated in clause 14(4); or

(b) the matter not getting resolved under clause 14(9) based on records placed,

and after affording a reasonable opportunity of being heard to both the parties.

(2) The Ombudsman shall also take into account, in addition, the principles of banking law and practice, directions, instructions and guidelines issued by the Reserve Bank from time to time and such other factors as may be relevant, before passing a reasoned Award.

(3) The Award shall contain, *inter alia*, the direction, if any, to the Regulated Entity for specific performance of its obligations and in addition to or otherwise, the amount, if any, to be paid by the Regulated Entity to the complainant by way of compensation for any loss suffered by the complainant.

(4) Notwithstanding anything contained in sub-clause (3), the Ombudsman shall not have the power to pass an Award directing payment by way of compensation, an amount which is more than the consequential loss suffered by the complainant or Rupees 20 lakh whichever is lower. The compensation that can be awarded by the Ombudsman shall be exclusive of the amount involved in the dispute.

(5) The Ombudsman may also award a compensation not exceeding Rupees one lakh to the complainant, taking into account the loss of the complainant's time, expenses incurred, harassment and mental anguish suffered by the complainant.

(6) A copy of the Award shall be sent to the complainant and the Regulated Entity.

(7) The Award passed under sub-clause (1) shall lapse and be of no effect unless the complainant furnishes a letter of acceptance of the Award in full and final settlement of the claim to the Regulated Entity concerned, within a period of 30 days from the date of receipt of the copy of the Award:

PROVIDED that no such acceptance may be furnished by the complainant if he has filed an appeal under sub-clause (3) of clause 17.

(8) The Regulated Entity shall comply with the Award and intimate compliance to the Ombudsman within 30 days from the date of receipt of the letter of acceptance from the complainant, unless it has preferred an appeal under sub-clause (2) of clause 17.

16. Rejection of a Complaint

(1) The Deputy Ombudsman or the Ombudsman may reject a complaint at any stage if it appears that the complaint made:

(a) is non-maintainable under clause 10; or

(b) is in the nature of offering suggestions or seeking guidance or explanation.

(2) The Ombudsman may reject a complaint at any stage if:

(a) in his opinion there is no deficiency in service; or

(b) the compensation sought for the consequential loss is beyond the power of the Ombudsman to award the compensation as indicated in clause 8(2); or

(c) the complaint is not pursued by the complainant with reasonable diligence; or

(d) the complaint is without any sufficient cause; or

(e) the complaint requires consideration of elaborate documentary and oral evidence and the proceedings before the Ombudsman are not appropriate for adjudication of such complaint; or

(f) in the opinion of the Ombudsman there is no financial loss or damage, or inconvenience caused to the complainant.

17. Appeal before the Appellate Authority

(1) There shall not be any right of appeal to a Regulated Entity for an Award issued for non-furnishing of documents/information under clause 15(1)(a).

(2) The Regulated Entity may, aggrieved by an Award under clause 15(1)(b) or closure of a complaint under clauses 16(2)(c) to 16(2)(f), within 30 days of the date of receipt of communication of Award or closure of the complaint, prefer an appeal before the Appellate Authority:

(a) PROVIDED that in the case of an appeal by a Regulated Entity, the period of 30 days for filing an appeal shall commence from the date on which the Regulated Entity receives the letter of acceptance of Award by the complainant:

(b) PROVIDED FURTHER that an appeal may be filed by a Regulated Entity only with the previous sanction of the Chairman or the Managing Director/Chief Executive Officer or, in their absence, the Executive Director/Official of equal rank.

(c) PROVIDED that the Appellate Authority may, if he is satisfied that the Regulated Entity had sufficient cause for not making the appeal within the time, may allow a further period not exceeding 30 days.

(3) The complainant may, aggrieved by an Award under clause 15(1) or rejection of a complaint under clauses 16(2)(c) to 16(2)(f), within 30 days of the date of receipt of the Award or rejection of the complaint, prefer an appeal before the Appellate Authority:

PROVIDED that the Appellate Authority may, if he is satisfied that the complainant had sufficient cause for not making the appeal within the time, may allow a further period not exceeding 30 days.

(4) The Appellate Authority's Secretariat shall scrutinise and process the Appeal.

(5) The Appellate Authority may, after giving the parties a reasonable opportunity of being heard:

(a) dismiss the appeal; or

(b) allow the appeal and set aside the Award or order of the Ombudsman; or

(c) remand the matter to the Ombudsman for fresh disposal in accordance with such directions as the Appellate Authority may consider necessary or proper; or

(d) modify the order of the Ombudsman or Award and pass such directions as may be necessary to give effect to the order of the Ombudsman or Award so modified; or

(e) pass any other order as it may deem fit.

(6) The order of the Appellate Authority shall have the same effect as the Award passed by Ombudsman under clause 15 or the order rejecting the complaint under clause 16, as the case may be.

18. Regulated Entity to Display Salient Features of the Scheme for Knowledge of the Public

(1) The Regulated Entity to which the Scheme is applicable shall facilitate the smooth conduct of the Scheme by ensuring meticulous adherence to the requirements under the Scheme, failing which, the Reserve Bank may take such action as it may deem fit.

(2) The Regulated Entity shall appoint a Principal Nodal Officer at their head office who shall not be a rank less than a General Manager or an officer of equivalent rank and shall be responsible for representing the Regulated Entity and furnishing information on behalf of the Regulated Entity in respect of complaints filed against the Regulated Entity. The Regulated Entity may appoint such other Nodal Officers to assist the Principal Nodal Officer as it may deem fit for operational efficiency.

(3) The Regulated Entity shall display prominently for the benefit of their customers at their branches/places where the business is transacted, the name and contact details (Telephone/mobile number and E-mail ID) of the Principal Nodal Officer along with the details of the complaint lodging portal of the Ombudsman (*https://cms.rbi.org.in*).

(4) The Regulated Entity to which the Scheme is applicable shall ensure that the salient features of the Scheme are displayed prominently in English, Hindi and the regional language in all its offices, branches and places where the business is transacted in such a manner that a person visiting the office or branch has adequate information on the Scheme.

(5) The Regulated Entity shall ensure that a copy of the Scheme is available in all its branches to be provided to the customer for reference upon request.

(6) The salient features of the Scheme along with the copy of the Scheme and the contact details of the Principal Nodal Officer shall be displayed and updated on the website of the Regulated Entity.

CHAPTER V
MISCELLANEOUS

19. Removal of Difficulties

If any difficulty arises in giving effect to the provisions of the Scheme, the Reserve Bank may make such provisions not inconsistent with the Reserve Bank of India Act, 1934, or the Banking Regulation Act, 1949, or the Payment and Settlement Systems Act, 2007, or the Scheme, as it may consider necessary or expedient for removing any difficulty.

20. Repeal of the Existing Schemes and Application to Pending Proceedings

(1) The Banking Ombudsman Scheme, 2006, the Ombudsman Scheme for Non-Banking Financial Companies, 2018, and the Ombudsman Scheme for Digital Transactions, 2019, hereby stand repealed.

(2) The adjudication of pending complaints, appeals and execution of the Awards already passed, as on the date of commencement of the Reserve Bank - Integrated Ombudsman Scheme, 2021, shall continue to be governed by the provisions of the respective Ombudsman Schemes and instructions of the Reserve Bank issued thereunder.

ANNEX.

FORM OF COMPLAINT (TO BE LODGED) WITH THE OMBUDSMAN

[Clause 11(2) of the Scheme]

(TO BE FILLED UP BY THE COMPLAINANT)

All the fields are mandatory except wherever indicated otherwise

To

The Ombudsman

Madam/Sir,

Sub.: Complaint against .... (place of Regulated Entity's branch or office) of .... (name of the Regulated Entity)

Details of the complaint:

1. Name of the complainant ....
2. Age (years) ....
3. Gender..
4. Full address of the complainant ....

   ....

   ....

   Pin Code ....

   Phone No. (if available) ....

   Mobile Number ....

   E-mail (if available) ....
5. Complaint against (Name and full address of the branch or office of the Regulated Entity) ....

   Pin Code ....
6. Nature of relationship/account number (if any) with the Regulated Entity

   ....
7. Transaction date and details, if available

   ....

   (a) Date of complaint already made by the complainant to the Regulated Entity

   (*Please enclose a copy of the complaint*)

   ....

   (b) Whether any reminder was sent by the complainant? Yes/No

   (*Please enclose a copy of the reminder*)

   ....
8. Please tick the relevant box (Yes/No)

Whether your complaint:

(i)	is sub-judice/under arbitration[1]?	Yes	No
(ii)	is made through an advocate, except when the advocate is the aggrieved party?	Yes	No
(iii)	has already been dealt with or is under process on the same ground with the Ombudsman?	Yes	No
(iv)	is in the nature of general complaint/s against Management or Executives of a Regulated Entity?	Yes	No
(v)	is on account of a dispute between Regulated Entities?	Yes	No
(vi)	involves employer-employee relationship?	Yes	No

9. Subject matter of the complaint

   ....

10. Details of the complaint:

    (*If space is not sufficient, please enclose a separate sheet*)

    ....

    ....

    ....

11. Whether any reply has been received from the Regulated Entity within a period of 30 days of receipt of the complaint by it? Yes/No

    (*if yes, please enclose a copy of the reply*)

12. Relief sought from the Ombudsman

    ....

    ....

    (*Please enclose a copy of documentary proof, if any, in support of your claim*)

13. Nature and extent of monetary loss, if any, claimed by the complainant by way of compensation (please refer to clauses 15 (4) & 15 (5) of the Scheme)

    Rs...

    ....

14. List of documents enclosed:

Declaration

(i) I/We, the complainant/s herein declare that:

  (a) the information furnished above is true and correct; and

  (b) I/We have not concealed or misrepresented any fact stated above, and in the documents submitted herewith.

(ii) The complaint is filed before the expiry of a period of one year reckoned in accordance with the provisions of clause 10(2) of the Scheme.

Yours faithfully

(Signature of the Complainant/Authorised Representative)

1 Complaint is sub-judice/under arbitration if the complaint in respect of the same cause of action is already pending/dealt with on merits by any Court, Tribunal or Arbitrator or any other Authority, whether individually or jointly.

AUTHORISATION

If the complainant wants to authorise a representative to appear and make submission on her/his behalf before the Ombudsman, the following declaration should be submitted:

I/We .... hereby nominate Shri/Smt .... as my/our authorised representative whose contact details are as below:

Full Address ....

....

Pin Code ....

Phone No: ....

Mobile Number ....

E-mail ....

(Signature of the Complainant)

REGISTRATION OF ASSIGNMENT OF RECEIVABLES (RESERVE BANK) REGULATIONS, 2022

(Noti. No. DOR.FIN.081/CGM(JPS)-2022, dt. 14-1-2022)

In exercise of the powers conferred by section 19 (1A) read with Section 31A of the Factoring Regulation Act, 2011 (12 of 2012), the Reserve Bank of India, hereby makes the following regulations pertaining to the manner of filing of particulars of transactions with the Central Registry by a Trade Receivable Discounting System (TReDS) on behalf of Factors.

1. Short title and commencement

(1) These regulations may be called the Registration of Assignment of Receivables (Reserve Bank) Regulations, 2022.

(2) These regulations shall come into force on the date[1] of their publication in the Official Gazette.

2. Definitions

For the purpose of these regulations, unless the context otherwise requires:

(1) "Act" means the Factoring Regulation Act, 2011 (12 of 2012);

(2) "Central Registrar" means a person appointed as such under sub-section (1) of section 21 of the Securitisation and Reconstruction of Financial Assets and Enforcement of Security Interest Act, 2002 (54 of 2002);

(3) "Central Registry" means the Central Registry set up under section 20 of the Securitisation and Reconstruction of Financial Assets and Enforcement of Security Interest Act, 2002 (54 of 2002).

3. Registration of assignments of receivables transactions

(1) Where any trade receivables are financed through a Trade Receivables Discounting System (TReDS); the concerned TReDS on behalf of the Factor shall, within a period of ten days, from the date of such assignment or satisfaction thereof, as the case may be, file with the Central Registry the particulars of

(a) Assignment of receivables in favour of a Factor in Form I, which shall be authenticated by the authorized person using a valid electronic signature.

(b) Satisfaction of any assignment of receivables on full realization of the receivables in Form II, which shall be authenticated by the authorized person using a valid electronic signature.

(2) If the particulars referred in the sub-regulation (1) are not filed within the period specified therein, the Central Registrar may, on being satisfied on an application made in this behalf stating the reasons for the delay, allow the said particulars to be filed within such additional time not exceeding ten days as he may specify, upon payment of the fee as prescribed by GoI in Registration of Assignment of Receivables Rules, 2012, as amended from time to time.

1 Enforced w.e.f. 17-1-2022.

(3) Every Form for registration of any transaction relating to assignment of receivables or satisfaction of receivables on realisation shall be accompanied by the fee, as prescribed by GoI in Registration of Assignment of Receivables Rules, 2012, as amended from time to time, to be paid to the Central Registrar in the manner as may be specified by the Central Registrar from time to time.

FORM I

ASSIGNMENT OF RECEIVABLES IN FAVOUR OF FACTOR BY TReDS

(Particulars of assignment of receivables)

1. (a) **Category of the Assignor of receivables (Fill up only one category):**

☐ Individual
☐ Proprietorship Firm
☐ Limited Liability Partnership Firm (LLP)
☐ Partnership Firm
☐ Company
☐ Trust
☐ HUF

(b) **Whether the receivables are free from any encumbrance?**

☐ Yes
☐ No

(c) If not, name and address of the Bank or Financial Institution holding any Security interest over the receivables.	Name of Bank/Financial Institution:
	Address of Bank/Financial Institution
(d) If security interest over receivables is held by Consortium of Banks, name and address of the Leader.	Name and address of Leader of Consortium
(e) If security interest over receivables is held by Multiple Banks, name and address of the bank authorised to act on behalf of other Banks.	Name and address of the Bank representing Multiple banks

Note: If there is no single Bank representing Multiple Bank names of all the Banks may be furnished.

2. **Assignor**

(a) **Individual**

(i) Name Title .... (Mr./Mrs./Ms.)
Surname .... Name ....
Father's/Husband's Name ....
Date of Birth .... (dd/mm/yyyy)

(ii) Permanent Account Number (PAN) of Individual Assignor ....

OR

(b) Proprietorship Firm

(i) Name of Proprietorship Firm ....

(ii) Permanent Account Number (PAN) of Proprietorship Firm ....

(iii) Name of the Proprietor ....

(a) in case of company

Corporate Identity Number of Proprietor Company ....

(b) in case of individual

Title (Mr./Mrs./Ms.) ....

Surname .... Name ....

Father's/Husband's Name ....

Date of Birth .... (dd/mm/yyyy)

Permanent Account Number (PAN) ....

OR

(c) Limited Liability Partnership Firm (LLP)

(i) Limited Liability Partnership (LLP) Firm Name ....

(ii) Name of the partner or partners who is/are making assignment of receivables belongings to the Limited Liability Partnership (LLP) Firm

(1) Title .... (Mr./Mrs./Ms.)

Surname .... Name ....

Father's/Husband's Name ....

Date of Birth .... (dd/mm/yyyy)

(2) Title .... (Mr./Mrs./Ms.)

Surname .... Name ....

Father's/Husband's Name ....

Date of Birth .... (dd/mm/yyyy)

(Above details for multiple partners can be captured multiple times)

(iii) Permanent Account Number (PAN) of Limited Liability Partnership Firm (LLP) ....

OR

(d) Partnership Firm

(i) Partnership Firm Name ....

(ii) Name of the partner or partners who is/are making assignment of receivables belongings to the Partnership Firm

(a) Title .... (Mr./Mrs./Ms.)

Surname .... Name ....

Father's/Husband's Name ....

Date of Birth .... (dd/mm/yyyy)

(b) Title .... (Mr./Mrs./Ms.)

Surname .... Name ....

Father's/Husband's Name ....

Date of Birth .... (dd/mm/yyyy)

(Above details for respective partners can be captured multiple times)

(iii) Permanent Account Number (PAN) ....

OR

(e) **Company**

(i) Company name ....

(ii) Company Identity Number (CIN) or foreign company registration number..

OR

(f) **Trust**

(i) Name of the Trust ....

(ii) Whether Private Trust or Public Trust ....

(iii) If Public Trust, registration number as such Trust, if any ....

(iv) Trust Permanent Account Number ....

(v) Name of the Trustee/person who is making assignment of receivables belonging to the Trust

Title .... (Mr./Mrs./Ms.) ....

Name .... Surname ....

Father's/Husband's Name..

Date of Birth .... (dd/mm/yyyy)

OR

(g) **HUF**

Title of HUF .... (Mr./Mrs./Ms.)

Name of Karta .... Surname ....

Father's/Husband's Name..

Date of Birth .... (dd/mm/yyyy)

Permanent Account Number (PAN) of HUF ....

3. **Address of the Assignor**

Shop/Flat/House No. ....

Plot No. ....

Building No. .... Building Name ....

Street Name/No. ....

Village..

Taluka .... District ....

State/UT .... PIN Code ....

Basic Statistical-Return Code (BSR) Code if any assigned to Assignor ....

Note: In the case of companies the address of Registered Office and in the case of others the address of principal place of business may be furnished.

4. **Particulars of the Factor being the Assignee of receivables**

Name of Assignee ....

Corporate Identity Number ....

Permanent Account Number (PAN) ....

Address..

Shop/Flat/House No. ....

Plot Number..

Building Number .... Building Name ....
Street Name/No. ....
Village ....
Town ....
Taluka ....
City ....
District ....
State/UT ....
Pin Code ....
E-mail ID ....
Telephone ....

5. **Particulars of the TReDS, filing the particulars with the Central Registry on behalf of the Factor**

Name of TReDS ....
Corporate Identity Number ....
Permanent Account Number (PAN) ....
Address ....
Shop/Flat/House No. ....
Plot Number ....
Building Number .... Building Name ....
Street Name/No. ....
Village ....
Town ....
Taluka ....
City ....
District ....
State/UT ....
Pin Code ....
E-mail ID ....
Telephone ....

6. **DEBTOR (Buyer)**

(a) DEBTOR (Buyer) Limit ....

(b) **Particulars of Debtor**

(i) Individual Debtor

(i) Title .... (Mr./Mrs./Ms.)
Surname .... Name ....
Father's/Husband's Name ....
Date of Birth .... (dd/mm/yyyy)

(ii) Individual debtor Permanent Account Number (PAN) ....

OR

(ii) Proprietorship Firm Debtor

(i) Name of Proprietorship Firm ....

(ii) Proprietorship Firm Permanent Account Number (PAN) ....

(iii) Name of the Proprietor

(a) in case of company ....

(b) in case of individual

Title .... (Mr./Mrs./Ms.)

Surname .... Name ....

Father's/Husband's Name ....

Age ....

Date of Birth .... (dd/mm/yyyy)

OR

(iii) Partnership Firm Debtor

Partnership Firm Name ....

Partnership Firm Permanent Account Number (PAN) ....

Name of the partner or partners of debtors:

Title .... (Mr./Mrs./Ms.)

Surname .... Name ....

Father's/Husband's Name ....

Age ....

Date of Birth (dd/mm/yyyy) ....

OR

(iv) Limited Liability Partnership Firm (LLP)

Limited Liability Partnership (LLP) Firm Name ....

LLP firm Permanent Account Number (PAN) ....

Name of the partner or partners:

Title .... (Mr./Mrs./Ms.)

Surname .... Name ....

Father's/Husband's Name ....

Age ....

Date of Birth .... (dd/mm/yyyy)

OR

(v) Company

Company name ....

Company Identity Number (CIN) or foreign company registration number

....

Company PAN ....

OR

(vi) Trust

Name of the Trust ....

Type of Trust (Private/Public) ....

If Public Trust, registration number as such Trust, if any ....
Trust Permanent Account Number ....
Name of the Trustee/person who is making assignment of receivables belonging to the Trust
Title.............................. (Mr./Mrs./Ms.)
Name .... Surname ....
Father's/Husband's Name..............................
Age..............................
Date of Birth .... (dd/mm/yyyy)

OR

(vii) HUF

Title of HUF .... (Mr./Mrs./Ms.)
Name of Karta:
Title .... (Mr./Mrs./Ms.) ....
Surname .... Name ....
Father's/Husband's Name..............................
Age..............................
Date of Birth .... (dd/mm/yyyy)
Permanent Account Number (PAN) of HUF

(c) Address of the Debtor

Shop/Flat/House No. ....
Plot No. ....
Building No. ....
Building Name ....
Street Name/No. ....
Village/Town ....
Taluka .... District ....
State/UT .... PIN Code ....
E-mail ID ....
Telephone ....

(In case of multiple debtors in respect of a single assignor, the details of multiple debtors may be provided)

7. Assignment Details

(a) Financial Details of the Assignment

(i) Total Limit/Facility sanctioned under the agreement ....
(in case the amount is in Foreign currency, rupee equivalent to be stated)
(Rupees .... only)

(ii) Expected realisation or repayment period (in days) ....

(iii) Amount receivables assigned or given as Security for loan/credit limit..............................

(b) Whether assignment is absolute without recourse to assignor

☐ Yes

☐ No

If not, amount of loan or credit limit secured by receivables: (Rupees ....only

from ....

DD MM YYYY

Payment schedule of the loan or period which assignment subsists

to ....

DD MM YYYY

If credit limit renewable from time to time and secured by specific receivables, or pre-sent and future receivables, please mention:

Particulars of specific receivables ....

Description of future receivables ....

8. **Description of Document by which the receivables are assigned:**

Assignment Deed or assignment as security for a loan

Name of parties (1) ....

(2) ....

Date of Document ....

Place of execution ....

Taluka..

District .... State ....

Pin code ....

Description of receivables which are assigned or given as security in favour of the Factor

(i) Whether the assignment is on (a) whole turnover basis

(b) Invoice basis (non-whole turnover basis)

(a) In case of Whole Turnover Basis:

(i) Brief description of goods or services ....

(ii) Sub-Limit sanctioned for the goods and services ....

(iii) Sale proceeds of goods manufactured and sold or services provided/ rendered or to be provided/ rendered for the period from .... to ....

OR

(i) Brief description of goods or services ....

(ii) Sub-Limit sanctioned for the goods and services ....

(iii) Sale proceeds of goods sold or to be sold or services rendered or to be provided/ rendered as trader/selling Agent/retailer for the period from .... to ....

(Above details for different goods type can be captured multiple times depending upon the number of types of goods)

(b) In case of Invoice Basis (non-whole turnover basis):

(i) Invoice No. ....

(ii) Date..

(iii) Amount of invoice ....

(iv) Serial numbers or any other identification marks (e.g. Chassis No. for vehicles)..

(v) Brief Description of goods ....

(vi) payable by date (DD/MM/YYYY) ....

9. **Brief particulars of the principal terms and conditions of the assignment agreement**

A. Discount..

B. Margin amount details ....

C. Extent and operation of the charge ....

D. Others..

10. **Electronic signature of the authorised representative of TReDS**

....

Central registry

FORM II

SATISFACTION ON REALIZATION OF RECEIVABLES

(Particulars for Satisfaction on realization of receivables)

1. Assignor Permanent Account Number (PAN) ....

2. (a) Name of the Assignor ....

(b) Address of the Assignor

Building No...

Building Name...

City..

State/UT...

3. Assignment registration ID number

(a) Particulars of TReDS, who has filed the details of the assignment with the Central Registry...

(b) Particulars of the Assignee Factor ....

Permanent Account Number ....

Name..

Address...

Building No. ....

Building Name ....

City...

State/UT..

(c) Particulars of registration of assignment of receivables:

(i) Registration date .... (dd/mm/yyyy)

(ii) Final amount assigned (in Rupees) ....

4. **Date of realization of receivables or repayment of loan in full**

.... **(dd/mm/yyyy)**

For office use only

It is certified that the above document for charge satisfaction is hereby registered

Electronic signature of the authorised officer at the Central Registry ....

Electronic signature of the authorised officer at the Central Registry ....

REGISTRATION OF FACTORS (RESERVE BANK) REGULATIONS, 2022

(Notification No. DOR.FIN.080/CGM(JPS)-2022, dt. 14-1-2022)

In exercise of the powers conferred by section 3 read with Section 31A of the Factoring Regulation Act, 2011 (12 of 2012), the Reserve Bank of India, hereby makes the following regulations pertaining to the manner of granting Certificate of Registration to companies which propose to do factoring business.

1. Short title and commencement

(1) These regulations may be called the Registration of Factors (Reserve Bank) Regulations, 2022.

(2) These regulations shall come into force on the date[1] of their publication in the Official Gazette.

2. Definitions

For the purpose of these regulations, unless the context otherwise requires:

(1) "Act" means the Factoring Regulation Act, 2011 (12 of 2012);

(2) "Reserve Bank" means the Reserve Bank of India constituted under Section 3 of the Reserve Bank of India Act, 1934 (2 of 1934);

(3) "Company" means a company as defined in clause (20) of section 3 of Companies Act, 2013 (18 of 2013);

(4) "Non-Banking Financial Company – Factor (NBFC-Factor)" means a non-banking financial company as defined in clause (f) of section 45-I of the Reserve Bank of India Act, 1934, which has its principal business as per Regulation 4 of these regulations and has been granted a Certificate of Registration (CoR) under section 3 of the Act;

(5) "Non-Banking Financial Company- Investment and Credit Company (NBFC-ICC)" means any company which is a financial institution carrying on as its principal business - asset finance, the providing of finance whether by making loans or advances or otherwise for any activity other than its own and the acquisition of securities, and granted a CoR under Section 45IA of the Reserve Bank of India Act, 1934 (2 of 1934); and is not any other category of NBFCs as defined by the Reserve Bank in any of its Master Directions.

3. Net Owned Fund (NOF)

Every company seeking registration as NBFC-Factor shall have a minimum Net Owned Fund (NOF) of Rs. 5 crore, or as specified by the Reserve Bank from time to time.

4. Principal Business Criteria (PBC)

An NBFC-Factor shall ensure that its financial assets in the factoring business constitute at least fifty per cent of its total assets and its income derived from factoring business is not less than fifty per cent of its gross income.

---

1 Enforced w.e.f. 17-1-2022.

5. Registration and matters incidental thereto

(1) Every company intending to undertake factoring business shall make an application to the Reserve Bank for grant of certificate of registration (CoR) as NBFC-Factor under the Act and shall ensure compliance with PBC as stipulated in regulation 4 of these regulations.

(2) Any existing NBFC-ICC, intending to undertake factoring business, shall make an application to the Reserve Bank for grant of CoR under the Act if it satisfies the following eligibility criteria:

(a) not accepting or holding public deposits;

(b) total assets of Rs. 1,000 crore and above, as per the last audited balance sheet;

(c) meeting the NOF requirement as prescribed in regulation 3 of these regulations;

(d) regulatory compliance.

(3) Any existing NBFC-ICC, which does not satisfy the above conditions but intends to undertake factoring business, shall approach the Reserve Bank for conversion from NBFC-ICC to NBFC-Factor. Such NBFC-ICCs shall comply with the PBC as specified in regulation 4 of these regulations.

(4) Application for such conversion shall be submitted with all supporting documents meant for new registration as NBFC-Factor, together with surrender of original CoR issued by the Reserve Bank to the NBFC-ICC under Section 45IA of the Reserve Bank of India Act, 1934.

(5) An entity not registered with the Reserve Bank under the Act, may conduct the business of factoring, if it is an entity mentioned in Section 5 of the Factoring Regulation Act, 2011, i.e., a bank or a body corporate established under an Act of Parliament or State Legislature, or a Government Company.

(6) NBFC-Factor or eligible NBFC-ICC which has been granted CoR by the Reserve Bank under these regulations, shall commence factoring business within six months from the date of grant of CoR.

6. Conduct of business and prudential regulations

NBFC-Factors or eligible NBFC-ICCs which have been granted CoR under the Act shall conduct the factoring business in accordance with the Act and rules and regulations framed under the Act or the directions and guidelines issued by the Reserve Bank from time to time.

****

Commercial Law Publishers (India) Pvt. Ltd.

Bare Act List

ISBN	Book Name	Price
	Aadhaar (Targeted Delivery of Financial & other subsidies, benefits & services) Act, 2016 with allied Rules, Regulations & Orders	120
	Actuaries Act, 2006 alongwith Allied Rules	80
978-93-5603-329-0	Administrative Tribunals Act, 1985 alongwith Allied Rules	195
978-93-5603-602-4	Advocates Act, 1961	80
978-93-90303-38-0	Aircraft Act, 1934 alongwith Rules and Allied Rules	400
	Air Force Act, 1950 alongwith Rules, 1969	200
978-93-5603-926-1	Air Prevention and Control of Pollution Act, 1981	100
	Ancient Monuments and Archaeological Sites and Remains Act, 1958 alongwith allied Acts & Rules	120
978-93-5603-321-4	Anti Hijacking Act, 2016	70
	Antiquities & Art Treasures Act, 1972 with Antiquities & Art Treasures Rules, 1973	40
978-93-5603-595-9	Anusandhan National Reseach Foundation Act, 2023	80
978-93-5603-756-4	Apprentices Act, 1961 with Rules	250
978-93-5603-856-1	Arbitration and Conciliation Act, 1996	250
	Architects Act, 1972 alongwith Rules and Regulations	70
978-93-5603-317-7	Armed Forces Tribunal Act, 2007	70
978-93-90926-28-2	Arms Act, 1959 alongwith Rules, 2016	265
	Army Act, 1950 with Rules, 1954	250
978-93-87983-87-8	Bankers' Books Evidence Act, 1891	40
978-93-5603-558-4	Banking Regulation Act, 1949 with Allied Acts and Rules	395
978-93-5603-738-0	Banking Law	550
978-93-5603-697-0	Banning of Unregulated Deposit Schemes Act, 2019 Alongwith Banning of Unregulated Deposit Schemes Rules 2020	95
978-93-5603-287-3	Bar Council of India Rules, 1975 under the Advocates Act, 1961	295
	Beedi and Cigar Workers (Conditions of Employment) Act, 1966	60
978-93-5603-645-1	Bharatiya Nagrik Suraksha Sanhita, 2023	395
978-93-5603-634-5	Bharatiya Nyaya Sanhita, 2023	250
978-93-5603-605-5	Bharatiya Sakshya Adhiniyam, 2023	160
978-93-5603-795-3	Biological Diversity Act, 2002 alongwith Rules	120
978-93-91005-01-6	Black Money (Undisclosed Foreign Income and Assets) & Imposition of Tax Act, 2015 with Rules, 2015	160
978-93-5603-885-1	Boilers Act, 1923 alongwith Allied Rules	120
978-93-5603-291-0	Bonded Labour System (Abolition) Act, 1976 alongwith Rules, 1976	60
	Border Security Force Act, 1968 alongwith Rules, 1969	100
978-93-87983-53-3	Building and Other Construction Workers' (Regulation of Employment and Conditions of Service) Act, 1996 with Rules	260
	Bureau of Indian Standards Act, 2016 with Rules, 1987 alongwith allied Rules, Regulations and Orders	250
	Cable Television Networks (Reg.) Act, 1995 with Rules & Regulations	250
	Cable Television Networks (Regulation) Act, 1995	60
978-93-91005-96-2	Cantonments Act, 2006	550
978-93-90926-12-1	Carrier Laws (Air, Land, Ship)	120
978-93-5603-565-2	Mannula on Motor vehicles laws	1695
978-93-9092-611-6	Central Civil Acts (Covering complete text of 115 Central Acts) [Set of 2 Vols.]	2695
978-93-5603-761-8	Central Electricity Authority Regulations (As amended in Sept. 2023)	595
978-93-5603-136-4	Central Excise Act, 1944 with Appeal Rules, Cenvat Rules and Allied Rules	425
978-93-5603-504-1	Central Motor Vehicles Rules, 1989 (as Amended in 2023)	1095
	Central Reserve Police Force Act, 1949 alongwith Rules	75

	Central Sales Tax Act, 1956 with Rules	70
978-93-92141-97-3	Central Vigilance Commission Act, 2003 alongwith Allied Acts	100
	Charitable and Religious Trusts Act, 1920 alongwith Charitable Endowments Act, 1890 and Religious Endowments Act, 1863	50
	Chemical Weapons Convention Act, 2000 alongwith Chemical Weapons Convention Appeals Rules, 2005	120
978-93-5603-712-0	Child and Adolescent Labour (Prohibition and Regulation) Act, 1986 alongwith Rules, 1988 and Children (Pledging of Labour) Act, 1933	120
978-93-89564-38-9	Chit Funds Act, 1982	90
978-93-5603-810-3	Christian Marriage Act, 1872	90
978-93-5603-793-9	Cigarettes and Other Tobacco.....Act, 2003 alongwith Rules, 2004	120
	Cine-workers and Cinema Theatre Workers (Reg. of Employment) Act, 1981 alongwith Rules, 1984 with allied Acts & Rules	65
978-93-5603-543-0	Cinematograph Act, 1952 with Rules	160
978-93-5603-623-9	Citizenship Act, 1955 with Rules, 2009	170
	Coal Mines (Special Provisions) Second Ordinance, 2014	80
978-93-5603-308-5	Code of Civil Procedure, 1908 (HB)	460
978-93-90926-220	Code of Civil Procedure, 1908 [As Amended by The Mediation Act, 2023	360
978-93-90303-43-4	Code on Social Security, 2020	180
978-93-89564-08-2	Code on Wages, 2019 along with Code on Wages (Central Advisory Board) Rules, 2021	70
978-93-5603-361-0	Commercial Courts Act, 2015 (Act, 4 of 2016) As Amended by the Mediation Act, 2023	100
978-93-5603-757-1	Commissions For Protection Of Child Rights Act, 2005	110
978-93-5603-476-1	Commissions of Inquiry Act, 1952	65
978-93-5603-326-9	Companies Act, 2013 (without notes)	495
978-93-5603-248-4	Companies Act, 2013	695
978-93-5603-342-9	Competition Act, 2002 alongwith Allied Rules	350
978-93-5603-859-2	Constitution of India As amended by The Constitution (One Hundred and Sixth Amendment) Act, 2023 dt. 28-9-2023	275
978-93-5603-723-6	Consumer Protection Act, 2019 alongwith Rules & Regulations	225
978-93-5603-671-0	Contempt of Courts Act, 1971 alongwith Rules to Regulate Proceedings for Contempt of Supreme Court, 1975	100
978-93-5603-715-1	Contract Act,1872	110
978-93-5603-324-5	Contract Labour (Regulations & Abolition) Act, 1970	145
978-93-5603-760-1	Copyright Act, 1957	195
978-93-91005-49-8	Court Fees Act, 1870	100
	Credit Information Companies (Regulation) Act, 2005	60
978-93-5603-439-6	Criminal Law (Amendment) Act, 2013	75
978-93-5603-438-9	Criminal Law (Amendment) Act, 2018	130
978-93-5603-714-4	Criminal Manual (PKT Edition)	645
978-93-5603-584-3	Criminal Manual	845
978-93-89564-56-3	Criminal Minor Acts (Covering complete text of 160 Central Acts) [Set of 2 Vols.]	1795
978-93-5603-336-8	Criminal Procedure Code, 1973 (HB)	460
978-93-5603-134-0	Criminal Procedure Code, 1973 (PB)	360
978-93-5603-177-7	Criminal Procedure Identification Act, 2022 with Rules	60
978-93-5603-971-1	Customs Act, 1962 (As amended up to date)	400
978-93-92141-61-4	Dam Safety Act,2021	70
	Dangerous Machines (Regulation) Act, 1983 alongwith Rules, 1984	40
	Delhi (Right to Citizen to Time ...... Services) Act, 2011 with Rules, 2011	50
	Delhi Circle Rates, w.e.f. 23-9-2014	150
978-93-5603-533-1	Delhi Co-operative Societies Act, 2003 alongwith Rules, 2007	360
	Delhi Development Laws	140

	Delhi Excise Act, 2009 alongwith Delhi Excise Rules, 2010	250
	Delhi Land Reforms Act, 1954	90
	Delhi Luxuries Tax Act, 1996 with Rules	75
	Delhi Metro Railway (O & P) Act, 2002 with Rules	150
	Delhi Motor Vehicle Rules alongwith Delhi Motor Vehicles Taxation Act, 1962 and Delhi Motor Accident Claims Tribunals Rules, 2008	150
978-93-92141-19-5	Delhi Municipal Corporation Act, 1957 with Rules	450
	Delhi New Rates of Stamp Duty	60
978-93-5603-600-0	Delhi Rent Control Act, 1958 with Rules, 1959, Delhi Rent Act, 1995, Slum Areas (Improvement & Clearance) Act, 1956 with Rules, 1957	175
	Delhi Right to Information Act, 2001	45
	Delhi Sales Tax on Works Contract Act, 1999 alongwith Rules, 1999	45
	Delhi Special Police Establishment Act, 1946	60
	Delhi Value Added Tax Act, 2004	395
	Depositories Act, 1996 with Rules & Regulations	125
978-93-91005-00-9	Designs Act, 2000 with Rules, 2001	100
978-93-5603-546-1	Digital Personal Data Protection Act, 2023	75
978-93-91005-24-5	Disaster Management Act, 2005 along with Epidemic Diseases Act	150
978-93-5603-706-9	Divorce Act, 1869	100
	Dock Workers (Regulation of Employment) Act, 1948 alongwith Rules, 1962	45
978-93-5603-695-6	Dowry Prohibition Act, 1961 with Rules	80
978-93-5603-633-8	Drugs & Cosmetics Act, 1940 alongwith Rules, 1945	1095
978-93-5603-149-4	Drugs & Magic Remedies (Objectionable Advertisements) Act, 1954 alongwith Rules, 1955	50
978-93-5603-534-8	Drugs (Prices Control) Order, 2013 alongwith National Pharmaceutical Pricing Policy (NPPP-2012)	150
978-93-5603-039-8	Drugs and Cosmetics Act, 1940 alongwith Drugs (Control) Act, 1950	80
978-93-5603-728-1	Easements Act, 1882	85
978-93-5603-016-9	Electricity Act, 2003 along with Electricity Rules and allied Regulations	450
	Emblems and Names (Prevention of Improper use) Act, 1950 alongwith Rules, 1982	35
978-93-5603-754-0	Emigration Act, 1983 alongwith Rules, 1983	75
978-93-5603-677-2	Employees' Compensation Act, 1923	170
978-93-5603-275-0	Employees' Provident Funds & Miscellaneous Provisions Act, 1952 with Scheme, 1995	475
978-93-5603-227-9	Employees' State Insurance Act, 1948 with Rules & Reg.	325
	Employers' Liability Act, 1938	30
	Employment Exchanges (Compulsory Notification of Vacancies) Act, 1959	30
978-93-90926-466	Enemy Property Act, 1968	100
	Energy Conservation Act, 2001 alongwith Rules, 2003 and Allied Rules	160
978-93-5603-610-9	Environment (Protection) Act, 1986 with Rules	895
978-93-5603-354-2	Environment Laws	395
978-93-5603-221-7	Equal Remuneration Act, 1976 with Allied Rules	65
978-93-5603-904-9	Essential Commodities Act, 1955 with Essential Commodities (SP) Act, 1981 and Colliery Control Order, 2000	120
978-93-92141-57-7	Evidence Act, 1872 (Indian)	95
978-93-92141-26-3	Explosives Act, 1884 and Explosive Substances Act, 1908 and Rules, 2008 alongwith Ammonium Nitrate Rules, 2012	495
978-93-5603-882-0	Factories Act, 1948	150
978-93-5603-709-0	Family Courts Act, 1984	75
978-93-90303-98-4	Farmers Act & Rules	90
978-93-5603-435-8	Fatal Accidents Act, 1855	65
978-93-5603-912-4	Fertiliser (Inorganic, Organic or Mixed) (Control) Order, 1985	425

978-93-5603-753-3	Food Safety and Standards Act, 2006	120
978-93-92141-68-3	Food Safety and Standards Act, 2006 alongwith Rules, 2011 & allied Regulations, Orders	2195
978-93-90303-33-5	Foreign Contribution (Regulation) Act, 2010 with Rules, 2011 and Allied Rules, 2012	100
978-93-56031-07-4	Foreigners Act, 1946 alongwith Foreigners Orders, 1948	100
978-93-92141-102	Foreign Exchange Management Act, 1999	70
978-93-91005-87-0	Foreign Marriage Act, 1969 alongwith Foreign Marriage Rules, 1970	50
	Foreign Trade (Devel. and Reg.) Act, 1992 alongwith Rules & Order	60
	Freedom of Information Act, 2002	30
	Fugitive Economic Offenders Ordinance, 2018	40
	Fugitive Economic Offenders Ordinance, 2018 with allied Rules	80
978-93-5603-216-3	Gas Cylinders Rules, 2016 alongwith Allied Rules and Orders	250
978-93-5603-606-2	General Clauses Act, 1897	80
978-93-91005-88-7	Geographical Indications of Goods (R&P) Act, 1999 with Rules, 2002	150
978-93-88798-28-0	GST Acts 2017	225
978-93-5603-618-5	GST Acts and Rules, 2017 with Forms (as amended by the finance Act, 2024)	1395
978-93-5603-625-3	GST Acts with Rules, 2017	695
978-93-5603-693-2	Guardians and Wards Act, 1890	80
	Guide to Contract Labour (S. Krishnamurthi)	250
	Guide to Delhi Sales Tax Act with Rules	160
	Guide to Payment of Gratuity Act (S. Krishnamurthi)	200
978-93-92141-43-0	Haryana New Labour & Industrial Code Along with Draft Rules	995
978-93-5603-286-6	Hindu Adoption & Maintenance Act, 1956	60
978-93-5603-553-9	Hindu Law	150
978-81-5603-288-0	Hindu Marriage Act, 1955	60
978-93-5603-302-3	Hindu Minority and Guardianship Act, 1956	60
978-93-5603-306-1	Hindu Succession Act, 1956	60
	Hire-Purchase Act, 1972 alongwith Hire Purchase (Repeal) Act, 2005	35
978-93-90926-38-1	HIV & AIDS (Prevention & Control) Act, 2017	65
978-93-5603-441-9	Identification of Prisoners Act, 1920	70
	Immoral Traffic (Prevention) Act, 1956	80
	Indecent Representation of Women (Prohibition) Act, 1986 with Rules	40
978-93-5603-707-6	Indian Forest Act, 1927	295
978-93-5603-174-6	Indian Penal Code, 1860 (IPC)	220
978-93-88798-13-6	Indian Penal Code, 1860 (IPC) [Pkt. Edn.]	90
978-93-5603-851-6	Indian Succession Act, 1925	175
	Industrial Development Bank of India Act, 1964	35
978-93-88798-24-2	Industrial Disputes Act, 1947 with Rules, 1957	175
978-93-5603-223-1	Industrial Employment (SO) Act, 1946 with Rules	65
978-93-90303-46-5	Industrial Relations Code, 2020	100
	Industries (Developments & Regulation) Act, 1951	50
978-93-5603-353-5	Information Technology Act, 2000 wth Allied Rules	350
978-93-5603-047-3	Inland Vessels Act, 2021	275
978-93-5603-591-1	Insecticides Act, 1968 with Rules	250
978-93-5603-569-0	Insolvency & Bankruptcy Code, 2016	1325
978-93-5603-312-2	Insurance Act, 1938	435
	Insurance Regulatory and Dev. Auth. Act, 1999 with Rules & Regs.	280
	Insurance Regulatory and Development Authority Act, 1999	40
978-93-5603-355-9	Intellectual Property Laws	395
	Inter-State Migrant Workmen (Reg. of Employment & Conditions of Service) Act, 1979	70

	Interest on Delayed Payments to Small Scale & Ancillary Ind. .... Act, 1993	30
	Jammu and Kashmir Reorganisation Act, 2019 with Orders, 2019	100
978-93-5603-545-4	Jan Vishwas Amendment of Provisions Act, 2023	150
978-93-91005-13-9	Juvenile Justice (Care......Children) Act, 2015	80
978-93-5603-915-5	Juvenile Justice (Care...Children) Act, 2015 Alongwith Rules and Regulation	450
978-93-5603-813-4	Labour & Industrial Laws	360
978-93-5603-635-2	New Labour & Industrial Laws	450
	Labour Laws (Exemption from Furnishing Returns........Certain Establishments) Act, 1988	35
978-93-5603-065-7	Labour Laws (Manual)	995
978-93-5603-442-6	Land Acquisition Act, 1894	150
978-93-5603-807-3	Law of Contract — The Indian Contract Act, 1872	325
978-93-5603-415-0	Legal Metrology Act, 2009 alongwith Rules	895
978-93-5603-946-9	Legal Services Authorities Act, 1987 alongwith Rules, 1995	165
	Life Insurance Corporation Act, 1956	45
978-93-5603-536-2	Limitation Act, 1963	95
978-93-90926-54-1	Limited Liability Partnership Act, 2008	100
978-93-5603-731-1	Limited Liability Partnership Act, 2008 with Rules, 2009	550
978-93-5603-466-2	Lokpal and Lokayuktas Act, 2013	120
	Maharashtra Control of Organised Crime Act, 1999	75
978-93-5603-382-5	Maintenance and Welfare of Parents and Senior Citizen Act, 2007	90
	Majority Act, 1875	30
978-93-90926-52-7	Major Ports Authorities Act, 2021 with Major Port Trust Act	100
978-93-87983-00-7	Manual on Drugs & Cosmetics	2195
978-93-87983-93-9	Manual on Intellectual Property Law (Pkt. Edition) (H/B)	325
	Manual on Intellectual Property Law	1095
978-93-88798-70-9	Manual on Labour & Industrial Law (Pkt. Edition Hard Bound)	695
978-93-88798-69-3	Manual on Labour & Industrial Law	1095
978-93-5603-313-9	Manual on Marriage & Divorce Law	425
978-93-89564-11-2	Manual on Motor Vehicles Laws	995
978-93-91005-64-1	Manual on Telecom Regulatory Authority of India Act, 1997 alongwith allied Rules & Regs.	1195
978-93-5603-307-8	Manual on Women Laws	450
978-93-5603-548-5	Marriage & Divorce Laws	450
978-93-5603-640-6	Marine Aids to navigation Act, 2021 with Rules	150
978-93-88798-19-8	Maternity Benefit Act, 1961 alongwith Rules, 1963	70
978-93-5603-619-2	Mediation Act, 2023	80
	Medical Council Act, 1956 alongwith Regulations	360
978-93-5603-646-8	Medical Termination of Pregnancy Act, 1971 alongwith Rules & Reg.	85
	Medicinal Central Council Act, 1970 alongwith Allied Regulations	60
978-93-5603-443-3	Mental Health Act, 1987	100
978-93-92141-06-5	Mental Healthcare Act, 2017 with Rules, 2018	160
	Merchant Shipping Act, 1958 alongwith allied Rules	380
978-93-5603-122-7	Micro, Small and Medium Entp. Dev. Act, 2006 with Rules	125
978-93-5603-838-7	Mines Act, 1952 with Rules	295
978-93-5603-638-3	Mines and Minerals (Development and Regulation) Act, 1957	1195
978-93-5603-394-8	Minimum Wages Act, 1948 with Central Rules, 1950	150
	Minor Acts (Covering Stamp Act, Regu. Act, Court Fees & Suit Valuation Act)	100
	Monopolies and Restrictive Trade Practices Act, 1969 (MRTP)	50
978-93-5603-893-6	Motor Vehicles Act, 1988	295
978-93-5603-943-8	Multi State Co-operative Societies Act, 2002 along with Rules, 2002	225
978-93-5603-315-3	Muslim Laws (Containing Six Acts)	100

978-93-5603-609-3	National Green Tribunal Act	150
978-93-5603-421-1	Narcotic Drugs & Psychotropic........Act, 1985 with Rules & Order	325
978-93-90303-40-3	National Commission for Indian System of Medicine Act Along with Homeopathy & Ayurveda Institute	175
978-93-5603-941-4	National Company Law Tribunal Rules, 2016 alongwith allied Rules	295
978-93-5603-554-6	National Dental Commission Act, 2023	80
978-93-5603-475-4	National Food Security Act, 2013 with Rules, 2015	100
978-93-5603-74-41	National Highways Act, 1956 alongwith Allied Act and Rules	250
978-93-92141-01-0	National Investigation Agency Act, 2008	40
978-93-89564-15-0	National Medical Commission Act, 2019 along with Rules, 2019	120
978-93-5603-654-3	National Nursing and Midwifery Commission Act, 2023	100
978-93-91005-71-9	National Security Act, 1980	50
978-93-5603-220-0	National water ways Act, 2016	65
978-93-92141-22-5	Negotiable Instruments Act, 1881	95
978-93-5603-714-4	New Criminal Laws.....Criminal Manual Covering : (Pocket Edition)	645
978-93-5603-584-3	New Criminal Laws.....Criminal Manual Covering : (Regular Edition)	945
978-93-5603-426-6	New Drugs and Clinical Trial Rules 2019 along with allied Acts & Rules	595
978-93-56030-47-3	New Labour & Industrial Code Along with Draft Rules	1095
978-93-5603-779-3	Notaries Act, 1952 with Rules, 1956	95
978-93-91005-79-5	Oaths Act, 1969	50
978-93-90303-45-8	Occupational Safety Health and Working Conditions Code, 2020	150
978-93-5603-422-8	Official Secrets Act, 1923	60
978-93-5603-450-1	Parsi Marriage and Divorce Act, 1936	60
978-93-5603-771-7	Partition Act, 1893	80
978-93-5603-920-9	Partnership Act, 1932	80
978-93-5603-872-1	Passports Act, 1967 alongwith Rules	220
978-93-5603-660-4	Patents Act, 1970 with Rules, 2003	325
978-93-5603-831-8	Payment of Bonus Act, 1965 alongwith Rules, 1975	105
978-93-5603-283-5	Payment of Gratuity Act, 1972 alongwith Rules, 1972	140
978-93-5603-589-8	Payment of Wages Act, 1936 alongwith allied Rules	150
978-93-5603-648-2	Payment and Settlement System Act, 2007	80
978-93-5603-218-7	Pension Fund Regulatory and Development Authority Act, 2013	60
978-93-5603-215-6	Petroleum Act, 1934 alongwith Rules, 2002 and Petroleum Minerals Pipeline (Acquisition…) Act with Rules	260
978-93-5603-337-5	Police Act, 1861	100
978-93-5603-479-2	Prisons Act, 1894	110
978-93-5603-983-4	Post Office Act, 1898	80
978-93-5603-901-8	Power-of-Attorney Act, 1882	80
	Practice Guide to Industrial Disputes Act (H.S. Sharma)	150
978-93-5603-924-7	Pre-conception and Pre-Natal Diagnostic Techniques.........Act, 1994 with Rules As Amended by The Jammu & Kashmir Reorganisation Act, 2019	130
978-93-5603-551-5	Press & Registration of Books Act, 1867 along with Rules & Order	80
978-93-5603-895-0	Press and Registration of Periodicals Act, 2023	80
978-93-5603-750-2	Pharmacy Act, 1948	80
978-93-5603-981-0	Prevention of Corruption Act, 1988	100
978-93-5603-339-9	Prevention of Cruelty to Animals Act, 1960 alongwith Rules	275
978-93-5603-573-7	Prevention of Damage to Public Property Act, 1984	65
	Prevention of Food Adulteration Act, 1954 alongwith Rules, 1955	480
978-93-5603-123-4	Prevention of Money Laundering Act, 2002 alongwith Allied Rules	250
	Preventive Detention Laws (Containing 4 Acts)	50
978-93-90303-72-4	Private Security Agencies (Regulation) Act, 2005 along with Model Rules, 2020 and Misc. Rules	70

	Prize Chits and Money Circulation Schemes (Banning) Act, 1978	30
978-93-5603-331-3	Probation of Civil Rights Act, 1955 alongwith Rules, 1977	65
978-93-5603-911-7	Probation of Offenders Act, 1958	80
978-93-90926-29-9	Prohibition of Benami Property Transactions Act, 1988 with Rules, 2016	100
978-93-91005-04-7	Prohibition of Child Marriage Act, 2006 with Child Marriage Restraint Act, 1929	60
	Prohibition of Employment as Manual Scavengers and their Rehabilitation Act, 2013 along with the Employment of Manual Scavengers and Construction of Dry Latrines (Prohibition) Act, 1993	50
978-93-5603-774-8	Protection of Children from Sexual Offences Act, 2012 with Rules, 2020	80
978-93-9092-655-8	Protection of Human Rights Act, 1993	120
	Protection of Plant Varieties & Farmers' Rights Act, 2001 alongwith Rules, 2003	150
978-93-5603-574-4	Protection of Women from Domestic Violence Act, 2005 with Rules	120
978-93-5603-540-9	Provincial Insolvency Act, 1920	95
978-93-5603-808-0	Public Examinations (Prevention of Unfair Means) Act, 2024	80
978-93-90926-11-4	Public Gambling Act, 1867	50
	Public Liability Insurance Act, 1991 alongwith Rules, 1991	35
978-93-87983-92-2	Public Premises (Eviction of Unauthorised Occupants) Act, 1971 & Rules, 1971	60
	Railway Property (Unlawful Possession) Act, 1966 & Allied Rules	60
978-93-5603-309-2	Railway Protection Force Act, 1957 alongwith Rules, 1987	195
978-93-5603-305-4	Railways Act, 1989	285
978-93-5603-703-8	Recovery of Debts..... Act, 1993 alongwith allied Rules & Regulations	140
978-93-5603-295-8	Registration Act, 1908 with State Amendments	120
978-93-5603-647-5	Registration of Births & Deaths Act, 1969 alongwith Births, Deaths & Marriages Registration Act, 1886	90
978-93-92141-52-2	Representation of the People Act, 1950 & Representation of the People Act, 1951 alongwith allied Rules	395
978-93-91005-07-8	Reserve Bank of India Act, 1934	200
978-93-5603-982-7	Right of Children to Free & Compulsory Education Act, 2009 alongwith Rules	120
978-93-5603-303-0	Rights of Persons with Disabilities...Act, 2016 alongwith Rules & Delhi Rules, 2018	275
978-93-5603-958-2	Right to Fair Compensation and Transparency in Land Acquisition, Rehabilitation and Resettlement Act, 2013 with Rules, 2016	150
978-93-5603-934-6	Right to Information Act, 2005 alongwith Rules and Allied Act	150
978-93-5603-825-7	Sale of Goods Act, 1930	70
978-93-5603-219-4	Sales Promotion Employees (Conditions of Service) Act, 1976	50
978-93-5603-035-0	SC/ST (Prevention of Atrocities) Act, 1989 with Rules	175
978-93-90926-37-4	Securities and Exchange Board of India Act, 1992 with Allied Rules	495
978-93-90926-25-1	Securities Contract (Regulation) Act, 1956 alongwith Rules	180
978-93-5603-228-6	Securitisation and Reconstruction of Financial Assets and Enforcement of Security Interest Act, 2002 alongwith Rules and Allied Rules	250
978-93-5603-985-8	Seeds Act, 1966 with Rules, 1968	110
978-93-5603-141-8	Service Tax with Rules and Allied Rules	525
978-93-5603-847-9	Sexual Harassment of ..... (Prevention, Prohibition & Redressal) Act, 2013	95
978-93-5603-446-4	Sick Industrial Companies (Special Provisions) Act, 1985 with Rules	150
978-93-90926-03-9	Societies Registration Act, 1860 alongwith State Amendments	80
978-93-5603-419-8	Special Economic Zones Act, 2005 with Rules, 2006	295
978-93-5603-951-3	Special Marriage Act, 1954	80
978-93-92141-59-1	Specific Relief Act, 1963	70
978-93-5603-947-6	Stamp Act, 1899 As amended by The Finance Act, 2023	150
	State Bank of India Act, 1955	50
978-93-90303-41-0	State Financial Corporations Act, 1951	70
978-93-5603-642-0	Street Vendors (Protection of Livelihood and Regulation of Street Vending) Act, 2014 with Delhi Street Vendors ... Rules, 2017 and Scheme, 2019	95
978-93-5603-786-1	Suits Valuation Act, 1887 with State Amendments	65

	Supreme Court Rules, 1966 alongwith allied Rules & Regulations	120
978-93-5603-837-0	Surrogacy Regulation Act, 2021 along with Assisted Reproductive Technology (Regulation) Act, 2021 and Allied Rules	150
978-93-5603-599-7	Telecommunication Act, 2023	395
	Telecom Regulatory Authority of India Act, 1997 with Rules	525
978-93-5603-461-7	Telegraph Act with Rules & Regulations	175
978-93-89564-42-6	The International Financial Services Centre Authority Act, 2019	50
P-23	The Prevention of Food Adulteration Act, 1954	480
978-93-5603-479-2	The Prisons Act, 1894	110
978-93-5603-604-8	The Real Estate (Regulation and Development) Act, 2016	150
978-93-92141-53-9	The Recycling of Ships Act, 2019	100
	Trade and Merchandise Marks Act, 1958 with Rules	80
978-93-5603-721-2	Trade Marks Act, 1999 with Rules, 2017	275
978-93-87983-71-7	Trade Unions Act, 1926 alongwith Central Regulations, 1938	50
978-93-92141-64-5	Transfer of Property Act, 1882	95
978-93-90303-47-2	Transgender Persons (Protection of Rights) Act, 2019 Along with Rules, 2020	60
978-93-5603-437-2	Transplantation of Human Organs and Tissues Act, 1994 alongwith Rules, 2014	120
978-93-92141-17-1	Tribunal Reforms Act, 2021 with Tribunal Reforms (Conditions ...) Rules, 2021	80
978-93-5603-854-7	Trusts Act, 1882	75
978-93-5603-561-4	Unlawful Activities (Prevention) Act, 1967 alongwith Rules, 1968	115
978-93-5603-593-5	Waqf Act, 1995 As Amended by The Jammu & Kashmir Organisation Act, 2019 alongwith Central Waqf Council Rules, 1998 with Delhi Waqf Rules	195
	Warehousing (Development and Regulation) Act, 2007 with Rules & Regulations	80
978-93-90926-18-3	Water (P&CoP) Act, 1974 alongwith Cess Act & Rules	150
978-93-5603-217-0	Whistle Blowers Protection Act, 2011	50
978-93-5603-327-6	Wild Life (Protection) Act, 1972 alongwith Allied Rules	395
	Working Journalists and Other Newspaper Employees (Conditions of Service) and Miscellaneous Provisions Act, 1955 with Allied Rules	65
	Workmen's Compensation Act, 1923 alongwith Allied Rules (Employees' Compensation Act, 2017)	100
	Young Persons (Harmful Publications) Act, 1956 with Rules	30

Commercial Law Publishers (India) Pvt. Ltd.

Showroom : 4239/1, Shakahar Bhawan, Ansari Road, Darya Ganj, New Delhi-110002
Phones : 011-43011562, 43502008, 43502007, 43452009
E-Mail : Commercialhouse@yahoo.co.in • naveen.commercialhouse@gmail.com
website : www.commeciallawpublishers.com